Galileo Galilei

Institute for
World Concerns Series

GALILEO GALILEI

Toward a Resolution of 350 Years of Debate — 1633-1983

Edited by Paul Cardinal Poupard
With Epilogue by John Paul II

Translation by Ian Campbell
Foreword by Donald S. Nesti, C.S. Sp.

 Duquesne University Press
Pittsburgh, PA

First published in French
under the title *Galileo Galilei:*
350 ans d'histoire 1633–1983
© *Desclée International, Tournai, 1983*

English translation copyright
©1987 by Duquesne University Press
All Rights Reserved
Manufactured in the United States of America

Published in United States of America
by Duquesne University Press
600 Forbes Avenue, Pittsburgh, PA 15282

Library of Congress Cataloging in Publication Data

Galileo Galilei. English.
    Galileo Galilei: toward a resolution of 350 years of debate.

    Includes bibliographical references.
    Contents: Galileo and Copernicus / Bernard Vinaty —
Galileo and the professors of the Collegio Romano at the
end of the sixteenth century / William A. Wallace —
Galileo and the philosophy of his time / Mario Vigano —
Galileo and the theology of his time / François Russo — [etc.]
    1. Science, Renaissance. 2. Science—Philosophy—
History. 3. Astronomy—History. 4. Galilei, Galileo,
1564–1642. I. Poupard, Paul. II. Title.
Q125.2.G35513 1986   509'.024   86–24125
ISBN 0–8207–0193–9

Contents

Foreword to the English Edition

The issue of Galileo has largely dominated the historical relationship between the Catholic Church and science for the last three and one-half centuries. The present work is designed to explore the movement begun in 1979 towards a new consideration of that controversy. Specifically encompassing a multidisciplinary approach within the context of culture, each essay in this volume approaches Galileo from a different perspective. In almost all respects, of course, this reflects the universality of the subject, for surely Galileo himself was a historical figure whose rich and varied personality and work cannot be understood within a limited prism. For its part, moreover, the Church has heroically struggled to come to terms with the evolution of this specific topic and the concurrent growth of modern science. That dialogue between the Church and science, manifesting the truly dramatic nature of the debate, can be accurately captured only by an unlimited intellectual vision.

Such a vision is represented in these pages which further constitute the fruit of the spirit of Pope John Paul II who has sought a true understanding of this issue. His unexpected announcement in 1979 to re-examine the Galileo affair has met with expected enthusiasm. Numerous scholars have now undertaken the painstaking research and reflection which alone can result in mature judgment. Their contributions to this volume serve as the cutting edge of future investigations, and in that sense, they are pathbreaking contributions to this subject.

We at Duquesne University are proud to be a part of this significant effort. The publication of this volume in English by our University Press thereby permits us to take an active role in fulfilling the mandate enunciated by the Holy Father in reevaluating the Galilean condemnation. Moreover, the publication brings to the English-speaking world one of the first major achievements in the chain of events designed to recast a compelling historical problem. It is a tribute to the wisdom and courage of all parties to this event that such a publication has taken place to confront the truth.

Donald S. Nesti, C.S.Sp.
President, Duquesne University

Foreword to the French Edition

On November 10, 1979, during the plenary session of the Pontifical Academy of Sciences and in the context of an address on the relationships between science and religion, Pope John Paul II expressed the desire that "theologians, scientists, and historians, animated by a spirit of sincere collaboration, would deepen the examination of the Galileo case and, loyally recognizing errors from one or the other side, dispel the mistrust that this affair still arouses in many minds to the detriment of a fruitful collaboration between science and faith, between the church and the world." The Holy Father promised his full support to those who would work to establish universally acceptable agreement, in this way reopening the door to future collaboration.

Encouraged by the acclaim from all parts of the world of science and culture that greeted this unexpected declaration, the pope decided to entrust the mission of realizing his desire to a group of experts especially qualified in the various scientific sectors involved in this affair.

In the thought of the Holy Father, the research would follow its course in the context of frank and loyal collaboration between science and the church. It was a matter of retiring a mortgage, not by seeking to win a battle of apologetics, as had long been the end sought, but in order to pursue a joint work that, in full conformity to truth, would bear witness to the possibility of fertile relationships between the church and science, in an area easily exploited. It was not a matter of revising or revalidating a trial, but of serene and objective reflection.

The study commission set up to supervise this project was constituted by Cardinal Carlo Martini, for exegetical questions; Bishop Paul Poupard, for cultural questions; Professors Carlo Chagas and George Coyne for scientific and epistemological questions; Rev. Michele Maccarrone and Professor Mario D'Addio, for historical questions. Rev. Enrico di Rovasenda, director of the Chancellery of the Pontifical Academy of the Sciences, was the secretary.

In his letter instituting the commission, the Holy Father raised a certain number of questions, and requested Bishop Poupard to assume responsibility for directing the project. In addition he expressed his desire "that the work should be carried out without delay and so as to lead to concrete results."

It is not for me to enter into the details of all that has been accomplished in each sector, though the results are impressive. Here I wish only to salute the estimable volume realized by the clear-sighted leadership of Bishop Poupard.

I call this an "estimable" work: it is such by the richness of the studies and by the exceptional value of the collaboration in each aspect of the problem. They witness to the interest that the Galileo question has not ceased to inspire. I advise readers, after having acquainted themselves with the Introduction and before entering into the details of the following chapters, to first read the pages written by Professor George Béné (chap. 8). They convey a perfect idea both of the spirit in which the work has been conceived and of the climate in which the Galileo question is treated and should be treated today—that is, not from any partisan point of view.

Cardinal Gabriel Marie Garrone
Coordinator of the Study Commission

Abbreviations

EN, *Edizione Nazionale delle Opere di Galileo Galilei*, 20 vols., by Antonio Favaro, Isidoro Del Lungo, and Umberto Marchesini (Florence, Giunti Berbera, 1890–1909; reprinted, 1929–1939). Cited here by volume and page (e.g., EN, VI, 199).

LCL, "Lettre à Christine de Lorraine, grande-duchesse de Tosçane" (EN, V, 309–48), French translation by François Russo, in *Galilée, aspects de sa vie et de son oeuvre* (PUF, 1968), pp. 331–59.

LS, Libero Sosio, editor, manual edition of Galileo's *Dialogo sopra i Massimi Sistemi del Mondo* (Turin, Einaudi, 1982).

PUF, Presses Universitaires de France, Paris.

Galileo Galilei: 350 Years of Subsequent History

Paul Cardinal Poupard

Galileo Galilei was born in 1564 and died in 1642. He was the object of a condemnation by the Catholic Church in 1633. What, then, is the significance of the 350th anniversary of that condemnation (1983)? And what is the reason for this present publication, undertaken under the auspices of a coordinative committee for theological, scientific, and historical research, a publication intended to contribute to an even better clarification of the relationships between Galileo and the Catholic Church, and more generally the Ptolemaic-Copernican controversy of the 16th and 17th centuries?

The anniversary is that of the condemnation issued on June 22, 1633, against Galileo in these terms: that he had "made himself suspect of heresy by this Holy Office, as having believed and held a doctrine false and contrary to the holy and divine scriptures — namely, that the sun is the center of the universe, that it does not move from east to west, that the earth moves, and is not the center of the universe."

The Declaration of John Paul II

Within the framework of three and a half centuries of history, during the centenary celebration of the birth of Albert Einstein by the Pontifical Academy of Sciences on November 10, 1979, Pope John Paul II stated:

> Galileo and Einstein have characterized an epoch. *The greatness of Galileo is known to all*, as is that of Einstein; but with this difference, that by comparison with the one whom we are honoring today before the College

xiii

of Cardinals in the Apostolic Palace, the first had much to suffer — we cannot conceal it — at the hands of men and organizations of the church. The Second Vatican Council has recognized and deplored certain undue interventions: "May we be permitted to deplore" — it is written in §36 of the Conciliar Constitution *Gaudium et Spes* — "certain attitudes that have existed among Christians themselves, insufficiently informed as to the legitimate autonomy of science. Sources of tension and conflict, they have led many souls to consider that science and faith are opposed." The reference to Galileo is clearly expressed in the note appended to this text, which cites the volume *Vita e opere di Galileo Galilei* by Pio Paschini, published by the Pontifical Academy of the Sciences.

Proceeding from this position of the Council, I urge theologians, scientists, and historians, motivated by a spirit of sincere collaboration, to deepen an examination of the Galileo case, and in a loyal recognition of errors, from whatsoever side they come, put an end to the mistrust to which this affair still gives rise in many minds. This will lead to a fruitful concord between science and faith, between the church and the world. I give my full support to this task, which can honor the truth of the faith and of science, and open the door to future collaboration.[1]

It was to this proposal that on July 3, 1982 Pope John Paul II constituted four working parties in the fields of exegesis, science and epistemology, history and culture.

Since I was in charge of the last-named sector, I thought I could not do better than promote multidisciplinary research bereft of any apologetic preoccupation, with the aim of witnessing to the conviction professed by John Paul II before the Pontifical Academy of Sciences. "The agreements between religion and science are more numerous and above all more important than the misunderstandings from which has sprung the bitter and sad conflict that has dragged itself out in the course of succeeding centuries."

These two strata of truth are in fact not of the same order. And they can never contradict one another, as the Second Vatican Council declared in *Gaudium et Spes* (§36). The declaration echoes the convictions of Galileo expressed in his famous letter to Marie-Christine de Lorraine, grand duchess of Tuscany, in 1615.[2] Referring to this text, John Paul II expressly underlines it:

The ecclesiastical magisterium admits the plurality of rules of interpretation of Holy Scripture. It expressly teaches, in fact, with the encyclical *Divino Afflante Spiritu* of Pius XII, the presence of different genres in the sacred

1. Epilogue, below, p. 315.

2. Galileo, "Lettre à Madame Marie-Christine de Lorraine," in F. Russo, *Athéisme et Dialogue*, Vatican City, September 1980, pp. 162–176; English trans. by Prof. Stillman Drake in *Discoveries and Opinions of Galileo* (New York: Doubleday Anchor Books, 1957).

books and hence the necessity of interpretations conforming to the character of each of them.

The various agreements that I have recalled do not by themselves solve all the problems of the Galileo affiar, but they help to create a point of departure favorable to their solution, a frame of mind propitious for an honest and loyal resolving of long-standing oppositions.[3]

A Clarification

The chapters that follow were not written in an attempt to justify the 1633 condemnation of Galileo, as has sometimes been alleged. Nor were they written in a juridical frame of reference, which is outside their competence. They are a work of clarification elaborated by scholars desirous of understanding and of helping others to understand. The matter concerns the location of Galileo, first in relation to his predecessors, particularly Canon Copernicus on the one hand, and to his contemporaries, particularly the professors of the Roman College on the other hand; then in the philosophical and theological context of his time; and finally in the course of the centuries from the era of the Enlightenment to the scientific circles of today.

Readers will make their own readings of the pages that follow. Speaking for myself, in the charge entrusted to me by the Holy Father of serving as the executive president of the Pontifical Council for Cultural Affairs, this book has clarified the past, and provided me with a conviction about the future.

Without doubt the datum from the past is:

> The theological amalgam, hardly discussed in the first decades of the 17th century, which the great centuries of medieval synthesis had made between the message of the Christian faith itself and a conception of the world essentially derived from the Aristotelian tradition.[4]

The conviction with respect to the future is:

> There are lessons of history that one has no right to forget. Revelation is not on the plane of a cosmogony. Divine assistance has not been given to the church in the perspective of problems of a positive scientific order. The unhappy condemnation of Galileo is there to remind us of this. That is its providential aspect.[5]

Truth and Freedom

Human beings are searching for the truth. And their spirit can do this only in freedom. These are convictions that animate the entire interna-

---

3. Epilogue, below, p. 317.
4. D. Dubarle, *"Autour de Galilée," Athéisme et Dialogue,* December 1980, p. 242.
5. Philippe de la Trinité, *Divinitas,* 25 (April 1959) 36.

tional scientific community, across all the cleavages that separate its members. The Catholic Church, met in council, has made these convictions its own by its historic declaration on religious freedom, *Dignitatis Humanae Personae*, December 7, 1965. Everyone is in search of truth. But truth imposes itself only by its own force, which penetrates the spirit with as much gentleness as strength. Accordingly, no one should be constrained to act against their own conscience, in private or in public. We have the duty to seek truth and to cleave to it. Furthermore, in accord with our nature as rational and responsible persons, we cannot meet this obligation unless, in addition to psychological freedom, we also enjoy immunity from all external constraint. The limits of this freedom are the rights of others, our duties toward other persons, and the common good of all. Therefore there must be granted to everyone the maximum degree of freedom, constrained only, and only to the degree required, when true necessity dictates.[6]

Thus there is no reason on the part of church or state that can justify an illegitimate constraint with regard to the inalienable rights of thought. As is well known, this firm conviction of the Second Vatican Council has been subsequently reaffirmed in forthright terms by Pope John Paul II before international forums, the UN in New York, UNESCO in Paris, in Africa and Latin America, from the far boundaries of Asia to the age-old heart of Europe.

Faith and Scholarship

There is no doubt that progressive elucidation of doctrinal questions, still confused at the time of Galileo, nowadays permits us to dissociate religious faith from a geometric or nongeometric cosmology, in contradistinction to Galileo's judges. Their misfortune was that the Catholic faith for centuries had become so linked with a particular understanding of the world that the Copernican revolution seemed capable of shattering the entire theological edifice. Accordingly, his judges thought, in good faith, that prohibition of Copernican opinions was required by Catholic doctrine. Their error is a salutary warning of the danger of confusing the faith with its purely human vehicle, necessary, it is true, for each epoch, but reformable from epoch to epoch. Copernicanism posed the hitherto unheard-of problem of the relativity of the cultural connections between religious faith and the scientific conception of the universe.

Fraught with difficulties and besieged by conflict and distrust, it is a

6. See P. Poupard, *Le Concil Vatican II*, chap. 12, "*La liberté religieuse*" (PUF, 1983), pp. 105–111.

long road that the believing conscience has traversed over the three and a half centuries that separate us from the anti-Galilean sentence of 1633.

A Fundamental Consensus

Today different horizons menace freedom of thought, when allegedly scientific conceptions of social life are imposed on thinking persons who cannot accept them, and who find themselves deprived of their inalienable rights as free and responsible persons. It is the duty of scientists, in the name of conscience, to stand up to the intolerable pretensions of totalitarian states, and to reaffirm that scientific discoveries are not made by decree. The unfortunate Lysenko affair has tragically witnessed to this in our day. It is neither the spirit of faith nor the spirit of science that condemns matters to obscurantism. Today nonbelievers and believers agree on this point. And this fundamental consensus is a cultural fact important for our time.

Faith and Science

Furthermore, there has been a gradual enlightenment on the side of Christians, who nowadays understand better the well-known quip concerning the faith, which teaches us "not how the heavens go, but how we go to heaven!" The apparent contradictions between the biblical description of creation and the great cosmic structures gradually discovered by the natural sciences no longer trouble believers. They understand without confusion, as does the Dogmatic Constitution of the Second Vatican Council, *Dei Verbum*, the nature and object of revelation — namely, a divine teaching in human words, across expressions culturally circumscribed and dated, offered to all generations.

A pioneer amidst opposition and misunderstanding, Galileo was not only a man of science of undeniable genius, but also a man of faith, even though we know little of his religious sentiments. Perhaps it will suffice to quote here the very beautiful letter of his daughter, Sister Marie Céleste, to him after his condemnation:

> Most dearly beloved father,
>
> I have just learned unexpectedly about your new ordeal. Because of it I have suffered a great pain, which pierces my soul: what a terrible grief that this decision has finally been taken. It is as offensive to your work as to your person. It is from Signor Geri that I have received this news that torments me.
>
> Not having received a letter from you this week I have been greatly worried, sensing in this silence a forewarning of what has happened. Most

beloved and respected father, now is the moment to bring to bear the virtue of prudence that the Lord has given you. This blow must be borne with that strength of soul that your religious spirit and your age comport.

Truly, through many experiences, you have learned to know the falseness and instability of all the things of this wicked world. Do not make too much, therefore, of these storms, but rather have the hope that they will soon die down and that they will change into circumstances favorable for you.

As it seems to me, I would say that there are grounds for hope because clemency has been shown to you by the location of your detention in such an agreeable place.

It also seems to me that one can hope for a change more in accord with your desires and mine. May God permit this if it is the better thing for you.

I beg you always to continue to grant me the consolation that your letters bring. Please let me have details about your health and your state of soul.

I end this letter, but I continue to think about you and pray, asking the Lord to grant you peace and consolation. From S. Matteo in Arcetri, July 2, 1633.

Your loving daughter,

Sister Céleste[7]

How can we fail to emphasize that Pope Leo XIII, in his liberating encyclical *Providentissimus*, intentionally took up the very texts of St. Augustine quoted by Galileo in his letter to Marie-Christine de Lorraine, mentioned above. This was to bring out the difference, nowadays evident to us, between faith and science in reading the Bible, for "the Spirit of God has not wished to teach us things that are not of any use for our salvation."[8]

And again, "if it should happen that the authority of the Holy Scriptures is put in opposition to a manifest and certain reasoning, this means that the one who interprets the Scripture does not understand it in the proper fashion; it is not the meaning of Scripture that is opposed to truth, but the meaning the interpreter wished to give it; that which opposes Scripture is not that which is in it, but that which the interpreter has put there, believing that this constituted its meaning."[9]

Since then the Second Vatican Council has taught us the "legitimate

7. EN, XV, 167.
8. *De Genesi ad litteram*, 2, 9.
9. *Epistula Septima ad Marcellinum*, PL (Migne), 83, col. 589. The collection of scriptural and patristic citations found in the famous letter to Marie-Christine de Lorraine, grand duchess of Tuscany, was, it seems, prepared by others, in particular by Galileo's friend and confident, the Benedictine Benedetto Castelli, himself a notable man of science.

autonomy of terrestrial values."[10] And we have now no difficulty in agreeing with St. Augustine, quoted by Galileo to Marie-Christine de Lorraine:

> It very often happens that someone, not even a Christian, possesses knowledge of the earth, the sky, other elements of this world, movement, rotation, the very size and intervals of the stars, eclipses of sun and moon, the passage of the years and of the seasons, the nature of animals, plants, and stones, and a thousand other similar things — knowledge clearly demonstrated by reason and experience. [11]

As with St. Augustine, we are convinced that nonbelieving scientists, whenever they see Christians basing themselves, though in error, on their faith in scripture, and making mistakes in matters perfectly understood by nonbelievers' cannot believe "in holy books that speak to us of the resurrection of the dead, of hope, of eternal life, of the kingdom of heaven, when they see them full of errors about things that they can understand from experience."[12]

The Second Vatican Council

The council had the boldness to declare with sadness, summoning Christians to a true examination of conscience:

> In this respect believers themselves often bear a certain responsibility. For atheism, considered in its totality, does not find its starting point within itself; it finds it in various causes, among which must be counted a critical reaction vis-à-vis religions and, especially in some areas, vis-à-vis the Christian religion. That is why, in the genesis of atheism, believers can play a not insignificant part, to such an extent that, by neglecting the education of their faith, by false presentations of doctrine, and also by defects in their religious life, moral and social, one can say that they have veiled the authentic face of God and of religion, more than they have revealed it.[13]

As the ancients said, history is the mistress of life. The very history of the errors of churchmen instructs us, teaching us to delimit more accurately the domain of the ecclesiastical magisterium, which is in no way guaranteed to be free of error when it moves away from that domain. Good intensions are not enough to legitimate an intervention, and the end does not justify the means.

---

10. Pastoral Constitution, *Gaudium et Spes*, §36.
11. *De Genesi ad Litteram*, chap. 19.
12. Ibid.
13. *Gaudium et Spes*, §19.

The Long Search for Truth

Galileo sought to understand the universe by mathematicizing it, and in this way resolved the epistemological problem — namely, the elevation of that which is perceived to a universalizable ideal. It was more a matter of mathematical science than of philosophical knowledge of nature. Salviati declares, for example:

> And now we can say that the door is open, for the first time, to a new method already in possession of numerous and admirable results, which, in the years ahead, will command the attention of minds.[14]

Intelligibility came only at the end of a long effort of thought in which the human spirit, in search of truth, sought untiringly to decipher "this great book that is constantly open before all eyes (I mean the universe), but the philosophy of which cannot be grasped if one has not grasped the language and if one is ignorant of the characters in which it is written. This philosophy is written in mathematical language, its characters are triangles, circles, and other geometrical figures, without the aid of which it is humanly impossible to grasp even a few words, and without which one can only wander vainly in an obscure labyrinth."[15] What seems evident to us today in fact demanded a complex elaboration. The chief difficulty was that of freeing the mind from categories of thought that were totally inadequate.

From Experience to Scientific Explanation

Shorn of the polemics that surrounded a great adventure of intelligence, and remote from the outbursts that accompanied its appearance, Galileo's contribution is a far-reaching lesson in intellectual probity: to integrate all the facts of experience and to proceed to an intellectual analysis of the phenomena, as an obligatory prelude to any proposition considered to be truly scientific. A rational idealization of a hypothesis can be retained as satisfactory only if it enfolds in its perspectives all the experimental phenomena, including those that at first sight seemed the most recalcitrant with regard to insertion into the framework of a proposed explanation.

Thus, only a proposition really explicative of all the perceived data, beyond the empirical pseudo evidence of the senses, is recognized as true science. Such a quest for universal explicative intelligibility constitutes the very heart of the advent of the modern form of science, which, I may note in passing, is the exact opposite of scientism — pseudo science, science that has strayed beyond its limits.

14. EN, VIII, 267.
15. "*Il Dialogo sopra due Massimi Sistemi del Mondo*," EN, VI, 232.

Constructing a hypothesis, rendering its premises precise, testing its assets by developing its consequences — this was the great adventure in which Galileo was the pathbreaker. This is not the place to discuss his defects of character — they are undeniable — nor the intentions of his judges — doubtless irreproachable — but rather to recognize that all truth bears its own value, from the moment that it is rigorously established by the most appropriate methods, whatever may have been the historical and sociological encrustations that hindered its perception. Galileo's theological awareness — to some extent more clear-sighted than that of his judges of the Holy Office — lay in his perceiving with St. Augustine that the Bible, in its sole concern to open for us the paths of salvation, and not to explain to us the movements of the stars, is not at all concerned with the truth of a dated and perishable cosmology. No more than grace suppresses nature but perfects it, does faith oppose science. It is, as Pascal would have said, of another order. We know with Galileo that the word of God does not have as its aim to teach us that the earth goes around the sun, and by no means that the sun goes around the earth, as his judges believed, but as St. Paul said, it teaches that the world is for humankind, humankind is for Christ, and Christ is unto God.

The Infinite Distance, According to Pascal

No word from any churchman, whatever his authority in matters of faith, can prevent the movement of the earth according to the laws of nature imparted to it by the Creator, which it belongs to the human race to discover with all the resources of human intelligence, itself created in the image and resemblance of God. The immensity of the universe leads us to the infinity of thought, and it is the investigative freedom of thought that ends by paying homage to the excellence of charity, as did Pascal:

> The infinite distance from bodies to spirits prefigures the infinitely more infinite distance of spirits from charity, for the latter is supernatural.

> All bodies taken together, and all spirits together and all works together, are not worth the smallest movement of charity. That is of an order that is infinitely higher.

> Out of all bodies taken together, one would not be able to derive even a tiny thought; that is impossible, something of another order. Out of all bodies and spirits one could not draw the slightest movement of true charity; that is impossible, and of another order, supernatural.[16]

Three and a half centuries later things come to appear as they really

---

16. Pascal, *Pensées*, ed. Braunschweig, no. 793.

are: the image of the Ptolemaic world has fallen apart, that of Copernicus is affirmed, and the judges, who assuredly in good faith but certainly in the wrong, condemned Galileo are known to have committed an error. Their distant successors today know that the autonomy of scientific research cannot obscure the development of philosophical reflection and theological thought. And we recognize with Pascal that the distinction between science and faith should be maintained because of the infinite distance that separates the object of the first from the object of the second.

A Contribution to the Search for Truth

Today we know that Galileo was essentially right in adopting the astronomic theory of Copernicus, with the exception of his explanation of the movement of the tides: "The only proof that he proposed for the ebb and flow of the tides was absolutely worthless."[17]

We know that, above all, this was a matter of free discussion among free scholars. The very diverse contributions collected in the present volume are a living illustration of this. I have learned much by reading them. Written by men coming from cultural worlds as different as the disciplines they represent, their contributions cannot be summed up in a single statement, for they treat of diverse matters.

Their essential agreement lies in the freedom they display in research as in analysis. Perusing them, readers will be able to discover a history of Galileo that is doubtless more complex than they had imagined, as much as in Galileo's dependence upon his predecessors as in his independence of thought relative to his contemporaries. In fact readers will see how, from the Enlightenment to the present day, interpretations of the Galilean situation have evolved and certain myths have taken shape on the ground of an inadequate knowledge of the history involved.

Henceforth this will be better known, thanks to the studies in this volume. It should be added that criticisms will be very welcome. For this publication has no other aim than that of bringing its modest contribution to the search for the truth that is inscribed in creation by the finger of God, and which men and women, tirelessly and gropingly, struggle to decipher in their historical journey toward that full light, where Galileo's name is inscribed among the greatest.

During his memorable address to the Pontifical Academy of Sciences on November 10, 1979, John Paul II declared:

I wish to confirm anew the declarations of the Council on the autonomy of

17. *Encyclopaedia Universalis*, art. "Galilée," vol. 7, 1968, p. 441.

science in its function of engaging in research on the truth written in creation by the finger of God . . . . The greatness of Galileo is known to all.

I am happy to announce the publication of all the Galilean documents kept in the secret archives of the Vatican. This *definitive and authentic* edition, with a historical introduction and a juridical commentary on the trial of Galileo Galilei, has been prepared under the auspices of the Pontifical Academy of Sciences.

PART ONE

GALILEO'S PREDECESSORS

1

Galileo and Copernicus

Bernard Vinaty

In the course of the second day of the "Dialogue Concerning the Two Principal World Systems, the Ptolemaic and Copernican," Gianfrancesco Sagredo, Venetian patrician and one of the three persons taking part in the dialogue, recounts:

> Certain events had but recently befallen me, when I began to hear this new opinion [Copernican] talked about. Being still very young and having just finished my course of philosophy, which I subsequently neglected in order to devote myself to other occupations, there chanced to come into these parts someone from over the mountains, from Rostock — and I believe his name was Christian Wursteisen — a follower of the Copernican opinion, who gave two or three lectures on this subject in an academy, having many present in his audience, rather on account of the novelty of the subject, I think, than for any other reason. I did not attend, however, having convinced myself that such an opinion could only be a solemn oddity. Later, having questioned some of those who had been present, I found that they all made fun of it, except one, who told me that the matter was not at all absurd. Because I considered this man to be very intelligent and extremely circumspect, I was sorry I had not been there. Accordingly, from that moment, whenever I met anyone who upheld the Copernican opinion, I began to ask him if he had always thought thus; and however many I questioned, I did not find one who did not tell me that he had for a long time been of the contrary opinion, but had gone over to the new viewpoint, moved by the force of the reasons that rendered it persuasive. Then, having examined them one by one, to see to what extent they grasped the reasons for the counterarguments, I found them all very ready to expound them, so that I could not truthfully say that it was from ignorance or vanity or, because they wanted to show themselves clever, so to speak, that they had adopted this opinion.[1]

The one member of the audience who had heard the exposition of

---

1. EN, VII, 154–55; LS, 158–59.

Christopher Wursteisen[2] without finding anything to make fun of was Galileo himself. And inasmuch as Sagredo was his pupil in the Studium at Padua in 1597, it is probable that Galileo's first attraction to Copernicanism dates back to about 1595. Galileo had been named lector (lecturer) in mathematics in that city by the Senate of the Venetian Republic, effective September 26, 1592. Under this title he was obliged to give lectures in the disciplines of the traditional *quadrivium*: geometry, arithmetic, harmony, and astronomy.[3]

Galileo's Adoption of the Copernican Theory

We possess several copies of Galileo's teaching of the elements of cosmography — today, the rudiments of physical geography. In conformity with tradition, this teaching consisted of a commentary on the *Traité de la Sphère* of Sacrobosco.[4] After having demonstrated the elements and properties of the circle, the author of the *Traité*, and its commentators, described in Ptolemaic terms the principal circles having a cosmological function (horizon, equator, zodiac, and ecliptic) leading up to the explanation of the inequalities of days and seasons. The *Traité* concluded with the explanation of eclipses by the relative motions of the moon and the sun.[5] Strangely, Galileo makes no mention of Copernicus in his commentary. Two reasons may account for this. The copy that served for the official edition of Galileo's works, the *Edizione Nazionale delle Opere di Galileo Galilei* by Antonio Favaro and Isidoro Del Lungo,[6] dates from 1602, but represents the corrected version of a text that goes back to 1593, when Galileo had not yet gone over to the side of

2. Deceived by his memory, otherwise exceptionally good, the man Galileo calls Christian Wursteisen, was really named Christopher Wursteisen. A certain Christopher Wursteisen is in fact enrolled on the registers of the Faculty of Law of the University of Padua, for the date of November 5, 1595, whereas Christian Wursteisen from Basel, who died in 1588, never seems to have set foot in Padua. Rostock was the first European university in which Copernicanism was taught. In Peking, Copernicanism was taught at a very early date by Jesuit astronomers.

3. B. L. Van der Waarden, "The Earliest Form of Epicycle Theory," *Journal of the History of Astronomy*, 5 (1974) 175–78: on the formation of the *quadrivium*, see particularly pp. 179–82.

4. John of Holywood (Johannes de Sacro Bosco, in the Latin form of his name), who died in Paris in 1256, was the first to give a systematic presentation of the Ptolemaic system concerning the movements of the planets. His *Traité de la sphère* very soon became the scholastic manual of elementary cosmography. J. L. E. Dreyer comments of this in *A History of Astronomy from Thales to Kepler* (Cambridge University Press, 1906; numerous reprintings): "After the long undisputed reign of Pliny and of Martianus Capella, Ptolemy finally reached the first rank" (p. 233).

5. The Barberini collection in the Vatican Library includes a manuscript copy of the *Traité de la Sphère* by Galileo (call number, 4.371).

6. Florence, Giunti Barbèra, 20 volumes, 1890–1909; reprinted, 1929–1939.

Copernican astronomy. Another reason seems more pertinent: apart from the elementary course on cosmography, the syllabuses foresaw an advanced course on planetary astronomy, in which the professor commented on Ptolemy's *Almagest*.[7] No note of this course has survived. Nothing could have prevented Galileo from introducing into the corrected text of his *Traité de la Sphère*, if not under the title of a retractation, at least as a supplement, some indications on the doctrines of Copernicus. If he did not do this, it is probably because the new Copernican astronomy changed nothing of the traditional framework of cosmography, and it played a role of the first rank in the explanation of the apparent irregularities of planetary motions (stations and retrogradations).[8]

The statement by Sagredo is of interest in raising the question, How did one become a Copernican fifty years after the death of Copernicus?[9] Two letters of Galileo, representing his first two explicit professions of Copernicanism, help us to answer this question.

The first, dated May 30, 1597, is addressed to Jacopo Mazzoni (1548–1598), a former colleague of Galileo at the Pisa Studium. Galileo congratulates him on the appearance of his work *De comparatione Aristotelis et Platonis* (Padua, 1597) and replies to an objection lodged against Copernicus by the author:

> To speak the truth, although as to the other conclusions I remain assured, on the question of the first point I remain confused and cautious, because I see Your Excellency attacking with such frank resolve the opinion of the Pythagoreans and Copernicus on the movement and location of the earth. Because I hold the latter to be much more probable than the opinion of Aristotle and Ptolemy, this causes me to open my ears wide as to the reasoning you have invoked.[10]

7. *"Ptolemäus"* (art. by B. L. van der Waerden) in Pauly-Wissowa, *Realencyklopädie der classischen Altertumswissenschaft*. See also Derek J. Price, *The Equatorie of the Planetis* (Cambridge University Press, 1955), pp. 93–117.

8. Stations and retrogradations are the apparent movements of the superior planets — that is, the planets whose orbits lie outside the annual orbit of the earth around the sun, when these movements are observed from the earth. As viewed from the earth, when a planet has the same celestial longtitude as the sun it is said to be in conjunction with the sun, and it then moves on the celestial sphere from west to east, in the same direction as the sun. On the contrary, whenever the celestial longitude of a planet differs by 180° from that of the sun, it is said to be in opposition to the sun; it then appears to move in retrograde direction of the celestial sphere — that is, from east to west, in the opposite direction to the movement of the sun.

9. Copernicus died in Frauenburg on May 25, 1543. On the very day of his death he received a copy of his work *De revolutionibus orbium celestium* that Joachim Rheticus had arranged to have printed at Nuremberg. See *Des révolutions des orbes célestes*, introduction, translation of the first ten chapters, with notes, by Alexandre Koyré (Paris, A. Blanchard, 1934; new impression, 1970).

10. EN, II, 198.

In the second letter, dated August 4, 1597, Galileo thanks Johannes Kepler for having sent him a copy of his work *Prodromus dissertationum cosmographicarum continens mysterium cosmographicum* ("Forerunner of cosmographic dissertations, containing the cosmographic mystery") (Tübingen, 1596). In his letter we read:

> I promise you I will read your book attentively in serenity of spirit, because in it I am sure to find very beautiful things. Truly, I will do it all the more willingly because for many years I have accepted the doctrine of Copernicus, and because starting with these principles I have discovered the causes of many natural effects that remain inexplicable by current theories. I have composed many studies in favor of this [opinion] and against the contrary doctrines, which I have not hitherto ventured to publish, frightened by the fate of our Master, Copernicus himself, who, if he has gained immortal renown in some quarters, has become a laughingstock and has been banned in others — so great, in fact, is the number of blockheads. If those who think like you were more numerous, I would certainly have the courage to publish my reflections; but because this is not the case, I prefer in such circumstances to wait.[11]

The Copernican Projection

The letter to Mazzoni raises the question, Was it, then, necessary to be a Platonist in order to become a Copernican? The letter to Kepler allows a glimpse not so much of a program, properly speaking, as, more probably, a projection of Copernican research activities. Of what did this projection consist?

Furthermore we are going to be involved in the animated history of relationships with Kepler, which cannot be passed over in silence when one is examining the relationships of Galileo with the thought of Copernicus.

Alexandre Koyré has maintained that Platonic thought constituted the conceptual intermediary that led to acceptance of Copernicanism. This thesis has recently been subjected to a number of critical reevaluations. Galileo did not know Greek, and of Plato he knew only those doctrines that the Florentine Academy had integrated into general learning.[12] It could be that reading Mazzoni's work had helped to fix in his mind the memory of several cosmological conjectures, in particular the "admirable speculation" of the *Timaeus* concerning the formation of the solar system, to which he referred thirty years later in the first day of the "Dialogue."[13] But all in all, the "divine" Archimedes exercised a

11. EN, XX, 67–68.

12. Carlo Maccagni, *Riscontri platonici relative alla matematica in Galileo e Torricelli* (Pisa, Domus Gelileiana).

13. EN, VII, 53–54; LS, 37–38.

more profound and wider influence on Galileo's thought than did Plato.

In fact, with what did Galileo's mind concern itself during these years? Essentially with mechanics, which he soon began to refashion. Until the Reinassance, mechanics occupied a subordinate and subsidiary position among the university disciplines; it was only the practical and empirical science of machines or engines, by its very nature foreign to rational science, the Greek *episteme*. Now Galileo had just composed "The Mechanics"[14] and a treatise *De motu*, which he carried about with him all his life, adding touches of improvement in the course of several successive editions, up to the point of discussing and commenting on the definitive version in the last of his major works, "Discourse and Mathematical Demonstrations concerning Two New Sciences Dealing with Mechanics and Local Motion."[15] In "The Mechanics" he elaborated a general theory of simple machines (the balance, the lever, the windlass and pulleys, the screw), starting from the Archimedean model of the lever. To explain the action of a weight he introduced the notion of "static moment" — that is to say, the product of a weight and the distance that separates it from the point at which it exerts a turning effect. In *De motu* he undertook a revision of the Aristotelian distinction between natural movements and constrained or violent movements. Observing that not all movement communicated to a body is necessarily a movement imposed on it, inasmuch as it is not contrary to its nature, he inserted, as a third term, neutral movements, which are neither natural nor constrained, and which prefigure inertial movements, about which he began to gain a clear idea after 1602. It is hardly an exaggeration to say that at the moment when he first turned to Copernicanism, Galileo was already working toward the construction of a rational mechanics that would allow the application of geometry to physical phenomena.

In the light of the above data, are we in a position to understand what in fact were the "natural effects" that Galileo claimed to explain in taking Copernican astronomy as a premise? Interpreters suspect that out of rivalry with Kepler, Galileo had exaggerated in speaking of "numerous studies over a period of many years." Stillman Drake dates

---

14. Galileo Galilei: *On Motion and On Mechanics*, English translation by E. I. Drabkin and Stillman Drake (University of Wisconsin Press, 1960). "The Mechanics" was not published in Italy until 1649, under the title *Della scienza mecanica e delle utilità che si traggono di quella*.
15. Galileo Galilei, *Discorsi e dimostrazioni matematiche intorno a due Nuove Scienza attenenti alla meccanica e moi vimenti locali*, work published by the Elseviers of Leyden in 1638. See the annotated edition by A. Carugo and L. Geymonat (Turin, Boringhieri, 1958).

to ca. 1595 Galileo's conversion to Copernican astronomy.[16] Interpreters agree in recognizing in Galileo's words an allusion to the explanation of ocean tides and the trade winds by combining the first two movements attributed to the earth by Copernicus — the annual revolution around the sun and the diurnal rotation about the axis of the poles. The first idea as to this explanation thus goes back to a time twenty years before the "Discourse on the Ebb and Flow of the Sea" (1616).

I dispute even less the supposition that in a notebook of the Servite, Fra' Paolo Sarpi, the celebrated theologian of the Venetian Republic and historian of the Council of Trent, friend of Galileo, there has been found a summary of the new explanation.[17] But I propose to complement it by another more general consideration. Research in mechanics led Galileo, progressively but rapidly, to undertake a revision of Aristotelian physics. He had begun by attacking the division of material elements into light and heavy, a division that Aristotle had to some extent "axiomatized." Galileo showed that all the effects attributed to levity were, in fact, due to relative differences in gravity — that is, to differences in "specific weights." In a word, Galileo extended Archimedean hydrostatics to aerostatics.

From that time on, Galileo asserted that a volume of air has weight in the air mass in which it resides, in the same way that a volume of water continues to have weight in the mass of water in which it is in equilibrium. This gave Galileo a way to refute the Aristotelian doctrine according to which gravity was a tendency of heavy bodies to occupy the "natural" place proper to them, just as levity brought light bodies to their proper place.

We are here touching on a central theme of Galilean thought, which served as a link between the new mechanics and Copernican astronomy: reflection on the fall of bodies, a "cosmological" phenomenon, if indeed it was one. Galileo came to ask himself, What information concerning the real constitution of the world can we gain from an attentive observation of the fall of bodies, always under the condition that reasoning is carried out after replacing the debatable Aristotelian premises by geometric theorems? At the same time as he posed this problem, Kepler posed to himself the same question, but in speculative terms that I willingly call Platonist, and even Kantian: How should most of the world be constructed that we can observe the effects due to gravity, such as they manifest themselves?

16. Stillman Drake, *Galileo at Work*, chap. 3, §2, pp. 36–37; idem, *Galileo Studies: Personality, Tradition and Revolution* (University of Michigan Press, 1970). chap. 10, "Galileo's Theory of the Tides," pp. 200–213.

17. Fra' Paolo Sarpi (1552–1623), *Scritti folosofici e teologici, editi ed inediti*, Romano Amerio, ed. (Bari, Laterza, 1951), Pensieri §§569–71, p. 115.

Undoubtedly Galileo (1564–1642) and Johannes Kepler (1571–1630) were the two greatest artisans of the Copernican revolution in their generation, much more so than Descartes, who in this matter occupies only a modest place.[18] However, almost everything set Galileo and Kepler in opposition. The contrast in the respective unfoldings of their thought was so great that their relationships via their correspondence very soon turned into misunderstanding and were broken off, to be resumed much later. In their mutual misunderstanding, doctrinal reasons had less weight than personal quarrels.[19]

The cosmological importance of gravity did not escape Copernicus, but he had hardly fathomed its exact significance:

> For myself, at least, I consider that gravity is nothing more than a natural appetition; by this means the divine Providence of the Architect of the world gives to [its] parts [the ability] to find themselves in their unity and integrality, gathering together in the form of a globe. And one can believe that this tendency belongs equally to the sun, to the moon, and to the other wandering stars, so that thanks to its efficacity, they remain in that sphericity in which they appear, even though in their divers ways they effect their circuits.[20]

Copernicus thus remained faithful to the traditional doctrine concerning gravity. His only revolutionary innovation, but a decisive one, was that of assigning to each star its own particular center of gravity, instead of considering that the earth was the center of gravity of the whole stellar world.

Whereas Kepler sought to make gravity conceivable in a world system, Galileo applied himself to rendering the fall of heavy bodies observable. For Kepler the world — one did not as yet speak of the universe, except in the works of Giordano Bruno (1548–1600) — was animated by forces: the forces that caused the moon to circle the earth, for example, was opposed to the force that tended to bring them together and merge them into a single body by virtue of their affinity.[21] Kepler was the first to speak of gravity in terms of a mutual attraction between two bodies linked by a certain material affinity. In 1609, in his

18. Basing himself on the relativity of local motion, Descartes attached little importance to the movement of the earth rather than that of the sun, while placing the sun at the center of the planetary system and counting the earth among the planets. See *Les principes de la philosophie, 3e partie, "Du monde visible,"* in particular chapters 11, 13, 15, 16, and 19. See also Léon petit "L'affaire Galilée vue par Descartes et Pascal," *XVII͏ᵉ siecle,* 28 (1955) 231–39.

19. Drake, *Galileo Studies,* chap. 6, "Galileo, Kepler and their intermediaries," pp. 123–39.

20. *De revolutionibus,* book 1, chap. 9 (in Koyré, *Des révolutions,* p. 101).

21. Johannes Kepler, *Astronomia Nova, Gesammelte Werke,* under the direction of Walther von Dyke and Max Caspar (Munich), vol. 3 (1937). There one finds: gravity is "the mutual material tendency of bodies of similar nature to unite and join together."

introduction to the "New Astronomy according to Causes; or Celestial Physics," he wrote: "It is not the stone that [in its fall] goes in search of the earth, it is the earth that attracts the stone."[22]

The falling stone does not tend toward the center of the earth, like a voyager seeking the terminus of his voyage, but the stone and the earth meet at their center of gravity, and if the stone had the same mass as the earth, their meeting would be at the midpoint of their initial distance of separation.[23] But Keplerian gravity had nothing to do with the gravitation of the stars, and we are still far from Newton's universal gravitation. In Kepler's eyes, a pulsive force emanated from the sun and set the planets in motion in their orbits; the sun communicated this same pulsive force to other planets so that these in turn, in a derivative and secondary fashion, caused their satellites to orbit — the term "satellite" was created by Kepler himself.[24] According to Kepler gravity and solar force act with an intensity inversely proportional to distance, as in the case of magnetic force, with which latter the gravitational and solar forces have many analogies of nature, whereas light is attenuated proportionally to the square of the distance from the luminous source.

By a kind of allergy, Galileo altogether rejected Kepler's thinking. In the influences and affinities of which Kepler spoke, Galileo believed that he could recognize the occult properties of Aristotelian "nature." He was later to write in the "Dialogue":

> Among all the great men who have philosophized on such an admirable effect of nature [the tides produced by the double movement of the earth], Kepler surprises me more than the others, and I am astonished that he, a free and perspicacious spirit, who had within his grasp the movements

22. *Ibid.* Kepler annotated the writing of his youth, *Somnium, seu Opus Posthumum de Astronomia Lunari*, an imaginary account of a voyage on the moon, which was published posthumously in 1634. In note 66 we read: "I define 'gravity' as a force of mutual attraction, similar to magnetic attraction. But the power of this attraction is greater for bodies close together than for bodies far apart. It follows that they show a greater resistance to separation when they are in the proximity of each other." See *Kepler's Somnium, The Dream or Posthumous Work on Lunar Astronomy*, translated and annotated by Edward Rosen (University of Wisconsin Press, 1967), p. 71.

23. Kepler, *Astronomia Nova*, p. 25. He adds: "Supposing that the lunar matter had the same density as terrestrial matter, then the earth would climb toward the moon by a 54th part of their distance of separation, while the moon would descend toward the earth by the remaining 53 parts of the separation."

24. The first time we meet with the term "satellite," in print, is in the "Account of the Proper Observations of Four Satellites of Jupiter" written by Kepler and signed September 11, 1610. Some months previously, on May 3, Kepler had sent to Galileo his *Dissertatio cum Sidereo Nuntio* ("conversation with the celestial messenger"), in which he indifferently designated the Medici stars by the expressions "circumjovial planets" or "satellites of Jupiter." See "Kepler's Conversation with Galileo's Sidereal Messenger," first complete translation, with notes and introduction, by Edward Rosen, in *The Sources of Science* (New York and London, 1965), p. 76–77.

attributed to the earth [by Copernicus], subsequently lent his ear and his assent to supremacies over the waters and to occult properties, as well as to other infantilities.[25]

Strangely, the Galilean universe is deprived of forces, as if the very idea of force had to be exorcised. Galileo analyzes movements, and for him physical explanation consists in showing that one physical movement results from another. To the essentially dynamic thought of Kepler there is opposed the essentially kinematic thought of Galileo. And in this sense, the Galilean mechanism is much more radical.

During the years of Padua (1592–1610), Galileo arrived at three important results concerning the fall of heavy bodies:

1. Contrary to the teaching of Aristotle, bodies do not fall with a speed proportional to their mass. If Galileo had not yet arrived at the actual formulation, *"in vacuo* all bodies fall with the same speed," it is because he thought that the theoretically possible vacuum was physically impossible. In effect, Galileo remained a partisan of the "abhorrence of a vacuum," which he moreover interpreted, in a mechanistic sense, as the resistance of different materials to deprivation of their cohesion. He did not see in what way this resistance/cohesion could be overcome. In any case, abstracting from the resistance of the medium (air or water, for example), and from aerostatic or hydrostatic upthrusts, bodies fall with the same speed, independently of their masses. Galileo had arrived at this result as early as the first years of his teaching in Pisa (1589–1592).

2. To sensible perception, the fall of bodies has always appeared to be the most natural movement that there is, the archetype of natural movements; and this is an accelerated motion. The Aristotelians in general considered that after the phase of initial accelaration by discontinuous increments of the initial speed, a body then continued its fall with a high but constant speed. Galileo established that the fall of heavy bodies is a naturally accelerated motion and that by "naturally accelerated" there should be understood "continuously and uniformly accelerated."[26] As early as 1602 Galileo had demonstrated the continu-

---

25. EN, VII, 486; LS, 545–46. The text of the *Somnium* alludes to oceanic tides on the moon. Kepler annotates this passage as follows: "It is matter of a probable conjecture that has not received a complete proof. Experienced mariners say that ocean tides are higher when the luminaries (the sun and moon) are in syzygy (conjunction or opposition) rather than in quadrature. The causes of the oceanic tides thus seem to be the attraction of the waters of the ocean by the sun and the moon. The earth, of course, similarly attracts its own waters, and we call this attraction 'gravity'. What then hinders us from saying that the earth equally attracts the lunar waters as the moon attracts the terrestrrial waters?" (note 22 to the *Somnium*, p. 123).

26. Drake, *Galilean Studies*, chap. 11, "The Fall and Uniform Acceleration," pp. 214–40.

ous character of acceleration during fall. From 1604 Galileo was in possession of a law of uniformly accelerated motion, but it was incorrect, because at that time he considered that the speed of the body was proportional to the distance traversed from the commencement of the fall. Although after 1604 he knew that distances traversed in the fall are proportional to the square of the time elapsed, it is probably only in 1615 that he arrived at the exact law of the proportionality of the speed, at a given instant, to the time elapsed since the beginning of the fall.

3. Finally if the fall of bodies is natural movement par excellence, the uplifting of bodies is the archetype of violent movements, and the contrariety of these two species of movement is illustrated by their reversibility. In fact, a perfectly elastic body rebounds to the same height as that from which it has fallen. Starting from this conclusion, Galileo conceived the existence of a perfectly neutral movement, neither natural nor violent, in the course of which a body moves without losing or gaining height — that is, a horizontal movement that one can imagine on a surface polished so as to eliminate friction and to allow abstraction from it. With an ingenuity truly of genius, Galileo applied himself to studying the oscillations of the pendulum, which clearly represent the reversibility of descents and re-ascents, and also to the study of rolling motions along inclined planes, which amount to prolonged and retarded falls. By a bold transition to the limit, considering planes of progressively reduced inclination, he deduced that if a body rolling down one inclined plane climbs to the same height up another inclined plane of the same slope, then uniform motion — that is, with no acceleration — should be prolonged indefinitely on a horizontal plane. In this way Galileo discovered the formulation that we today call the principle of inertia.

The laws of uniform motion, exemplified in inertial motion, and the laws of uniformly accelerated motion, exemplified in the fall of bodies, were expounded in their definitive form in the "Discourses and Demonstrations" of 1638. They are one of Galileo's principal claims to glory. But what bearing did they have on what is conveniently called the "Copernican revolution"? On a number of occasions Galileo returned to the consideration that the geometric notion of a horizontal plane is physically realized on the earth's surface, which is a spherical surface.[27] Let us say that, for Galileo, the surface of the sea, abstracting from tides and waves, is something more than a simple local reference frame for

27. EN,VII, 37; LS, 53–54: "Motion along a horizontal line, neither ascending nor descending, is circular motion about a center: circular motion will therefore not come about naturally without a preceding rectilinear motion, but once it is established it will continue perpetually with a uniform speed."

defining horizontality. It is physically that surface on which inertial movements are verified. This view, which the best authorities were to regard as a gross mistake,[28] is not however without importance, because it induced Galileo to consider that the orbital movements of the stars are endowed with perenniality, because they are truly inertial. In their case gravity does not have any effect, because they follow a course at a fixed distance from a determinate center. Today we find it difficult to understand the Galilean conception of an inertial circular motion, because we are accustomed to consider velocities "vectorially." For us a velocity has a magnitude and a direction, and a uniform velocity can only be a velocity with a constant magnitude and an invariant direction; that is why we do not recognize any movement as inertial, apart from uniform rectilinear motion. Neither Galileo nor Descartes mastered the consideration of the direction of a velocity. It is only with Christian Huygens and Isaac Newton that this consideration is arrived at.

During the years 1600–1610 it was Kepler who most closely approached the goal being pursued. In effect, the second law of planetary motion formulated in the "New Astronomy" *(Astronomia Nova)* states that the radius joining an orbiting body to the sun covers equal areas in equal times. The law of areas to a certain extent integrated the direction and magnitude of velocity in the analysis of orbital displacements. But above all, starting with the consideration that the planet Mars has a greater velocity at perihelion (passage through the orbital point closest to the sun) and a lesser velocity at aphelion (passage through the orbital point farthest from the sun), Kepler concluded that planetary orbits could not be circular. After much hesitation, he assigned them the

28. Members of Fr. Mersenne's circle extensively discussed the axioms and conclusions expounded by Beaugrand in his *Géostatique* (1636). During a journey to Italy in 1635, he had met Bonaventura Cavalieri and Benedetto Castelli and had informed them of the work of Pierre Fermat. The "geostatic debate," forgotten today, had as its aim the confrontation of the purely geometric with the purely physical definition of verticality and horizontality. It was born from the rereading of the treatises by Archimedes, "On Floating Bodies" and "On the Equilibrium of Planes." The two principal questions debated were: (1) How to affirm that all vertical lines are parallel if they all converge to the center of the earth?, and (2) How to accommodate the horizontal plane to the terrestrial surface, if the latter is spherical?

Roberval and Descartes, disagreeing on everything else, were in agreement on rejecting Beaugrand's position, which returned to the view of or according precedence to the physical or "geostatic" definition over the geometric definition, to the point of distinguishing between the theory of balances of small dimensions and the theory of balances of large dimensions. Nevertheless Beaugrand at least had the merit of drawing attention to the problem of whether a body always had the same weight, no matter what its distance from the center of the earth, by asking if the same mass would act in an identical fashion if directly attached to a balance arm or if suspended at the end of a long string.

On the question of circular inertia in the thought of Galileo, one can consult Drake, *Galilean Studies*, chap. 13, "The Case against Circular Inertia," pp. 257–78.

elliptical form, propounding in the "New Astronomy" the first law of planetary motion: "The planets traverse orbits that are ellipses, of which one of the foci is occupied by the sun." Inasmuch as the variations in velocity of a particular planet are minimal, the eccentricities of its orbital ellipses are minute.

The circular inertia postulated by Galileo rendered the elliptical nature of planetary orbits unacceptable to him; and in fact, he never accepted the law established by Kepler. Furthermore, he always took it that the acceleration due to gravity is constant at any distance from the center of the earth. Consequently neither Galileo, nor even Kepler, ever made a distinction between the mass and the weight of a body. As to the question of the nature of gravity, this was a problem of little interest for Galileo, who was ready to admit that it lay outside the range of our judgment:

> SIMPLICIUS: The cause of this effect (the fall of bodies) is very well understood and everybody knows that it is due to gravity.

> SALVIATI: You are mistaken, Signor Simplicius; you ought to say that everyone knows that it is *called* gravity. But for my part, I do not ask of you the name but the essence of the thing, about which you know no more than you know about the essence that causes the stars to follow their orbits, apart from the name assigned to it, rendered familiar and current by the frequent experience of that which we see a thousand times every day. But it is not that we really understand what is the principle or virtue that moves the stone down better than that which raises it up, once it has left the hand of the thrower, nor that we understand it better than that which causes the moon to orbit, except, as I have said, the name we have assigned to it as the most singularly appropriate appellation, as also whenever we give to the principle of projectile motion the general term *virtus impressa*, to planetary motion the name "intelligence," "assistant," "informant," and to an infinity of other movements we attribute "nature" as cause.[29]

Despite all their differences, Galileo and Kepler were at least in agreement as to a project essential to the Copernican revolution: to construct a *universal* physics — that is, equally celestial and terrestrial, on the basis of a rational mechanics with laws valid from one end of the universe to the other. Thus the ancient division into celestial and sublunary worlds was abolished, and the planetary group could be organized into a true solar system, the existence of which had been foreseen and affirmed by Copernicus.

The Copernican Program

Though a genius at mechanics, in astronomy Galileo was certainly not

29. EN, VIII, 260–61; LS, 284–86.

of the same stature as Kepler, the greatest astronomer of his generation. But at the very moment when Galileo had returned to his research on the acceleration of falling bodies, he invented the telescope, which cast him willy-nilly into astronomy.[30] Henceforward, to the end of his life, mechanical research and astronomical observation were to alternate in an incessant interchange. In the end there came the publication of his two major works, the "Dialogue" (1632) and the "Discourses and Demonstrations" (1638), which followed each other in the reverse order of priority in their programing. It happened several times that Galileo, on the point of announcing an important proposition in mechanics, had to delay the communication because in the interim he found himself engaged in a polemic arising from an unexpected astronomical discovery, often, in fact, his own.

The moment had come for Galileo to pursue the astronomy of Copernicus in the open sky. Galileo constructed his first telescope in July 1609. In the first quarter of 1610, he gave himself up to astronomical observations with a fervor bordering on frenzy. As early as the autumn of 1609 he had observed the lunar mountains at length; on January 7 he discovered the three first satellites of Jupiter; on the 13th he discovered a fourth. In July, he discovered the strange appearance of Saturn, which he considered as being formed of three distinct bodies.[31] In September, when he finally left Padua to go to Florence, he observed the phases of Venus.

Guest of his friend Filippo Salviati in the villa "Le Selve," on the outskirts of Florence, he began the systematic observation of sunspots from January 1611 onward. In the spring, he compiled the tables of movements of the four satellites of Jupiter, and spent a long time bringing them to perfection. Stillman Drake, who has explored the textual notes of Galileo kept in the National Library of Florence, noticed that he had the good luck to observe, for the first time in history, the planet Neptune in December 1612, before its occultation by Jupiter in January 1613. Because it has a very long period of revolution — 165

---

30. Vasco Ronchi, *Il cannochiale di Galilei e la scienza del Seicento* (Turin, Boringhieri, 1958) 2nd ed. Edward Rosen, *The Naming of the Telescope* (New York, 1947). First called *perspicillium*, the instrument was publicly named "telescope" on April 14, 1611, according to Rosen. Geronimo Sirturi reported several pieces of information connected with the invention of the telescope in his work entitled precisely *Telescopium* (Frankfurt, 1618).

31. In 1655 Christian Huygens (1629–1695) was to discover Titan, a satellite of Saturn, together with a thin ring around the main planet (*Nouvelles observations des satellites de Saturne*, 1656). In addition, he explained the appearances of Saturn, observed by Galileo, by the phases of the ring inclined at 31 degrees to the plane of the ecliptic. In fact, the plane of the ring is inclined at 28 degrees to Saturn's orbital plane, which is in turn at an angle of 2 degrees 30 minutes to the ecliptic plane.

years — it was not identified as the eight planet of the solar system until 234 years later — and Galileo thought he had observed a fixed star of feeble luminosity![32]

As a result of these astronomical discoveries, what had the Copernican cause gained? It is customarily emphasized that from then onward, more and more analogies were drawn in support of the Copernican point of view. Apart from the dismantling of the ancient and medieval dogma of the unalterability of the heavens, a number of phenomena, hitherto apparent singularities, found corresponding entities within the solar system. The earth was not alone in being accompanied by a satellite; Venus showed phases similar to those of the moon; the surface of the latter did not have a mirrorlike polish, and the reliefs of "selenography" were altogether similar to those of the terrestrial geography.

The phases of Venus were particularly interesting. If the moon presents different aspects spread over a number of phases, it is because it revolves around the earth at the same time as it reflects the light of the sun. If Venus, viewed from the earth, presents similar phases, this can only be because it revolves around the sun while reflecting its light:

> The apparent diameter of Venus is at present about five times greater than it was at its first appearance at the vesper hour. From this marvelous experience I draw the sensible and certain demonstration of two great questions hitherto cast in doubt by the greatest intellects of the world.

> The first is that all the planets are by nature dark (the same thing applying to Mercury and Venus).

> The second is that of necessity Venus orbits the sun, as does Mercury and all the other planets, something that was firmly believed by the Pythagoreans, Copernicus, Kepler, and myself, but which had not been proved by the senses, as is now the case with Venus and with Mercury.[33]

Scholars have, mistakenly, neglected a line of thought that accompanied Galileo up to the writing of the "Dialogue" and that, alongside his reflection on the movement of a falling body under gravity, constitutes a second directive theme of his Copernican research. Very soon attacked on the allegedly fallacious nature of the image in the telescope, Galileo never conceded the slightest doubt as to its objectivity. He explained the matter in a letter to Piero Dini, dated May 21, 1611.[34] He advanced the principle that in every place reached by the light excited or reflected by

32. Stillman Drake, "Galileo and Satellite Prediction," *Journal for the History of Astronomy*, 10/28 (June 1979); idem, in collaboration with Charles T. Kowal, "Galileo's Observations of Neptune," *Nature*, 287/5780 (Sept. 25 1980).

33. Letter of Galileo to Giuliano de'Medici, ambassador to the grand duke of Tuscany in Prague, dated January 1, 1611; EN, XI, 11–12.

34. EN, XI, 105.

a body, it is possible to obtain an image of that body. An excellent practician and theoretician of perspective, which he had learned in the school of Guidobaldo del Monte and had applied in the design of fortifications, he had understood that every optical image reduces to a geometric construct obtained by projection. Thus it is not by recourse to a sensation, at least virtual, that illusions of visions are remedied, but by reasoning in accord with the laws of geometrical optics:

> That these gentlemen could entertain the doubt that there is illusion in the telescope seems to me a truly astonishing thing: because I know that they will not contradict me on the point that the detection of illusions and errors due to an instrument or to any other device rests with the competence of the one who is proficient in the art on which the instrument depends.[35]

An exceptional observer, Galileo knew from the outset how to draw the maximum results from a relatively rudimentary instrument. Recently received, in April 1611, into the Lincean Academy, founded in 1603 by his friend Prince Federico de Cesi, there had been no lack of occasions to praise the virtuosity of his telescope. But his gifts, unique rather than rare, were to be the root of unpleasant polemics. Martin Horky, pupil of the Bolognese astronomer Giovanni Antonio Magini, had taken part in a session of celestial observations in which Galileo had sought to demonstrate his discoveries before representatives of the University of Bologna. But they saw nothing, and the setback had been a bitter one. A correspondent of Kepler's, Horky, wrote to him: *[Perspicillium] in inferioribus facit mirabilia; in coelo fallit* (in terrestrial observations the telescope works marvels; in the heavens it fails).[36]

To hold to this diagnosis would have been to bring to trial the particularly significant Galilean project of utilizing the telescope to observe celestial appearances, particularly the appearances of the planets. Galileo knew that he could not resign himself to this without abandoning the hope of basing Copernican astronomy on "sensible experiences," because only the telescope permitted the determination of stellar diameters and parallaxes with some accuracy:

> SAGREDO: How, then, has this matter been hidden from Copernicus and manifest to you?
>
> SALVIATI: These things cannot be understood unless by the sense of sight, which nature has not accorded to all with sufficient perfection for them to be able to discern such differences. I would even say that it is the organ of sight itself that is the cause of its own hindrance. But after it had pleased God to grant to human intelligence, in our day, an invention so marvelous

35. Ibid.
36. Letter of April 27, 1611, to Kepler from Martin Horky, author of the *Brevissima Peregrinatio contra Nuncium Sidereum* (Modena, 1610).

that it can perfect our sight, multiplying it 4, 6, 10, 20, 30, and 40 times, innumerable objects that had been invisible to us because of their distance or because of their smallness, have become visible to us by means of the telescope. . . .

SAGREDO: Oh, Nicholas Copernicus, what would have been your satisfaction in seeing such clear experiences confirm this part of your system![37]

And, further on, Sagredo adds: "The error of these [the adversaries of Copernican astronomy] consists in being extremely mistaken in taking the apparent diameter of the fixed stars."[38]

Galileo had built the first telescopes by assembling a converging lens (the objective) and a divergent lens (the eye-lens), so that the eye-lens was located between one of its own faces and the focal point of its other face. He did not yet have a micrometric screw, but he put a wire grid on the objective so as to obtain a division into squares of the 30-fold enlarged image. He does not seem to have published anything on findings on the refraction of light rays obtained several years previously by Kepler — perhaps he was not even aware of them — expounded by Kepler in the "Compliments to Witelo, in which is Treated the Optical Part of Astronomy."[39] The ambassador of the grand duke of Tuscany in Prague, Giuliano de'Medici, applied himself to restoring relations between Galileo and Kepler. Through his intercession, Kepler obtained a telescope from Galileo's workshop.[40] He set to work to perfect it and develop the theory. He replaced the divergent eye-lens with a converging lens, which worked in the same way as in the microscope; thus he obtained better enlargement of the image. He immediately published his "Dioptric, or Demonstration of the Vision and Images Obtained by the Telescope."[41]

The most Copernican aspect of Galileo's reflections on the nature and properties of telescopic images concerns the formation of an image in the conditions of immensity proper to astronomy. Scholars have often neglected to mention that to the two premises of his system — the negation of the centrality of the earth and the affirmation of its mobility — Galileo added a third: the immensity of the sphere of fixed stars. Copernicus had deduced that, if the earth orbits the sun in the course of an annual revolution, then the so-called fixed stars are not absolutely

37. EN, VII, 363–67; LS, 401–5.
38. EN, VII, 387; LS, 429.
39. *Ad Vitellionem Paralipomena, quibus Astronomiae Pars Optica traditur*, Frankfurt, 1604.
40. See the review by Prof. Giorgio Tabarroni in *Physis*, 9 (1967) 253, of the article by Edward Rosen, "Galileo and Kepler: Their First Two Contacts," *Isis*, 57 (1966).
41. *Dioptrice, seu Demonstratio eorum quae visui et visibilibus propter Conspicilla non ita pridem inventa accidunt* (Augsburg, 1611).

fixed, but should appear to us as subject to an annual displacement in the sky detectable by a parallax — that is, by the angular separation of the two positions of the same star determined when the earth is at perihelion and aphelion. The extreme distance of the stars rendered their annual parallaxes practically indeterminable.[42] To Galileo belongs the merit of having methodically shown that it is precisely the conditions of immensity that render imperceptible the effects that are the consequences of Copernican astronomy. Galileo returns several times to this argument in the third day of the "Dialogue."

With the invention of the telescope, Galileo's Copernican project was transformed into a program that took into account writing as well as research. At the moment of negotiating his return from Padua to Florence, he entered into negotiations with Belisario Vinta, secretary of state to the Grand Duke Cosimo II. During the preceding year, in January 1610, he had published in Venice the "Starry Message,"[43] in which he announced to the world his first astronomical discoveries and in which he dedicated the four satellites of Jupiter to the glory of the Medici dynasty. In Prague a copy had been sent to Kepler by the ambassador Giuliano de'Medici, perhaps without Galileo's knowledge. Ever an enthusiast and incomparably magnanimous, Kepler wrote in April his "Conversation with the Starry Messenger," which was printed in August.[44] In it he confirmed the existence of the Medici stars and the other Galilean discoveries.

In May of the same year, Galileo addressed to Vinta a letter in which he traced out a detailed and articulate program of his current undertakings:

> I am determined in every way, seeing how the days pass by, to nail down the future that remains to me and to apply myself with all my strength to bring to a conclusion the fruits of the wearyings of all my past studies, from which I can hope to gain some renown. . . . The works that I have to bring to a conclusion are principally:

42. Copernicus, *De revolutionibus orbium caelestium*, I, 6, *in fine* (ed. Alexandre Koyré, p. 84). It was only in 1837 that the astronomer Bessel succeeded in determining by telescopic observation at the observatory of Königsberg the annual parallax of a star. The star was 61 Cygni and its parallax measured $0''. 294$. The nearest star to the earth is Proxima Centauri and its annual parallax measures $0''. 764$.

43. *Sidereus Nuncius, magna longeque admirabilia spectacula pandens, suspiciendaque proponens unicuique, praesertim vero philosophia atque astronomia, quae a Galileo Galilei . . . perspicilli nuper a se reperti beneficio sunt observata in Lunae facie, fixis innumeris, Lacteo Circulo, Stellis Nebulosis, apprime vero in quatuor Planetis circa Iovis Stellam . . . atque Medicea Sidera numcumpandos decrevit* (Venice, Tomaso Baglioni, 1610).

44. *Dissertatio cum Nuncio Sidereo nuper ad mortales misso a Galileo Galilei* (Prague, 1610). The Latin *nuntius* can be translated either "message" or messenger." Whereas Galileo addresses his "starry message" to the House of Medici and to the world, Kepler replies to him by praising the "Starry Messenger."

— two books *de systemate seu constitutione universi*, an immense concept, full of philosophy, astronomy, and geometry;

— three books *de motu locali*, an entirely new science, for up to now nobody else, ancient or modern, has discovered a single one of the many wonderful characteristics whose presence I have demonstrated in both natural and violent movements, so that I can reasonably call it a "new science" discovered by myself from its very foundation."[45]

One can here recognize the two principal works of Galileo, the "Dialogue," and the "Discourses and Demonstrations." The negotiations ended in July with his nomination as "First Mathematician and Philosopher of the Grand Duke of Tuscany," coupled with the appreciable dispensation from any necessity to teach. In the spring of the following year, Galileo went to Rome, where he stayed from the end of March to the beginning of June. There he met the Jesuit professors of the Roman College, who confirmed the truth of his discoveries by their observations at the *specola* (observatory) of the college. He was admitted to the Lincean Academy and feted there. The Academy decided to publish at its own expense the work he was in course of writing, "Description and Demonstration on the Subject of Sunspots."[46]

The Censure of Copernican Astronomy

From the end of 1612 events developed rapidly. Florence was rife with rumor, and anyone who knows the Florentines is aware that they have sharp tongues. Sacred eloquence had to involve itself in all this. From the pulpit of the monastery of St. Mark, the Dominican Niccolò Lorini took issue vigorously against "Ipernic" and the "diabolical sect of mathematicians," in November 1613.

A year later, on December 2, 1614, another Dominican, Tomasso Caccini, returned to the attack during an Advent sermon delivered in the monastery church of New St. Mary's. Before explaining the tenth chapter of the Book of Joshua, which relates how the latter stopped the sun on the plain of Gibeon until complete victory of the Israelite forces, Fr. Caccini cried out in the course of a moving peroration: "Men of Galilee [Galileo], why do you stand here looking up at the sky?"[47] Did

45. EN, X, 348–53.

46. *Istoria e Dimostrazioni intorno alle Macchie Solari e loro accidenti comprese in tre lettere scritte all'Ill.mo Sig. Marco Velseri Linceo dal Sig. Galileo Galilei Linceo* (Rome, Giacomo Macardi, 1613).

47. The fact is reported much later in the *Lettere inedite di Uomini Illustri* of Angelo Fabroni (Florence, 1773–1775), I, p. 47. The diatribes of Frs. Caccini and Lorini were probably inspired by the first refutation of Copernican astronomy, by the Dominican Giovanni M. Tolosoni. See I. S. Camporeale, O.P., "Umanesimo e Teologia tra' 400 e 500," *Memorie Domenicane*, new series, 8–9 (1977–1978), 414–16.

he count on winning over to his side those who laughed? But are we not in the full tide of the baroque? At that time one did not hold back from any effect or any abuse of figurative meaning.[48]

Uneasy at the turn of events in these attacks, Galileo wrote to his friend and close confidant, the Benedictine Benedetto Castelli, who was also his collaborator in the observations of the phases of Venus and the sunspots, a letter on the interpretation of the holy scriptures in matters of natural philosophy. This was the first of three letters on the same subject, called "Copernican letters," the other two being addressed to Piero Dini (February 16, 1615) and to Princess Marie-Christine de Lorraine, grand duchess (1615).

A misguided apologetic has reproached Galileo with having involved himself in questions not within his competence. This reproach was not leveled at him during his lifetime. The much-decried post-Tridentine mentality did not recognize a certain narrowness in exaggerated clericalism, a much more recent phenomenon. At that time it was admitted that the Bible is the patrimony of all Christians, even if its interpretation is determined by the ecclesiastical magisterium, ordinary or extraordinary.

More subtly, Galileo has been reproached with having put himself in the position of a buffoon, wanting to put the clergy under instruction, inasmuch as he had wished to use the Bible to prove the truth of Copernicanism. In my opinion, one should not be deceived by assuming even that Galileo took the position: "All things being considered, even I am able to have recourse to scripture to support what I propose, though basing myself on other reasons." A pugnacious polemicist by his gifts and by inclination, Galileo never gave up, and he hardly let pass occasions when he could argue by retort. But the basis of his thought is beyond doubt: God, in self-revelation to humankind through the words of human intermediaries, did not intend to give lessons in the natural sciences. Besides, even the planets known to the ancients are not mentioned in the books of the Bible.

The matter was brought before the Holy Office by a denunciation made by the Dominican Lorini, in February 1615. The theologian consulters delivered their expert conclusion in the session of February 23, 1616.

---

48. The play on words in the exclamation cited in the previous reference, referring to the Acts of the Apostles 1:11, is perhaps again to be found in the poem composed by Thomas Seggeth, inserted in the *Narratio de observatis a se quatuor Jovis satellibus* of Johannes Kepler (Frankfurt, 1611; reprinted in Florence in the same year). In writing "O Galilean, you have conquered the heavens," Seggeth could also have been thinking about the exclamation of the Emperor Julian the Apostate: "Thou hast won, Galilean!" One finds an allusion of the same nature in the letter of Bartolomeo Imperiali to Galileo, March 21, 1626 (EN, XIII, 314).

Two propositions attributed to Copernicus were censured. The proposition: "The sun is the center of the world [universe] and consequently is immobile" was judged "incongruous and formally heretical"; the second: "The earth is not the center of the world, and is not immobile, but is both wholly in motion, and also in diurnal rotation" was judged "meriting the same censure [as the first] in philosophy, and from the point of view of theological truth being also erroneous with regard to the faith."[49] Clumsy propositions and inadequate qualifications, emerging from a patched-up consultation, which had at no time been accompanied by serious debate. The censure was submitted to the General Congregation of the Inquisition, on February 25, and was ratified by Pope Paul V. At the session of the following week, on March 3, a decree was promulgated conferring executive validity on the censure; *De revolutionibus orbium caelestium* was inscribed in the Index of forbidden books "until corrected."[50]

Galileo had not been put into the role of a defendant, and one speaks improperly of a "first trial" that would have been held. It is nevertheless highly significant that on February 26, the day after the work of Copernicus had been put on the Index, Cardinal Robert Bellarmine of the Holy Office summoned Galileo to an audience in the presence of the commissioner general, the Dominican Michelangelo Seghizzi, to inform him of the condemnation of Copernicus's book and to invite him to cease teaching, publicly defending, and expounding Copernican astronomy. For the first time Galileo was officially recognized as the chief spokesman of Copernicanism.

How did the audience unfold? The answer to this question goes far behind anecdotal history, for it marks the beginning of a period of

49. Giorgio de Santillana, *The Crime of Galileo* (University of Chicago Press, 1955), chap. 7, "The Decree of Interdiction"; idem; "Nuove ipotesi sul processo di Galileo," in *Saggi su Galileo Galilei raccolti e pubblicati a cura di Carlo Maccagni* (publication of the National Committee for the Celebrations of the Fourth Centenary of the Birth of Galileo (Florence, G. Berbèra, 1972) pp. 474–87.

50. The decree of condemnation made a distinction between the astronomical hypothesis and its theological interpretation. Works such as those of the Carmelite Paul Foscarini, which proposed a reconciliation of Copernican astronomy with the biblical picture of the world, were proscribed and ordered to be destroyed. The *Commentaire du Livre de Job*, of the Augustinian Diego de Zuñiga, which gave favorable mention of the doctrines of Copernicus, had its dissemination suspended "until correction" of the incriminating passages. Copernicus's work fell under this latter kind of censure. The difference between the qualification of the correctors of the Holy Office and the decree of the censure of the Congregation of the Index of proscribed books is doubtless echoed in the report given by G. F. Buonamici in his *Journal*: "Paul V was of the opinion that it was necessary to declare the work of Copernicus to be contrary to the faith, whereas Cardinals Caetani and Maffeo Barberini openly opposed the pope, who ended by coming over to their good reasons" (EN, XV, 3).

Galileo's career that we can truly call Copernican and it imparts a disastrous turn of events to what follows. Let us say that it was to act as a time bomb.

Cardinal Robert Bellarmine had received from Cardinal Millini, prefect of the Holy Office, instructions as to the procedure to follow. At this point I need to invite the reader to follow me into the mysteries of canon law. To reduce Galileo to obedience, three successive stages were foreseen in order to meet three different eventualities:

1. Cardinal Bellarmine would invite Galileo by a "warning *(monitum)* to submit to the consequences of the censure incurred by the works of Copernicus.

2. In the event that Galileo objected, Cardinal Bellarmine should then proceed to a formal injunction *(praeceptum)*.

3. Finally, in the event that this did not suffice, Galileo should be formally indicted and arrested.

To the present day nobody knows exactly what transpired. Here I shall summarize one of the most likely scenarios, following the account of the facts proposed by Stillman Drake.[51] Cardinal Bellarmine, whose own "Controversies" had been placed on the Index by Sixtus V in 1590 "until corrected" *(donec corregetur)*, and who, himself a Jesuit, had consulted his professor confreres of the Roman College, was rather benevolent toward Galileo. He seems to have been content with the "warning," at the same time advising Galileo to speak of Copernicum astronomy only *ex hypothesi*, by way of supposition, while awaiting the time when he would be able to furnish more decisive proofs, if this should ever be possible. Seghizzi, more suspicious, was convinced that Galileo would not give in so easily, and that being so deeply committed, he would certainly raise objections. Thus, before the audience took place, he prepared the draft of the formal injunction that figures in the dossier of instructions of the affair. It was placed there inopportunely, all the more so because, without the signatures of the relevant authorities, it had no validity as a trial record.

The situation became increasingly complicated. The recommendation to keep to the cautious attitude of one who does not in any way speak of a confirmed hypothesis came to Galileo at the very moment when he had put the finishing touches to the physical proof that he thought he had discovered in favor of Copernicanism. In effect, despite the remonstrations of the grand duke's ambassador not to go there, Galileo

---

51. This interpretation is to be found in Appendix A of the English version of the book by Ludovico Geymonat, *Galileo Galilei* (Turin, Einaudi, 1957); transl. by Prof. S. Drake, New York, 1965). Appendix B gives the reply by Giorgio de Santillana (pp. 221–25).

arrived in Rome at the end of 1615 to make a final effort to save the Copernican cause. In the gardens of the Medici villa, residence of the ambassador, as a first salvo he had written the "Discourse on the Ebb and Flow of the Sea," which, on January 8, 1616, he had addressed to Alexander Orsini, who had just been made a cardinal.[52] The three letters to Mark Welser, published in 1613 under the title "History and Demonstrations concerning Sunspots," had been reprinted in Rome. Now the third of these "Roman letters" contains the first apology for Copernican astronomy published by Galileo. The ecclesiastical authorities allowed the republishing of this work without reacting. In it for the first time Galileo expounded an astronomical proof that he always held to be one of the strongest, derived from the observation of seasonal variations of the trajectory followed by sunspots.

He returns to it again in the "Dialogue" where the argument derived from the rotation of the sunspots is developed on the third day. He linked it with the argument from ocean tides taken up on the fourth and last day:

> From the discourse of these four days we have thus drawn great attestations in favor of the Copernican system; among which three have shown themselves to be sufficiently conclusive:
> — the first, the taking of the stations and retrogradations of the planets by reason of their approaches and recessions relative to the earth:
> — the second, from the revolution of the sun on its own axis and that which is observed in the sunspots;
> — the third, from the ebb and flow of the sea.[53]

These three major proofs follow the Aristotelian schema of reasoning *ex suppositione*:[54] granted the twofold movement of the earth, annual and diurnal, the explanation of planetary appearances, sunspot trajectories, oceanic tides, and trade winds becomes particularly simple and clear. Galileo had observed that sunspots appear on the eastern edge of the solar disc and disappear two weeks later on the western edge after having described the arc of an ellipse, the projection of a circle as viewed from earth. He had deduced that the sun is impelled by a rotation from west to east, taking a little less than a month. And he perceived as a consequence that when the earth, in its revolution around

---

52. Fourteen manuscript copies, of which twelve date back to the 17th century, of the "Discourse" published in vol. 5 of the *Edizione Nazionale*, pp. 371–95, are preserved to this day. The Barberini collection in the Vatican Library contains one of them (MS 4271).

53. EN,VII, 487, LS, 546.

54. William A. Wallace, O. P., *Prelude to Galileo: Essays on Medieval and Sixteenth-Century Sources of Galileo's Thought* (Hingham, Mass., D. Reidel Publ. Co., 1981), part 3, chap. 8, "Galileo and Reasoning *ex suppositione*," pp. 129–60.

the sun in the ecliptic, occupies a position such that the radius vector joining the earth's center to the sun's center is in the sun's equatorial plane, the sunspots then appear to follow rectilinear trajectories, instead of their usual elliptical trajectories. From this he concluded that the annual revolution of the earth associated with the semimonthly rotation of the sun sufficed to explain the annual cycle of variations of the monthly trajectories of the sunspots, even to the extent that, according to him, the annual rotation of the earth around the sun coupled with its daily rotation on its own axis (spin) explains the twice-daily period of the ocean tides:

> Such are the surprising mutations which, according to my host [Salviati is speaking of his friend the "Lincean Academician," Galileo], should appear periodically in the journeyings of the sunspots, if it is admitted as true that the earth has an annual movement, and that the sun, established at the center of the ecliptic, turns upon itself [spins] about an axis that is not perpendicular to but inclined to the plane of the ecliptic.[55]

The physical proof drawn from the tides was even more important for Galileo for two reasons. First, as an able polemicist he liked to have recourse to arguments *ad hominem* and by retort, for their argumentative value. Here he seems to be saying to his adversaries: "Ptolemaic astronomers and Copernican astronomers use the geometric construction of epicycles to explain the apparent irregularities of the planetary motions. The Ptolemaists place the earth at the center of deferent circles; the Copernicans, on the contrary, place the sun there. But the hypothesis of epicycles has never been able to settle matters between them and has never given judgment to one group rather than to the other. Well then, as for myself, I am going to use it to prove the truth of Copernican astronomy."

What is comprised in the hypothesis of epicycles? Interpreting the trajectory of a planet as the resultant of an epicyclic motion consists in making the given planet P orbit on the circumference of a circle (epicycle) that has a simple reference point C as its center (Fig. 1). This latter point in turn orbits on the circumference of a circle with its center at T (the earth, according to the geostatic or geocentric point of view). With the requisite geometric virtuosity, one will always succeed in finding a ratio of the radius CP of the epicycle to the radius TC of the deferent such that one can account for the periods of time in which the movement of P, as observed from T, seems to change direction (retrogradations) and the periods of time during which P slows down its progression to the point of seeming motionless to an observer located at

---

55. EN, VII, 372–73; LS, 412–20. The passage cited is found EN, VII, 379; LS, 419.

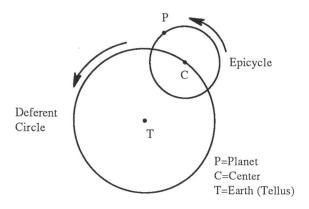

Fig. 1. The Epicycles of Ptolemy.

T (stations). Within the framework of epicycles it was more difficult but nevertheless not impossible to explain the variations in the luminosity of the planets as a function of their approaches and recessions with respect to the earth. Farthest recession or apogee is when the points P, C, T are aligned in the sequence TCP; close approach or perigee occurs when the points P, C, T are aligned in the order TPC.

Epicycles played the same role in the heliocentric system of Copernicus. In fact the *De revolutionibus* follows the *Almagest* of Ptolemy in strict parallelism, chapter by chapter and table by table. One can even regard the Copernican system as an astronomical simplification of the Ptolemaic system because the models chosen by Copernicus for the movement of each planet even more require circles. Morever, Copernicus was too scrupulous an astronomer, rigorously attentive to the relevant data, to locate the sun at the exact center of the planetary system;[56] he placed it at some distance from the geometric center of the orbits of the planets. He also drew attention to the lunar theory of Ptolemy and its incompatability with the observable parallaxes.[57] But it was above all the discussion of the distinction between inferior (inner) and superior (outer) planets that brought about confrontation between the Ptolemic and Copernican astronomic systems.[58] In brief, the greater

56. O. Neugebauer, *The Exact Sciences in Antiquity* (Providence, R. I., 2nd ed., 1957), § 82. A remarkably clear and simple exposition of the theory of epicycles is to be found in § 64.

57. Ibid., § 77.

58. Ibid., § 54.

simplicity of the Copernican system is of a different order from that of astronomical description: it is conceptual and cosmological. It laid the foundations for conceiving the solar system. One intuition in particular convinced Copernicus of the truth of his astronomic system: by imagining a planetary system nearly centered on the sun, he was finally able to gain an idea of the distances effectively separating the celestial bodies, in terms of heliocentric distance — that is, distances relative to the sun, something that the geocentric picture of the world did not allow.

Now let us come to the second particular feature of the physical proof — namely, explanation of the tides. Galileo had understood the thought of Copernicus in depth, even if he does not seem to have been an assiduous reader of *De revolutionibus*: the physical truth of Copernicanism interested him much more than its astronomic truth. Or let us say, more accurately, that for him, as for Kepler, astronomy is celestial physics, and that astronomic truth appeared to him to be a physical truth concerning the constitution of the world — physical, and even mechanical.

Galileo felt triumphant because he had thought of keeping to a proof that simultaneously involved terrestrial and celestial physics. Now this proof is strictly mechanical: it explains the periodic movement of the oceans by another movement, that of the earth. And luckily, the epicycles, which had hitherto served only as an expedient in astronomical descriptions, for the first time fulfilled a new function: they became a kinematic model.

In effect, if, as in Figure 2, we consider a point P on the terrestrial surface that rotates daily about the center of the earth, T, and if T in turn orbits annually around the sun, S, then once a day at P the speed of diurnal rotation adds to the speed of annual revolution; once a day at P the rotational speed substracts from the speed of revolution. The speed resulting from the two motions of the earth varies continuously; from P2 to P4 part of the rotational speed is subtracted from the annual speed of revolution; from P to P2 part of the rotational speed is added to the speed of revolution.

If, instead of considering an isolated point, we think of an arc of a circle that represents an ocean surface, we see that different points of the same ocean arc move at different speeds. Galileo allowed himself to be guided by an analogy:

> We can illustrate these effects [the tides] more clearly and render them more manifest to the sense [of sight] by the example of one of those barges that come from Lizzafusina, filled with fresh water for use in the city of Venice. Imagine, then, one of these barges coming at medium speed across the lagoon, placidly bearing the water in its hold. But then the barge slows

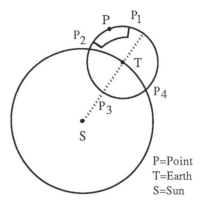

Fig. 2. The Tides and the Double Movement of the Earth according to Galileo.

down markedly, either to avoid shallow water or because of some other obstacle that opposes it. The water contained [in the hold] will not lose, to the same extent and in the same time, the impulse *(impetus)* that had been imparted to it; on the contrary, conserving its impulse, the water will flow toward the bow where it will rise significantly, while falling at the stern. On the other hand, if the same barge, in the setting of its uniform course, should undergo a significant increase in speed, the water contained [in the hold], before adapting itself to the new speed, persevering in its slowness, will remain behind — that is, toward the stern, where it will consequently rise, while falling at the bow. This effect is clear and beyond doubt, and can be experimentally tested at any time.[59]

It would be too hasty to retain from the Galilean explanation of the tides only its main fault — that of being erroneous. Certainly it has been definitively supplanted by the Newtonian explanation, which attributes the principal cause of the tides to the conjoint attractive influence of the moon and sun upon the earth. Nevertheless, it was not entirely erroneous. On the one hand, the effect due to the composition of the two movements of the earth is real, but the rise and fall of ocean waters that can be attributed to it is of the order of several centimeters, and would be quite insufficient to account for the tides that we observe. On the other hand, Galileo set forth valuable considerations on the oscillations of a liquid mass, which anticipated the results of a chapter in the history of the mechanics of fluids.

59. EN, VII, 450–51; LS, 503.

Winning Cause or Losing Cause?

After the censure of 1616, Galileo did not whisper a word about the Copernican cause for seven years, even though he held in his hand all the proof that he was to expound in the "Dialogue." He found himself engaged in two astronomical debates that did not involve Copernicanism, at least not directly:

The first had as its aim the identification of the nature of sunspots. Galileo's opponent was the Jesuit Christopher Scheiner, who taught mathematics and astronomy at Ingolstadt from 1610 to 1616, at Innsbruck from 1616 to 1620, and at Freiburg from 1620 to 1624. A specialist in the study of atmospheric refraction, Scheiner held that sunspots are produced by swarms of asteroids orbiting the sun, whereas Galileo maintained that it was a question of phenomena properly solar and whose location was the very surface of the sun.

The Galilean thesis dealt a new blow to the supposed immutability of the celestial world. A particularly tough adversary, Scheiner returned to the attack in the *Rosa Ursini sive sol* ["The rose or the sun of the Orsinis"], published in 1630 in Bracciano, the fief of the Orsini family. Galileo's disciples jokingly called it the *Ursa Rosina* ("the rose-colored bear"). Unshakeable, Scheiner was to set to work furiously at the moment of the trial directed against Galileo by writing in Vienna the *Prodromus pro Sole Mobili* ("the forerunner of the mobile sun"), the publication of which was to be forbidden by Jesuit superiors until 1651.

The second debate had as its aim to define the nature of comets and brought Galileo into opposition with the Jesuit astronomer Orazio Grassi at the Roman College. The positions were to some extent the reverse of the previous debate. Grassi was no fool. He had been a "supporter" of Galileo's astronomical discoveries, and it only needed the appearance of three comets in 1618 — an omen of disaster? — for friendship to be succeeded by animosity, followed by hatred. On this occassion, Grassi had given a public lecture, which he subsequently published anonymously under the title "Astronomical Disputation on the Subject of Three Comets."[60] In essence he was in the right: he upheld the celestial origin of the comets and their movement in a circular orbit. But he had a dull spirit: he reasoned in a manner that could be adopted only in Rome or Salamanca, deploying the entire arsenal of syllogistics, which could have been forgiven if he had not cluttered up his arsenal with a hodgepodge of classical erudition.

---

60. Orazio Grassi, S. J., *De tribus cometis Disputatio astronomica publice habita in Collegio Romano Societatis Jesu ab uno ex patribus eiusdem Societatis* (Rome, Jacopo Mascardi, 1619).

Galileo had inherited the very sure taste of the masters of the Renaissance, and in his eyes an esthetic fault was never found without an accompanying error of thought.[61] Furthermore he replied indirectly to the thesis defended by Grassi, through the mediation of Mario Giudicci, who published "The Discourse on the Comets" in Florence.[62] Riposte and counterriposte rapidly poisoned their relationship. In the form of an anagram, and under the pseudonym Lotario Sarsi, Grassi replied in 1619 with the *Libra astronomica ac philosophica* ("the astronomical and philosophical balance").[63]

Stung to the quick by this invitation to "weigh his arguments better," Galileo replied four years later in a polemical and methodological masterpiece, *Il Saggiatore* ("the assayer" — that is, the goldsmith's precision balance or scales).[64] The tale of lunges and counterlunges ends here. Grassi left the arena defeated, and the vanquished always cut a sorry figure, a thing he had in no way deserved. Galileo had administered to him an admirable lesson on how to reason scientifically, but had done so in the service of an erroneous thesis. Galileo continued in fact to think that comets were a meteorological phenomenon brought about by the action of the sun's rays in the higher regions of the earth's atmosphere.

Galileo had become an old man. Although painful arthritis, contracted during his years at Padua, periodically afflicted him, he had a robust constitution and a longevity exceptional for that time. Since the 1620s it is true that he found himself surrounded by young disciples, but many of those who had participated in his struggles for the Copernican cause had disappeared. The two friends to whom he had confided the discussion of his ideas in the "Dialogue" died before the definitive

61. See the celebrated essay of Erwin Panofsky, "Galileo as a Critic of the Arts," *Isis*, 47 (1956) 3–15. The author points out "the Galilean presupposition, in conformity with classicism, in favor of simplicity, of order, and of separation of genres, and on the contrary his opposition to complication, disorder, and any form of fusion" (p. 9). It has often been noted that Galileo preferred Aristotle to Tasso.

62. *Discorso delle Comete di Mario Guiducci, fatto de lui nell'Accademia fiorentina nel suo medesimo consolato* (Florence, 1619), reproduced in the Edizione Nazionale, vol 6.

63. *Libra astronomica ac philosophica, qua Gallilaei Galilaei opiniones da cometis a Mario Giudiccio in Florentina Academia expositae, atque in lucem nuper editae, examinaretur a Lothario Sarsi Sigensano* (Perugia, Marco Naccarini, 1619). *Lothario Sarsio Sigensano* represents the anagram of *Horatio Grassio Savonensi*. The anagram is imperfect, because instead of a "v" there is an "l," which caused Fr. Grassi's adversaries to say that he did not come from "Savona" but from "Salona," known for its buxom women.

64. *Il Saggiatore, nel quale con bilancia esquisita e giusta si ponderano le cose contenute nella libra astronomica e filosofica di Lotario Sarsi Sigensano, scritto in forma di lettere all'Ill.mo et Rever.mo Mons.re D. Virginio Cesarini, Acc.o Linceo . . .* (Rome, Giacomo Mascardi, 1623; EN, VI, 197–312). The *saggiatore* is the goldsmith's scales, which serve to weigh ounces of gold and carats of precious stones, and which is therefore much more precise than the cruder steelyard.

drawing up of the text, Filippo Salviati in 1614, and Gianfrancesco Sagredo in March 1620. Fra' Paolo Sarpi had departed this world in January 1623. The same fate had befallen the judges before whom Galileo had had to appear. Robert Bellarmine, worn out by his many duties carried out in the Roman Curia, died in Rome on September 17, 1621. Father Seghizzi, meanwhile nominated bishop of Lodi, carried with him to the grave the secret concerning the formal injuction. Had it been applied or not? It will probably never be made known.

A memorable day was to impart a new course to events: On August 16, 1623, the conclave of cardinals elected as successor to Pope Gregory XV (1621–1623) Cardinal Maffeo Barberini, who took the name Urban VIII. The unexpected but not entirely unpredictable choice was greeted with exultation at the Lincean Academy, and more generally by men of letters and intellectual pursuits. His nephew, a member of the academy and a cardinal of a year's standing, was then a legate in France. To replace him at the head of the Secretariat of State, the newly elected pope nominated his younger brother Antonio, whom he raised to the cardinalate with effect from October 1624.

In the course of his service as legate in France, Cardinal Francesco Barberini, who was a confrere of Galileo at the Roman Lincean Academy, spoke about him to a Provençal gentleman, a numismatist and bibliophile of great erudition, Nicolas Claude Fabri de Peiresc (1580–1637). He played an important role in the spread of Galilean thought in France. It was not long before it became known to Fermat, Descartes, and Roberval, as well as to all the friends and correspondents of the Minim friar, Marin Mersenne (1588–1648). On his return to Rome, Francesco Barberini directed the Vatican Library, where he established the precious Barberini collection.

In the month of April 1624, Galileo returned to Rome, this time to pay homage to a friend and patron, the new pope, and to offer him in person a copy of "The Assayer," which the Lincean Academy had published at its own expense at the end of the preceding year, and had dedicated to Pope Urban VIII. They had known and esteemed each other for a long time. When Pope Clement VIII (1592–1605) had charged Maffeo Barberini, not yet a cardinal, with the purification of the waters of Lake Trasimeno, he had found excellent expert hydrologists in Benedetto Castelli and Galileo. Later, in the dispute over floating bodies that took place in Florence during the summer of 1611, we find him on the side of Galileo.[65] Had the moment come to reopen the

---

65. *Discorso al Seren.mo don Cosimo II, Gran Duca di Tuscana, intorno alle cose che stanno in sù l'acqua, o che in quella si muovono* (Florence, Cosimo Giunti, 1612; EN, IV, 57–141).

Copernican cause? Galileo thought so, without any presentiment of a dramatic outcome.

It is quite significant that in 1624 Galileo had taken up his pen to reply to an attack launched eight years previously by Francesco Ingoldi, an active and enterprising member of the Roman Curia, in his *De situ et quiete terrae contra Copernici systema disputatio* ("disputed question on the site and quiescence of the earth against the system of Copernicus"). Galileo wrote him a long "Reply" when Ingoldi became secretary of Propaganda Fide, founded in 1622 by Pope Gregory XV and, as a man well versed in the knowledge of oriental languages, was working on the organization of the Vatican Polyglot Press and at the Urbanianum College for the training of missionaries. A man of vast designs, Urban VIII aimed at centering the administration of Catholic missions in Rome to distance them from colonial powers. It is in the remarkable "Reply to Francesco Ingoldi"[66] that there is to be found for the first time the thesis of the mechanical relativity of motions in the very terms that will be taken up again on the second day of the "Dialogue":

> SIMPLICIUS: According to the opinions of all groups of philosophers, sense and experience serve us as escorts when we philosophize; but in the position of Copernicus, it befalls the senses to deceive greatly, for they see close by and in the pure media very heavy bodies falling in a straight line by a hair's breadth. Now in all this, according to Copernicus, sight is deceived in this very clear perception, because the motion is not as straight as it seems, but is a mixture of rectilinear and circular.

> SALVIATI: This is the first objection raised by Aristotle and Ptolemy, and by all their disciples. This has been answered in full and has been shown to be a paralogism. It has been clearly illustrated how the movement that is common to us and to other mobiles is [for us] as if it had not been.[67]

It is a question of a mechanical relativity that adds something to the simple optical relativity of the displacement of a boat along a shore, a fact known and commented on since antiquity. Aristotle understood the optical relativity of displacements so well that he attributed the scintillation of the stars to a trembling of the eye, which has difficulty in keeping its sight fixed on such a remote object.[68] Galileo states precisely that in the cabin of a boat that traverses the sea at constant velocity, there results no mechanical effect that could help passengers to determine whether they are in motion or at rest. He gives this particularly striking example: A Venetian merchant, en route from Venice to Alexandria

66. *Lettera a Franceso Ingoli in risposta alla Disputatio de situ et quiete Terra*, 1624 e (EN, VI, 509–61); the text of the *Disputatio* of Ingoli is to be found in EN, V, 397–412.
67. EN VII, 273; LS, 301.
68. Aristotle, *De caelo*, book 2, 8.

and writing a letter in his cabin, moves his hand to form the letters in the same way as he would on dry land. Let us imagine for a moment that his hand had not participated in the movement of the boat: in order to form a single letter of the alphabet, it would have had to move an arms's length![69]

After reflections on motions caused by gravity and reflections on telescopic images formed in conditions of immensity, the consideration of the relativity of motions in inertial frames of reference and the consequences for the perception of mobility is the third of the themes that have contributed most to the advance of the Copernican cause and to the progressive transformation of Copernican astronomy into a new cosmology.

Urged by his friends, and in particular by his friends in Rome, Federico Cesi and Giovanni Ciampoli, to write a definitive version of *De systemate mundi*, Galileo finally set to work. But his health, which was from now on unsettled, put his initial enthusiasm under severe trial and the work dragged on from 1628 to 1629.

Scipion Chiaramonte, praised by Galileo in "The Assayer" for his position in the dispute over the comets, taught philosophy at Padua from 1627 to 1636, and reopened the Copernican debate. In two works he strove to save the Aristotelian thesis of the unalterability of the heavens by using syllogisms and risky astronomical demonstrations.[70] He went pell-mell at Tycho-Brahe, Kepler, and Galileo. A single example'of his syllogisms will suffice:

> If one admits the Copernican hypothesis of the mobility of the earth, three movements will be needed to explain it; now the earth, which is a simple body, cannot be activated by a threefold movement; the hypothesis of Copernicus should therefore be rejected.[71]

More subtle but also fragile were the objections raised by Chiaramonte:

> If the earth does not occupy the center of the world [universe], the celestial vault should appear to us as dissymetric; and if the earth has an annual revolution about the sun, the stars should seem to suffer displacement relative to fixed bodies.

We have already seen how Galileo, basing himself on the Copernican premise of the immensity of the universe, had demonstrated by a calculation of the parallaxes how the miniscule diameter of the earth's orbit around the sun relative to the earth's distance from the stars

---

69. EN, VII, 197–98; LS, 210–11.

70. Scipion Chiaramonte (1565–1652), *Antitycho* (Cesena, 1621); *De tribus novis stellis quae annis 1572, 1600, 1604 comparuere . . .* (Cesena, 1628).

71. Cited as a note by Libero Sosio, in his edition of the "Dialogue," LS, 300.

rendered imperceptible the consequences that one could properly draw from Copernican astronomy. Galileo expounds these results on the third day of the "Dialogue."

The intervention of Chiaramonte during the writing of the "Dialogue" was perhaps an inconvenience, burdening the composition of the work by several digressions, but it also had the advantage of renewing contacts between Galileo and Kepler. Kepler had sent Galileo a copy of his "Summary of Copernican Astronomy,"[72] but had found himself in disagreement with Galileo on the question of the comets. Always faithful in his friendships, Kepler defended the memory of his master Tycho-Brahe against Chiaramonte in the *Hyperaspistes*,[73] in an appendix to which he dealt with the disputes that had set Galileo against Grassi. He anticipated that there would be no lack of occasions for Galileo to withdraw the praises he had bestowed on Chiaramonte. Mathias Bernegger, friend and correspondent of Kepler, who was to translate the "Dialogue" into Latin several years later, followed the progress being made in the writing of the work.

At Christmas 1629 Galileo informed Cesi that the "Dialogue" was practically complete. At that time he thought of giving it the title "Dialogue Concerning the Ebb and Flow of the Sea." A month previously, in a letter dated November 19, 1629, Galileo had consulted Giovanfrancesco Buonamici, a diplomat of the grand duke's on service in Spain, an expert in navigation, and moreover Galileo's distant relative by marriage:

> Because we are engaged in talking about marine matters, Monseigneur should know that I am on the point of concluding some dialogues in which I treat of the constitution of the universe, and among the principal themes I write about the ebb and flow of the sea, giving to understand that I have found the true cause of this effect — a cause far removed from that to which it has hitherto been attributed. I take it to be true, and so do all those with whom I have spoken about it. And because I do not have the leisure to set out on a ,voyage, and because an abundance of particular observations could confirm what I am expounding, I wish to beg Monseigneur to be kind enough to confer with someone who has done much navigation and who has had the curiosity to make some observations on the data of nature in the course of his navigations. In particular I wish to be assured of the truth of something that would very suitably confirm my thoughts — namely,

72. Johannes Kepler, *Epitome Astronomiae Copernicanae, Libri I, II, III, de Doctrina Sphaerica* (Linz, 1618); *Liber IV, Physica Coelestis* (Linz, 1620); *Libri V, VI, VII, Doctrina Theorica* (Frankfurt, 1621).

73. *Tychonis Brahei Dani Hyperaspistes adversus Scipionis Claramontii Anti-Tychoneum* (Frankfurt, 1625). It was a Baroque title: *aspistes* is a soldier furnished with a buckler. It should thus be translated: The unconquerably armed defender of Tycho-Brahe against the Anti-Tycho of Scipion Chiaramonte."

whether it is true that while navigating on course to the West Indies between the tropics — that is, toward the equinoctial line, one finds a perpetual wind that blows from the levant and readily propels ships.[74]

From the evidence, Galileo was in the course of bringing complementary support to the physical proof that he drew from the tides, which he clung to because of the "geostrophic" explanation of the trade winds that he proposed. His theory of the trade winds is not entirely false, any more than is his theory of the tides; nevertheless the trade winds are only the secondary effect of a vast convection air current from the equator to the poles and from the poles to the equator. The question of the tides, moreover, imposed itself upon the attention of his contemporaries, and the Galilean explanation, as the letter to Buonamici shows, encountered rival explanations, that of Francis Bacon (1561–1626), for example, contained in the *Novum Organon* (1620), which incorporated the terminology of his own *De fluxu et refluxu maris* (of uncertain date), or that of the bishop of Spalato (Split), Marantonio de Dominis (1566–1624), in *Euripus sive sententia de fluxu et refluxu maris* (Rome, 1624).

Submitted to the Inquisitor of Florence, the manuscript of the "Dialogue" was sent to the Roman Inquisition, which entrusted its review to the master of the sacred palace, the Dominican Niccolò Riccardi, better known by his nickname *Padre Mostro* ("Father Monster") bestowed upon him by the king of Spain, who was as impressed by his erudition as by his corpulence. Fr. Riccardi was not particularly prejudiced against Galileo. Benedetto Castelli, who kept Galileo informed as to all the transactions going on in Rome, wrote to him on February 26, 1628:

> In the presence of His Excellency Ascanio Piccolomini, I have spoken to Father Monster, endeavoring to get him to say what he thought about the opposition from Sarsi [the Jesuit Grassi]. He tells me that your opinions do not run directly counter to the faith, because they are simply philosophical, and that he would do all that you might have asked of him; but that he had not intended to make a public showing, in order to be able to help you on any occasion that might bring you irritations on the part of the Tribunal of the Holy Office, where he is a qualificator. In effect, if he spoke out prior to an official hearing, he would not be able to speak then. And he told me

74. Letter of Galileo to Gianfrancesco Buonamici, dated from Florence, November 19, 1629 (EN, XIV, 54). Buonamici (1592–1669) in the course of 1629 had become an in-law of Galileo after Vincenzo, Galileo's son, had married his stepsister, Sestilia Bocchimeri. A diplomat in the service of the grand duke of Tuscany, he was at that time posted to Madrid. He should not be confused with Francesco Buonamici (1535–1613), Aristotelian professor at Pisa and author of a work *De motu* (Florence, 1591).

In his reply dated February 1, 1630, Buonamici directed Galileo to consult the observations of Lodovico Guicciardini and Antonio Herrera.

once more that on your account he had suffered some rough weather on the part of his colleagues.[75]

Things dragged on, which aroused mistrust on both sides. Galileo spent the months of May and June in Rome trying to obtain permission to have his work printed. At first he might well have believed that proceedings against him would come to nothing. Fr. Riccardi proposed revisions of matters of detail, which were nevertheless not insignificant, such as putting "the world" where Galileo had written "the universe"; modifying the title, which ought not to mention the tides, and above all, adding a preface in which he would recall the censure of the Copernican doctrine in 1616, and in which he would reaffirm his neutrality in expounding reasons for or against the Copernican system. This was asking him to dance on a tightrope. But Galileo agreed. The proofs of the preface were submitted to Pope Urban VIII on July 31, 1630. The pope demanded that at the conclusion of the work there should figure argumentation as to the divine omnipotence, to which he attributed particular importance.

From then on, vicissitudes and setbacks followed each other in a headlong rush. Galileo passed through a difficult time. Physically depressed by persistent fever, he witnessed the sorrows of bereavement multiplying the gaps around him: on August 1, 1630, he lost his friend and protector, Federico Cesi; Kepler, his companion in the Copernican struggles, died in Regensburg on November 30 of the same year. Plague raged in Rome. At the Roman College, where all the Barberinis had studied, sentiments with regard to him had radically changed. The marked esteem of the times of Fathers Paolo Valla, Muzio Vitelleschi, and Christopher Clavius had given way to a tenacious animosity against the one who had attacked the honor of the Society of Jesus. Galileo did not conceal the mistrust in which he held Fathers Scheiner, Grassi, and Cabeo:

> I believe that we will not witness greater subtleties than those to which the Reverend Fathers have accustomed us, subtleties that, in my opinion, are great trivialities in the matter of philosophy. In connection with this I hear it said that (*Rosa Ursini*) is having a long treatise *de maculis solis* printed in Bracciano; its length makes me suspect that it is full of blunders, which, by their infinite number, can truly blemish pages in which truth occupies only a small place.[76]

Having once more returned to Rome in the spring of 1631, Galileo

75. Letter of Benedetto Castelli to Galileo, February 26, 1628 (EN, XIII, 393–94). On the personality of Fr. Riccardi, see A. K. Eszer, O. P., "Niccolò Riccardi, O. P., *il Padre Mostro* (1585–1639)," *Angelicum*, 60 (1983) 3, 428–61.
76. Letter of Galileo to Cesare Marsili, April 21, 1629 (EN, XIV, 35–36).

lost his patience. Barely in possession of the imprimatur that Fr. Riccardi sent to him on April 25, on condition that the corrections be made to the text as foreseen, and that the "Dialogue" be printed in Rome, Galileo made a pretext of the danger of infection by the plague and took the manuscript to Florence where he had it printed in the Landini printery. It was a fatal mistake.

In February 1632 the first printed copies arrived in Rome. Taking advantage of a journey of the archbishop of Florence to the Holy Sea, Galileo entrusted to him two copies to transmit in homage. One of them was destined for Cardinal Francesco Barberini. The title of the work was "Dialogue . . . in which in the meetings of four days a dissertation is given on the two principal world systems, the Ptolemaic and Copernican, proposing indiscriminately the philosophical and natural reasons as much in favor of the one as of the other."[77]

Urban VIII was seized by extreme rage. The imprimatur was overruled and annulled. In August the Inquisition notified the Landini printery to suspend dissemination of the "Dialogue," and on September 23 a summons was served at Galileo's residence, requiring him to present himself without delay before the commissioner-general of the Holy Office, the Dominican Vincenzo Maculano. Galileo's first reaction was one of bewilderment: he procrastinated and excused himself on the basis of three medical opinions to the effect that he was unable to face the fatigue of the journey. The pope threatened him with a warrant for forcible transportation.

On February 13 Galileo arrived in a pitiable state in Rome, where, restricted to the premises of the Palace of the Holy Office, he was subjected to judicial interrogation (on April 12 and 30 and June 21). What were the chief points in the accusation? Essentially he was reproached with having disobeyed the formal precept enjoined on him in 1616. Galileo protested that he had received a simple warning, but Maculano, who was nevertheless not at bottom unfavorable to him, showed him the fateful unsigned draft of the formal precept. Galileo found himself in the humiliating position of one who has given reasons for doubting his good faith; and no survivor of what is conveniently called the "first trial" of 1616 was present to give witness. On the other

---

77. *Dialogo di Galileo Galilei Linceo, Matematico sopraordinario dello Studio di Pisa e Filosofo e Matematico primario del Serenissimo Gr. Duca di Toscana, dove ne i congressi di quattro giornate si discorre sopra i due Massimi Sistemi del Mondo, Tolemaico e Copernicano; proponendo indeterminatamente la ragioni folosofiche e naturali tanto per l'una, quanto per l'altra parte* (Florence, Gio. Battista Landini, 1632).
    The Latin translation by Matthias Bernegger, in Augsburg in 1635, after the condemnation of 1633, carried on its frontispiece a quotation from Seneca: *Inter nullos magis quam inter Philosophos esse debet aequa libertas.*

hand, a commission of three theologians, Oregio, Inchofer, and Pasqualigo, submitted the conclusions of their report on April 17: the "Dialogue" was declared to contravene in every respect the decree emanating from the Congregation of the Index in 1616.

On June 22, in the hall of sessions of the Inquisition adjoining the Dominican priory of St. Mary Minerva, Galileo was ordered to abjure the Copernican theory, and was condemned to imprisonment accompanied by penitential practices. All remaining copies of the "Dialogue" were ordered to be destroyed. On the same day Galileo read on his knees the official formula of renunciation and signed it. On the next day he was placed under guarded residence in the Medici villa, home of the ambassador of the grand duke of Tuscany at Trinità dei Monti. The curtain fell on the tragic denouement of the Copernican cause.

Was it the case that Urban VIII who, as late as May 1631 had received Galileo in audience with great marks of "esteem and affection," had thought himself mocked? It has often been claimed that he was offended at finding his own words put into the mouth of Simplicius:

> Always keeping before the eyes of the spirit the very solid doctine that I learned from a very informed and most eminent person, and in which one should rest, I know that both of you [Salviati and Sagredo], to whomsoever may ask you if God in His infinite power and wisdom could have conferred upon the aquatic element the alternating movement that we observed, in a way other than moving the receiver that contains it, I know, I say that you will reply that God could bring about and knows how to bring about this same effect in many ways, and even in ways unthinkable for our intellect.[78]

But it is not true that Simplicius was the dull and simple-minded interlocutor of whom the Dominican Tommaso Campanella wrote to Galileo: "He supplies the amusement in your philosophical comedy by showing at the same time the stupidity of his clique, its verbosity, instability, obstinacy, and all the rest."[79] Galileo loved sarcasm, but he

---

78. EN, VII, 488; LS, 548. It must be conceded that Maffeo Barberini (Pope Urban VIII) was quite logical in his thinking: he sought to uphold in theological argument, to which he so closely held, the distinction between astronomic hypotheses and theological interpretation, a distinction that he had defended in 1616 (see note 50, above). At the time of the condemnation, before Francesco Niccolini, ambassador of the grand duke in Rome and an in-law of Fr. Riccardi, he again alluded to "these difficulties from which we have preserved him [Galileo], since the time we became a cardinal." But what would science have been if it had always to leave the last word to theology? There cannot be true science without the autonomy of science: this was the conviction that gave meaning and significance to the Galilean struggle.

79. Letter from Campanella to Galileo, August 5, 1632 (EN,XIV, 366–67). In the same letter there is to be found: "We certainly have nothing for which to envy Plato. Salviati is a great Socrates who reveals much more than he conceals. As to Sagredo, there is a free intelligence, one not spoiled by the schools and judging all things with much sagacity."

always retained a sense of proportion, which often made him suspicious and reticent with regard to Campanella's opinions.

Urban VIII had explicitly demanded the insertion of the argument contained in the passage quoted in the conclusion of the whole "Dialogue." He was upset not because Galileo had twisted his thought, but because he recoiled sharply from the context that Galileo did not concede him convincing value. Could he yield on a point of this importance? The game was too decisive for him to back out. It was a matter of the autonomy of scientific knowledge relative to theology. For Galileo the explanation of the tides followed from reasoning *ex suppositione*: if the astronomy of Copernicus is true, then the tides are given a mechanical explanation, an explanation that is not only possible, but simple and easy, the most "natural" there could be. In a word it was a question of a physical proof, "experimental" (before the term was in use), based on a verifiable hypothesis.

For Urban VIII, who reasoned as a theologian, reasoning *ex suppositione* could arrive only at a plausible explanation, a "proof" of *convenientia*, congruity. But such a conclusion will never amount to apodictic proof. In his eyes it was presumptuous and strictly impious to claim to penetrate the designs of God in the constitution of the world by means of observation and explanation of a terrestrial phenomenon as limited as the tides of the ocean. One fact can only be the more or less probable token of another fact; only premises of universal validity can lead to rational necessity at the conclusion of a chain of reasoning.

Curiously, Urban VIII conducted his defense in the name of a nominalist theology, which speaks of divine wisdom only in order to make the point that the sole limit to divine power is that God cannot contradict the laws of metaphysics. Rational necessity can only be logical and *a priori*: any human experience whatsoever can serve to manifest it, but no human experience can condition it. Rational knowledge cannot therefore emerge from experimental science.

The Copernican cause emerged from the scene defeated. Galileo paid a heavy price in order that the autonomy of scientific research with regard to theological and metaphysical thought might be won definitively.

Today, no theologian or philosopher would seriously seek to put the matter in doubt.

From Copernican Astronomy to the New Cosmology

The recounting of the relationships of Galileo with the thought of Copernicus, in circumstantial detail, has been necessary to help the reader understand the slow maturing of a study program that gradually became a research program. In the work of Galileo the justification of Copernican astronomy led to the first program of scientific research in modern times. But it should not be forgotten that at no time in his career, not even at the most crucial and dramatic moment of the condemnation, did Galileo occupy his whole spirit, a very vast spirit, with the Copernican cause alone. The summons to appear before the tribunal of the Holy Office surprised him at a time when, worried by the lengthening shadows, he was engaged in the geometry of indivisibles, in the methodology of microscopic observations, in research on the resistance of solid bodies, corpuscular atomism, the nature of heat, and finally, a too often neglected aspect of his work, analysis of the perception of sensible qualities, in particular acoustic perception.

The thought of Galileo and that of Copernicus converge in the "Dialogue Concerning the Two Principal World Systems," a work that took more than twenty years to compose, as much time as Kant's *Critique of Pure Reason*. The "Dialogue," in its four days, has the solidity and complexity of works having undergone a protracted maturation. The first day dismantles the Aristotelian cosmos and designs a new world in which the frontiers between celestial and sublunar regions have been demolished.

The constitution of this world in motion is described on the second and third days. The second day demolishes, one after another, the four traditional objections lodged against the diurnal rotation of the earth from Ptolemy up to Tycho-Brahe: the perpendicular fall of heavy bodies, the identical ranges of artillery pieces in all directions, the everyday experience of the courses followed by clouds and flocks of birds, and the absence of the centrifugal effect observed in a turning wheel that throws off splashes of mud. Galileo showed that the anti-Copernicans would conclude only what they had already presupposed: they could not conceive the motility of the earth, because they did not know how to distinguish between active and passive motion, between the persistence and acquisition of motion.

The third day investigates why it is that the annual revolution of the earth around the sun in the immense universe of stars is imperceptible under ordinary conditions, and under what experimental conditions it would be possible to make it perceptible.

The fourth day dwells on the physical proof drawn from the tides and the trade winds. Mechanically reinterpreting the traditional division of the elements into earth, water, and air, which corresponds to the phenomenology of sensible perception, Galileo shows that these three elements have different inertial behaviors in the composition of the earth's rotational motion with its motion of annual revolution, and that these differences are at the origin both of the periodic movements observed in the oceans, and the perpetual current in the atmosphere in equatorial and tropical regions.

The "Dialogue" is a difficult, intricate, and surprising work. Alexandre Koyré sees in it above all "a war machine against the traditional science and philosophy," and he pronounces this judgment:

> "The Dialogue Concerning the Two Principal Systems of the World" claims to expound two vital astronomical systems. But in fact it is not a book of astronomy or even physics. It is above all a critical book; or a work of polemic and combat. It is at the same time a pedagogical work. And finally, it is a book about history: "The history of the spirit of Signor Galileo."[80]

Drawing the consequences of his interpretation, Koyré reserves no place for Galileo in his now classic study, *La révolution astronomique*.[81] It is divided into three parts: (1) Copernicus and the cosmic upheaval; (2) Kepler and the new astronomy; (3) Borelli and celestial mechanics. Such a drastic position arouses perplexity and indignation from the Italian side. But did not Stillman Drake, of whom it is no exaggeration to say that he knows the "Dialogue" by heart, and often finds himself in disagreement with Koyre's interpretations, "go one better" when he says:

> Galileo's concern with theoretical astronomy was never very great. Even his battle for Copernicanism was conducted mainly on physical grounds, centering as it did on a mechanical theory of the tides and on the removal of some fancied physical objections to the movement of the earth. So far as his Dialogue is concerned, the Copernican theory was presented in the absurdly simple form, with the sun at the exact center of concentric circular orbits — a scheme which Copernicus himself had recognized as untenable, and which could never have been reconciled with any astronomical tables ever compiled.[82]

80. Alexandre Koyré, *Estudes Galiléennes* (Paris, Hermann, 1966), p. 212. In the same passage, Koyré explains his point of view: "As to the new physics, mathematical, Archimedean, Galileo well knew that its establishment necessitated a recasting and rebuilding of all its concepts; and that it was necessary to base it, as solidly as possible, on a *philosophy*. Hence the subtle admixture in the Galilean work of 'science' and 'philosophy', and the impossibility for the historian — short of giving up the attempt to understand — of separating the two unifying elements of his thought."

81. Alexandre Koyré, *La Révolution astronomique: Copernic, Kepler, Borelli* (Paris, Hermann, 1961). Gianalfonso Borelli (1608–1679) was one of the principal Galileans of the generation following the death of the master. He belonged to the famous Accademia del Cimento, founded and protected by the Grand Duke Ferdinand II and above all by his brother, Prince Leopold. Active in the years 1657 to 1667, he is mainly known for the *Saggi di Naturali Esperienze* (Florence, 1667), which recounts his works.

82. Stillman Drake. "Galileo's 'Platonic' Cosmology and Kepler's Prodromus," *Journal for the History of Astronomy*, 4/3 (1973) 173–91; the passage quoted is on p. 174. Galileo had no deep knowledge of Copernicus's texts. See Edward Rosen, "Galileo's Mis-Statements about Copernicus," *Isis*, 49 (1959) 319–30.

Nevertheless, such as it is, the "Dialogue" remains one of the major works of scientific literature of all time. Recent rereadings witness to this.[83] The "Dialogue" will always be a marvelous treatise of argumentative logic. With an extraordinary dialectical agility, Galileo, who on many occasions placed himself under the patronage of Socrates, demonstrates how frequently it is difficult for discursive thought to escape a *petitio principii*, and why this is the case. He shows how we often ought to conclude the opposite of what we are in fact concluding, if we interpret more exactly and coherently the premises from which we are commencing. Finally Galileo applied himself methodically to make sensible experience (*esperienze sensate*) go hand in hand with geometrical demonstrations (*ragioni necessarie*). Thus he defined the ideal of a new knowledge that finds it expression in a discourse that is at the same time rational and experimental.

The "Dialogue" will also remain the manual of proofs in favor of Copernican astronomy. It is wrong to claim that Galileo did not prove what he put forward, just as it is erroneous to maintain that the decisive proof of Copernicanism came only with the first observation of the annual parallax of a star by the astronomer Friedrich Bessel in 1837, and in the invention of the pendulum experiment by the physicist Léon Foucault in 1851. It is not even necessary to await Newton's discovery of the law of universal gravitation for the Copernican truth to be confirmed by observation. Stillman Drake is right to affirm that "stellar parallax is hardly more conclusive proof of the earth's annual motion than was Jupiter's shadow as used by Galileo, which latter is merely harder to explain to lay readers."[84]

I shall continue to revere the "Dialogue" because in it I find the manifesto of a new philosophy of nature. As Galileo clearly announced from the first pages of the first day, the "Dialogue" was destined to replace the *De caelo* of Aristotle. The real greatness of Galileo consists in transforming the astronomy of Copernicus into a new cosmology. He explains himself, and it is suitable to leave the last word to him, a word that has become the first word for all science:

> May it be our lot, by the grace of the true Son, pure and immaculate, to learn from Him, with all other truths, that which we are now seeking,

83. William Shea, *Galileo's Intellectual Revolution* (London, MacMillan, 1972); Maurice A. Finnochiaro, *Galileo and the Art of Reasoning* (Hingham, Mass., D. Reidel Publ. Co., 1980); Stillman Drake, "The Organizing Theme of the Dialogue," lecture delivered at a colloquium organized by the Lincean Academy, on the occasion of the 350th anniversary of the publication of the "Dialogue," May 6 and 7, 1982.

84. Stillman Drake, "Ptolemy, Galileo, and Scientific Method," *Studies in History and Philosophy of Science*, 9/2 (June 1978) 99–115; the passage quoted is on p. 115.

blinded and groping our way as it were, about the other sun, material and covered with spots. . . .

But it does not seem to me that we should despair of coming to understand the properties of bodies very far from us, which are no less comprehensible than the properties of bodies nearer to us; it is possible, in fact, that we could grasp the former more exactly than the latter.[85]

85. Galileo, *Istoria e Dimostrazioni intorno alle Macchie Solari*; the passage quoted is to be found in the third letter (EN, V, 187).

2

Galileo and the Professors of the Collegio Romano at the End of the Sixteenth Century

William A. Wallace

Galileo's relationships with the Jesuits, especially those who taught at the Collegio Romano, have generally been viewed as hostile and antagonistic. The usual context is the controversy over sunspots, followed by that over the nature and position of comets, then culminating in the bitter argument over the Copernican system of the universe and the proofs alleged in its support. Fathers Christopher Scheiner (first while teaching at Ingolstadt and then later in Rome) and Orazio Grassi are singled out as Galileo's main adversaries. Not uncommonly they are vilified as ill-informed, bad-willed, and otherwise obstructionist in opposing the acceptance of the Pisan astronomer's progressive views.

The only Jesuit who has been accorded favorable treatment in the literature is Father Cristopher Clavius, who took an interest in an early mathematical composition of Galileo and helped him get his first teaching position at the University of Pisa. It was Clavius also who welcomed him in a triumphal visit to the Collegio Romano in 1611 after having confirmed, with the aid of other Jesuit astronomers, the telescopic discoveries he had announced in the *Sidereus Nuntius* of the previous year. But with Clavius's death in 1612, Galileo's friendship with the members of the Society of Jesus apparently terminated, and they became his bitter enemies over the thirty years that ended with his death in 1642.[1]

---

1. Representative treatments are those of L. Geymonat, *Galileo Galilei: A Biography and Inquiry into His Philosophy of Science* (New York, McGraw-Hill, 1965); and

Against the background of this common account there have recently come to light some surprising pieces of evidence that connect Galileo with Jesuit professors of the Collegio Romano around 1589–1591, the period when he was launching his teaching career at the University of Pisa. The discovery is an important one, for it shows that Galileo's early views on scientific methodology, on the relationships between celestial and terrestrial physics, and on the motion of heavy and light bodies were influenced by those of young Jesuits, colleagues and probably disciples of Clavius, who were concurrently teaching logic and natural philosophy in Rome. Not only this, but much of the Jesuit terminology for dealing with these matters was appropriated by Galileo and developed by him as an integral part of the *nuove scienze* he was to elaborate in his later writings. Thus there are hitherto unsuspected relationships between Galileo and the Jesuits — relationships more positive and collaborative than one would imagine from reading about his later controversies with Scheiner and Grassi.

These findings are quite recent and it will take some time before their full details and ramifications can be explored.[2] There seems no doubt, for example, that they will entail susbstantial revisions in textbook analyses of Galileo's role in the Scientific Revolution and its origins in late medieval and scholastic thought. Such revisionism, however, is not the aim of this essay. Its scope is more modest: to provide a brief account of the new evidence; to describe these Jesuits and the course materials they developed; to outline in summary form Galileo's overall debt to the Collegio Romano; and to draw a few conclusions about the bearing of this information on "the Galileo myth" and the "trial" of 1633.

Galileo's Early Latin Manuscripts

Since the end of the nineteenth century it has been suspected that two of Galileo's Latin manuscripts, one containing logical questions (MS 27)

S. Drake, *Galileo at Work: His Scientific Biography* (University of Chicago Press, 1978). A more critical assessment of Galileo's debates with Scheiner and Grassi may be found in W. R. Shea, *Galileo's Intellectual Revolution: Middle Period 1610–1632* (New York, Science History Publication, 1972).

2. Preliminary results are given in W. A. Wallace, *Prelude to Galileo: Essays on Medieval and Sixteenth-Century Sources of Galileo's Thought* (Dordrecht and Hingham, Mass., D. Reidel Publ. Co., 1981), and in a work by the same author with the tentative title, *Galileo and His Sources*, being readied for publication. A. C. Crombie and A. Carugo are also preparing for publication the results of their researches on Galileo's early writings.

and the other physical questions plus some memoranda on motion (MS 46), were derived and possibly copied from other sources.[3] The editor of the Edizione Nazionale (EN) of Galileo's works that began to appear in 1890, Antonio Favaro, speculated then that both were student notebooks — the first written by Galileo while he was at the Monastery of Vallombrosa in the late 1570s and the second while he was studying at the University of Pisa in 1584. Favaro transcribed the second manuscript and published its transcription under the title *Juvenilia* in the first volume of the EN.[4] The first manuscript he regarded as so insignificant that he excluded it from the edition, merely transcribing a few excerpts as "samples of some scholastic exercises of Galileo" and putting these in the ninth volume with other data pertaining to Galileo's youth.[5]

A third manuscript, however, which contains drafts of Galileo's early writings on motion (MS 71), Favaro did transcribe and publish in its entirety, and rearranged the writings to conform to his idea of how they were composed.[6] This last manuscript Favaro fortunately assigned to the period of Galileo's teaching at Pisa, 1590–1591. Of all Galileo's early Latin compositions it has caught the attention of scholars because of its obvious relationship to his later writings *De motu*, on which his fame as "father of modern science" obviously rests.

Because of Favaro's dating and handling of these three manuscripts in the EN, the connections between them have been overlooked. Recent scholarship, partially inspired by renewed interest in medieval and Renaissance science, has redirected attention to them and has yielded some interesting results. The third manuscript (MS 71) was the first to be studied in an attempt to understand the ordering of its materials.[7] Not only was Favaro's rearrangement found to be questionable, but the entire contents were discovered to be a progressive development of the memoranda on motion following the physical questions in the second manuscript (MS 46).

Then this second manuscript was subjected to close scrutiny and its sources gradually uncovered.[8] Rather than notes copied by Galileo in

3. These manuscripts are preserved in the Galileiana collection of the Biblioteca Nazionale Centrale, Florence; the numbers are those of the codices there in the Galileo font.
4. I, 1–177.
5. EN, IX, 273–92.
6. EN, I, 243–408.
7. The pioneer work here was a doctoral dissertation done at the University of Montreal by R. Fredette, a portion of which was published as "Galileo's *De motu antiquiora*" in *Phusis*, 14 (1972) 321–48. The same author contributed an important paper, as yet unpublished, entitled "Bringing to Light the Order of Composition of Galileo Galilei's *De motu antiquiora*," to the 1975 Workshop on Galileo at Blacksburg, Virginia.
8. See A. C. Crombie, "Sources of Galileo's Early Natural Philosophy," in *Reason,*

1584 while attending the lectures of Francesco Buonamici at Pisa, as Favaro had speculated, they were seen to be based on the writings of Clavius and other Jesuits of the Collegio Romano. Because the Jesuit materials could be dated, evidence began to accumulate that MS 46 was actually written, as an earlier curator of the Galileo manuscript font had indicated, "around 1590." This, of course, made it contemporaneous with the *De motu antiquiora* of MS 71 and could explain the curious relationship of its memoranda on motion to the contents of the longer work.

Finally, the first manuscript was recovered from the oblivion to which Favaro had consigned it. Study of it is still in progress, but preliminary indications are that it contains the greatest surprise of all.[9] Instead of being based on the teachings of a Vallombrosan monk around 1578, as Favaro conjectured, they are Galileo's adaptation of a sophisticated series of lectures on Aristotle's *Posterior Analytics* given by a Jesuit professor at the Collegio Romano, Paolo Valla (or Vallius), during the academic year 1587–1588.[10] Apart from the important analysis of scientific methodology they contain, they provide evidence that Galileo was seriously studying Jesuit course materials on logic and natural philosophy while occupying his first teaching post at Pisa between 1589 and 1591. All three manuscripts (MSS 27, 46, and 71) therefore date from approximately the same period — actually one of great productivity for Galileo, during which he laid the foundations on which his later work would be based.

The research on which these conclusions are founded is rather complex, employing paleographical techniques, word-counts, and statistical correlations that do not yield absolute certitude, but whose cumulative effect leaves little room for doubt. Two samples of the type of evidence available may suffice to give some idea of the probative force.

The first example shows the dependence of a brief passage in MS 27 on the 1588 lecture notes of Paolo Valla, which unfortunately are no

---

continuation

Experiment, and Mysticism in the Scientific Revolution, M. L. Righini-Bonelli and W. R. Shea, eds. (New York, Science History Publications, 1975), pp. 157–75 and 303–5; and W. A. Wallace, *Galileo's Early Notebooks: The Physical Questions, A Translation from the Latin with Historical and Paleographical Commentary* (University of Notre Dame Press, 1977).

9. The manuscript (MS 27) has been transcribed by W. F. Edwards of Emory University, Atlanta, Georgia, and by A. Carugo of the University of Venice, neither of whom has thus far published his reading of it. The excerpts from this manuscript cited below are my own transcriptions.

10. Arguments in support of this statement are given in my *Galileo and His Sources* (note 2, above).

longer extant but have come down to us through their having been plagiarized and published by another author, Ludovico Carbone, in 1597.[11] A careful comparison of the plagiarized text (referred to as that of Valla-Carbone) with Galileo's composition strongly suggests that the two derive from a common exemplar. Both texts are reproduced below in parallel columns, with Valla-Carbone's on the left and Galileo's on the right (identical or synonymous phrases are given in italics):

VALLA-CARBONE

Prima positio: esse subiecti tota-lis scientiae nulla ratione *in propria scientia demonstrari potest.*

Dixi "in propria" quia in superiori probari, *sicuti in propria aliquo pacto declarari potest* illius existentia, ut Themistius docet. . . .

Secunda positio: esse subiecti principalis nullo genere demonstrationis potest probari in propria *scientia.*[12]

GALILEO

Dico primo: esse subiecti totalis in propria scientia neque demonstratione a priori neque a posteriori *probari potest.*

Dixi "in propria scientia" quia in superiori poterit *probari, sicut* et *in propria poterit aliquo modo declarari.* . . .

Dico secundo: esse subiecti principalis non potest ullo genere demonstrationis probari in scientia.[13]

The passage reproduced records two responses to a question, "Can a science demonstrate the existence of its adequate subject?," as Galileo poses it, or "of its adequate and total subject?," as Valla-Carbone records it more fully.[14] The answers are the same in both: first, no science can demonstrate the existence of its own total subject, although this may be demonstrable in a higher science or may be "declared" in some way in the science itself; and secondly, it is in no way possible to demonstrate the existence of the principal subject within a science.

In the first paragraph Galileo omits the *scientiae*, which is not neces-

11. For information on Valla, consult the index of *Prelude to Galileo* (note 2, above) and *Galileo's Early Notebooks* (note 8, above) pp. 17–18 and passim. The plagiarized text may be found in L. Carbone, *Additamenta ad commentaria D. Francisci Toleti in Logicam Aristotelis* (Venice, G. Angelerius, 1597), fols, 38–55.

12. L. Carbone, *Additamenta*, fol. 48v.

13. MS 27, fol. 8v, lines 18–29.

14. Galileo's title reads *An scientia possit demonstrare de suo obiecto adequato esse existentiae* (fol. 8r, lines 19–20), whereas Carbone's reads *An scientia possit probare existentiam sui subicit adaequati et totalis* (fol. 48r).

sary for the sense, and in place of Valla-Carbone's *nulla ratione* ("by no reasoning") has the fuller *neque demonstratione a priori neque a posteriori* ("not by demonstration a priori or a posteriori"), which possibly is closer to the exemplar. In the second paragraph the wording is practically identical for both, except that Valla-Carbone identifies Themistius as the authority, whereas Galileo does not. Here, as in the title of the question, Valla-Carbone seems to reflect better the original. The third paragraph is almost the same in the two, and so gives striking evidence of common derivation.

An isolated passage of this sort, as has been said, cannot offer conclusive proof, but when esoteric questions of this type are being asked through page after page of two compositions, and when the same answers continue to be given to them in identical or synonymous wording, the conclusion is inescapable that they either derive one from the other or else come from a common source. But it is known, on Valla's own testimony, that the Carbone text of 1597 was plagiarized from his lectures at the Collegio, which were not completed until August of 1588 and not made available to his students until "shortly thereafter."[15] Inasmuch as the chances that Valla would have copied his 1588 lectures from Galileo are negligible, and even more so that both would have copied them practically word for word from yet an earlier source and that Valla would then have complained of plagiarism, only one reasonable alternative is left. Galileo must somehow have obtained a copy of Valla's lecture notes similar to those used by Carbone and from them written out the very interesting material contained in MS 27.

The dating and provenance of MS 46 is more difficult to ascertain, though the task is simplified by the fact that the physical questions contained in it are treated in precisely the same fashion as the logical questions of MS 27, and its internal references to the logical questions establish that it was composed some time after they were. Textual parallels point to a number of possible Jesuit professors as its source, but here too Valla emerges as the most likely candidate. A brief passage analogous to that reproduced above will provide a second example of the type of evidence available to establish the identity of Galileo's exemplar:

VALLA	GALILEO
Respondet primo *Achillinus . . .*	*Respondet Achillinus, gravi-*
gravitatem et levitatem dupliciter	*tatem et levitatem posse duplici-*

---

15. See the prefaces to both volumes of Paulus Vallius, *Logica* (Lyons, L. Prost, 1622) for an account of the details of Carbone's plagiarism.

sumi posse: primo, *in actu primo, et hoc modo est forma substantialis*; secundo, *in actu secundo, et hoc modo est qualitas* et accidens elementi.

Contra: quia . . . *operatio gravitatis est* motus vel *actio; ergo male ponitur* ab Achillino *in qualitate*. . . .

Sed *gravitas et levitas* aliquibus *sunt* accidentia, ut patet *in Sanctissimo Sacramento, ubi nulla est substantia* naturalis; ergo.

Respondet Achillinus *ibi non esse gravitatem* in actu primo sed in actu secundo, *supplente Deo gravitatem* in actu primo.

Contra: ibi est gravitario, quae fieri non potest sine gravitate in actu primo . . . ; secundo, *non sunt multiplicanda miracula sine necessitate*.[16]

ter considerari: vel *in actu primo, et sic sunt formae substantiales* elementorum; vel *in actu secundo*, idest ratione gravitationis et levitationis, *et sic dicuntur qualitates*.

Sed *contra: gravitatio* et levitatio sunt in praedicamento *actionis* et passionis; *ergo non sunt qualitates*.

Adde, quod *in Sanctissimo Sacramento est gravitas et levitas*, et tamen *ibi nulla est substantia*.

Respondet: Deum facere ibi gravitatem et levitatem, *loco gravitatis* et levitatis *quae non adsunt*.

Contra: non sunt multiplicanda miracula sine necessitate.[17]

The context is the reply to a question about the forms of the elements, to which both Valla and Galileo respond that they are substantial forms hidden from us but knowable through their qualities. Achillini, on the other hand, taught in his *De elementis* that the forms of the elements are their motive qualities, *gravitas* and *levitas* — a position rejected by both Valla and Galileo as part of their initial reply. Then follow the above passages as objections drawn from Achillini, together with their counterarguments. Galileo's text may be translated into English as follows:

> Achillini replies that gravity and levity can be understood in two ways: in first act, and so they are the substantial forms of the elements; or in second act, i.e., by reason of gravitation and levitation, and so they are said to be

16. Valla, Cod. APUG/FC 1710 (no foliation): *Tractatus quintus, De elementis; Disputation prima, De elementis in genere; Pars prima, De essentia elementorum; Quaestio tertia, De forma et materia elementorum.*

17. EN, I, 131–32.

qualities. But, to the contrary: gravitation and levitation are in the category of action and passion; therefore they are not qualities. Add to this: there is gravity and levity in the Most Blessed Sacrament, and yet there is no substance there. He replies: God makes gravitation and levitation to be there in place of the gravity and levity that are not present. To the contrary: miracles are not to be multiplied without necessity.[18]

Valla's arguments are obviously the same as Galileo's, although the latter's are occasionally expressed in different terms and are somewhat more abbreviated. This may readily be seen in the third paragraphs of the parallel texts, where Valla states that there is no *substantia naturalis* in the Eucharist, which Galileo abbreviates to say that there is no *substantia* there — a statement that is theologically inaccurate. The last paragraphs provide a more striking illustration: Valla gives a twofold refutation, whereas Galileo settles for his second, in terms well known to every student of scholastic theology.

What complicates the dating of Valla's lectures is the fact that he taught this particular matter in 1585–1586, again in 1586–1587, and finally in 1589–1590, but because the codex containing his notes is undated, one cannot be certain which version would have been available to Galileo. Only a small protion of Valla's physical questions have survived, morever, and thus it is not possible to make textual comparisons throughout all of MS 46. For the portions that are extant, however, Valla's notes show the best correlation with Galileo's, and this circumstance, plus the extensive parallels with Valla throughout the logical questions, argues for this Jesuit as the most likely source of Galileo's notetaking in MSS 27 and 46.[19]

Jesuit Professors and their Courses

Thus far discussion has centered on Galileo's first two manuscripts, which are clearly propadeutic to his third, MS 71, with its important essays on motion. The third manuscript does not have the signs of copying apparent in the other two, but it contains a series of drafts building up to a final treatise, which argues for its being a record of work in progress during Galileo's teaching years at Pisa. A number of themes that characterize these writings are to be found in the notes of other Jesuits at the Collegio Romano. Add to this the fact that both MSS 27 and 46 are incomplete, and provide internal evidence that they are but the surviving portions of what at one time was a complete course in Galileo's hand on logic and natural philosophy, and one has an impor-

18. *Galileo's Early Notebooks* (note 8, above), p. 190, par. S12.
19. Details are forthcoming in *Galileo and His Sources* (note 2, above).

tant incentive for investigating the offerings in these subjects at the Collegio in the years on either side of Valla's professorship.

The Collegio Romano was founded by St. Ignatius Loyola in 1551, and quickly grew to a position of prominence and prestige, so that by the end of the 1580s it had become the foremost university run by the Jesuits and indeed in all of Europe.[20] The early professors of philosophy at the Collegio were mainly Spaniards, the most influential being Francesco Toledo, who had studied under Domingo de Soto at Salamanca before becoming a Jesuit, and Benito Pereyra, a Valencian who was later to make his mark as a scripture scholar. Both wrote manuals of philosophy that were first published in the 1570s and reprinted often thereafter, although they last taught such courses themselves in the 1560s. Toledo's texts show him to be an eclectic Thomist along the lines pioneered by Soto, combining elements of nominalism and Scotism within an overall Aristotelian synthesis. Pereyra's writings are similar, although he manifests considerably more interest in Averroist themes and became suspect on that account — a factor that may explain his "promotion" to the scripture faculty of the Collegio in 1576.

Apart from the textbooks produced by these professors, and then the *Cursus philosophicus* of the Coimbra Jesuits that appeared at the end of the century, there is little published information about the materials covered in the courses at the Collegio. Fortunately, however, a large number of extant manuscripts contain the lecture notes or *reportationes* of lectures of the various professors, and these are a rich source of data on this subject. For purposes of this essay the lectures of Antonio Menu, who taught natural philosophy and metaphysics from 1577 to 1579 and then logic, natural philosophy, and metaphysics again from 1579 to 1582, mark the indispensable starting point for the study of influences on Galileo.[21] Menu began teaching the year after Pereyra's *De communibus omnium rerum naturalium principiis et affectionibus* was published, but he broke rather radically with many of Pereyra's theses. Instead of adopting a conservative Averroist stance, he imported within a general Thomistic framework a progressive Aristotelianism that owed much to the *Doctores Parisienses* and to the fourteenth-century calculatory tradition of Oxford and Paris.

Many of Menu's ideas in natural philosophy, of which a rather complete record is preserved, were taken up by Valla in the portions of

---

20. For a documented history of the Collegio, see R. G. Villoslada, *Storia del Collegio Romano dal suo inizio (1551) alla soppressione della Compagnia di Gesù (1733)*, Analecta Gregoriana No. 66. (Rome, Gregorian University Press, 1954).

21. For information on Menu, consult the index of *Prelude to Galileo* (note 2, above) and *Galileo's Early Notebooks* (note 8, above), pp. 16–18 and passim.

his course that survive. Menu, as already noted, taught logic (1579–1580) then natural philosophy (1580–1581), and finally metaphysics (1581–1582), following a sequence that was quite usual at the Collegio, wherein each professor would take his class through the entire three years of the philosophy curriculum.[22] Valla pursued the same cycle in the years 1587 to 1590, followed by Muzio Vitelleschi in the years 1588 to 1591, and then by Ludovico Rugiero in the years 1589 to 1592. In the cases of Vitelleschi and Rugiero, copies of their complete courses in philosophy are available, and these manifest an essential continuity with the teachings of Menu and Valla.[23] Rarely would one professor repeat his predecessor's positions word for word, and signs of disagreement within the faculty are not totally absent, but on the whole there is remarkable consensus on most of the matters that show up in Galileo's MSS 27 and 46, to say nothing of the topics treated in his MS 71.

Such consensus, it may be noted, is one of the complicating factors that makes dating the exemplar of MS 46 difficult. By statistical analysis, however, it can be shown that Galileo's composition correlates best with Valla's text, followed closely by Vitelleschi's, and then by Rugiero's. On this basis Valla's teachings between 1588 and 1590, at which time this colleagues in the philosophy cycle were Vitelleschi and Rugiero, emerges as the most likely source for the physical questions of MS 46.

In connection with Rugiero it should be mentioned that an excellent copy of his entire course, in seven manuscript volumes, is now kept in the Staatsbibliothek at Bamberg.[24] The copy is apparently the work of a professional scribe, and is extraordinary in that all of the lectures are numbered in the margins; moreover, the dates on which various tracts were begun or ended are clearly indicated.

Beginning on November 3, 1589, and ending on August 24, 1590, Rugiero gave 310 lectures on the *Organon* of Aristotle, ending with 94 lectures devoted exclusively to the *Posterior Analytics*. The following year, again starting on November 3, he delivered 207 lectures on the *Physics*, up to May 21, 1591, after which he gave 74 more on the *De caelo*, finishing its fourth book on August 7 of the same year. Concurrently, starting on July 7, he covered the *Meteorology* in about 75 lectures. Aristotle's *De generatione* he did not teach until his third year,

22. A *rotulus* of professors and the courses they taught in the various years at the Collegio has been prepared by I. Iparraguirre and is appended to Villoslada's history (note 20, above), pp. 321–36. From this list the various course sequences and cycles can readily be ascertained.
23. Some details are given in *Galileo's Early Notebooks* and in *Prelude to Galileo*, for which consult the indexes of both.
24. Cod. SB Bamberg. Misc. Class. 62. 1–7.

beginning on November 4, 1591, and completing its second book on February 12, 1592, with a total of 125 lectures. It is in this portion of his notes that Rugiero covers the motion of heavy and light bodies, as did his colleagues, so one should look here for adumbrations of the materials in Galileo's MS 71. In February, finally, he began two concurrent courses, one consisting of about 200 lectures on the *De anima* and another of 99 lectures on the *Metaphysics*, which brought him to mid-September of 1592 and the end of the philosophy cycle. The erudition, clarity, and detail of his teaching are incredible, and even a cursory examination of these codices will enable one to see why the years between 1587 and 1592 are regarded as the "golden age" of the Collegio Romano.

Galileo's Debt to the Jesuits

From the foregoing it is apparent that an extensive body of knowledge, methodological and scientific in the sense then accepted of science, was being covered each year at the Collegio Romano. Paralleling these "philosophical" investigations, there was also a heavy concentration on mathematics, and here the principal architect of the Collegio program was the German mathematician, Christopher Clavius. Himself from Bamberg, but having studied with Pedro Nuñez at Coimbra before coming to Rome, Clavius was preeminent in his field, "the Euclid of the sixteenth century," as he was known. Not only was he concerned with providing the Jesuits with men properly trained in pure and applied mathematics, but he was aware that mathematical knowledge is essential for the development of the natural sciences and on this account stressed its importance in the philosophy curriculum also. Pereyra, it may be noted, had fostered an antimathematical attitude in his philosophy courses, following in this the lead of the "peripatetics" then teaching in the Italian universities. Through Clavius's influence this mentality was overcome, and by the late 1580s and early 1590s mathematical astronomy was being taught concurrently with the *De caelo* and "calculatory" arguments were being discussed in the tracts on the continuum and on the elemental bodies.

Galileo's first contact with Clavius came in 1587, during a visit to Rome after having left his studies at the University of Pisa to pursue a career in mathematics. A year earlier he had composed an original treatise, *Theoremata circa centrum gravitatis solidorum*, which he wished to circulate among prominent mathematicians for their critique.[25] Apparently he left a copy of this with Clavius in late 1587, for

25. EN, I, 179–208.

there is an interchange of correspondence between them concerning it in 1588.[26] Clavius was very impressed with Galileo's work, and in fact collaborated with Guidobaldo del Monte to secure the young mathematician a teaching position in one of the universities. With regard to the *Theoremata*, however, he had a difficulty: Galileo's logic was not flawless, for it involved a *petitio principii* — it presupposed the very point it attempted to prove.

Because of the coincidence of dates and subject matter — note that this was 1588 and the problem related to the role of *suppositiones* in demonstration, precisely the matter covered in Valla's *Logica* and finished in that same year — it is tempting to look to Clavius as the intermediary through whom Galileo gained access to Valla's lecture notes. There is no mention of this in their correspondence, but the fact that Valla distributed them and that Carbone had secured a set argues for their availability at precisely the time Galileo would have benefited from studying them. If Clavius did Galileo this favor, once Galileo saw the thoroughness with which logical questions were treated at the Collegio, perhaps as contrasted with his own previous instruction, it would have been reasonable for him to seek additional lecture notes on the heavens, the elements, and the local motion of bodies. These, after all, were topics in which he was greatly interested, on whose mathematical treatment he would soon be (or already was) lecturing at the University of Pisa.

In the absence of apodictic proof, this seems about the best way to account for Galileo's acquaintance with the works of the young Jesuits discussed earlier in this essay. And if one peruses carefully their courses in logic and natural philosophy, and then studies Galileo's later compositions — not only MS 71 but most of his treatises down to the *Two New Sciences* of 1638 — one finds unmistakable Jesuit influences in Galileo's work. These influences have been detailed elsewhere, but they are worthy of brief mention here so as to round out the thesis being developed.[27]

With regard to the *De motu antiquiora* of MS 71, one of Galileo's distinctive contributions is his proposal there of the possibility of a motion intermediate between natural motion and violent motion, a *motus medius* that would be *praeter naturam* and once initiated could, in the absence of impediments, endure forever. Another is his acceptance of the possibility of noninstantaneous motion in a void, for which no

26. EN, X, 22–24, 27–29.
27. See W. A. Wallace, "Aristotelian Influences on Galileo's Thought," to appear in the proceedings of an international congress of the theme, *Aristotelismo Veneto e Scienza Moderna*, held at the University of Padua in September 1981.

medium would be required, contrary to the teaching of the Averroists of his day. Yet another is his arguing for the likelihood of continuity between a motion downward and the upward motion that preceded it — that is, for the nonexistence of rest at the turning point of motion. Still others are Galileo's identification of both nature and *gravitas* as internal causes of accelerated motion, his use of concepts deriving from Archimedes to develop the notion of specific gravity (*gravitas propria*, as he then called it), and his arguing against Aristotle that elemental bodies retain their *gravitas* when in their proper places — for example, that air has weight in air. Related to these is Galileo's advocacy of the concept of *virtus impressa* as necessary to explain projectile motion and also to account for the velocity increase experienced by bodies when falling freely in nonresistive media.

All these topics were discussed in the lecture notes of Menu, Valla, Vitelleschi, and Rugiero, in some instances in far greater detail than in Galileo's compositions, and generally favoring the same positions and with the same arguments for and against their adoption.[28] It is unlikely, as already remarked, that Galileo adhered as closely to the Jesuit lectures here as he did in writing MSS 27 and 46, for MS 71 gives clear signs of being a free composition, but its ideas are already contained in these Jesuit notes. It would seem too coincidental were those notes to have exerted no influence whatever on Galileo's thought.

Other themes that continue to resurface in Galileo's writings, and figure prominently in the lectures of these same Jesuits, are more methodological in character. One of them is Galileo's enduring concern with the *suppositiones* that lie behind demonstrative reasoning and his development of techniques of demonstrating *ex suppositione* in matters relating to the motions of celestial and terrestrial bodies.[29] Another is his concern with the subject of a science and the knowledge required of its existence — for example, the conditions under which naturally accelerated motion can be said to exist in the presence of physical *impedimenti*, antecedent to demonstrating its various properties. Yet another is Galileo's continued interest in finding the causes of natural phenomena, for he often distinguished between primary and secondary causes and between those that are essential and merely accidental — not only in his early writings but also in his mature studies of floating bodies,

28. Some details are given in the essay just cited (note 27) and in *Prelude to Galileo*, parts III and IV.

29. See W. A. Wallace, "Aristotle and Galileo: The Uses of *Hypothesis* (*Suppositio*) in "Scientific Reasoning," in *Studies in Aristotle*, D. J. O'Meara, ed. (Washington: The Catholic University of America Press, 1981), pp. 47–77.

the motion of the tides, the strength of materials, and projectile motion.[30]

Above all Galileo was intent in following out Clavius's program of applying mathematics to the study of nature and to generating a mathematical physics that could provide valid causal explanations for astronomical as well as physical phenomena. The same mentality characterizes the Jesuit writings already discussed, and again it seems no mere coincidence that it is in the background of many of Galileo's contributions.

Lest one imagine that the claim is being made that Galileo was indebted to the Collegio Romano for *all* his science, it perhaps should be expressly stated that such is not intended. What is being proposed is that, by the end of the sixteenth century, while Galileo was doing the seminal work that would fructify in the *nuove scienze* of his later years, he had already laid secure foundations on which these could be erected. He had already acquired a realist "mind-set" that placed great confidence in the ability of the human mind to grasp the truth about nature through both physical and mathematical reasoning. Undoubtedly this would be perfected through the skill he quickly developed as an experimenter and through his mathematical genius, which enabled him to apply limit concepts and other techniques to the mathematical solution of physical problems.

Other sources and other interests undoubtedly came to influence him, and there is no doubt that the Galileo who wrote the "Dialogue" of 1632 had matured far beyond the young mathematician who taught at the University of Pisa from 1589 to 1591. The Jesuit influence was mainly in Galileo's formative period, and to propose that this had a lasting and detectable effect on his writings is not to maintain that it dominated his entire life and work. Galileo has a clear and undisputed title as the "father of modern science," and this is not at question here. But such a title, as has been observed, does not rule out a "grandfather" or other progenitors behind the birth of the new physics.[31]

Some Recurrent Myths

The discovery of these unexpected relationships between Galileo and the Jesuits offers the possibility of dissolving a number of legends and

30. See W. A. Wallace, "The Problem of Causality in Galileo's Science," forthcoming in *The Review of Metaphysics*.

31. A press release attending the publication of *Prelude to Galileo* identified Paolo Valla as "the grandfather" of modern science and received extensive notice in North America and European communications media.

myths that have grown up around the Italian physicist. One of the most famous, to be sure, is that of the Leaning Tower of Pisa, where it is believed that Galileo obtained conclusive experimental proof of his law of falling bodies while he was teaching at the university there. A close study of MS 71 and its reference to the experiments of Girolamo Borri (which are also referenced in the Jesuit lectures, by the way) reveals what actually happened at that time — namely, in 1590 or 1591.[32] Galileo probably did drop objects from the Leaning Tower, but during his residence in Pisa he was not yet in possession of the law of falling bodies. His tests were of the kind then being used to see whether a wooden object or a leaden object would fall faster in air — a matter of dispute related to the problem of whether air has weight in air. Inasmuch as such evidence was then being discussed and evaluated in the philosophy course at the Collegio, there is nothing particularly original about this alleged episode in the life of Galileo.

Related to this is a general myth about the originality of Galileo's scientific thought. Historians of science following the lead of the postivist Ernst Mach have fostered the view of a sharp discontinuity between late medieval and early modern science. Galileo they see as a kind of Melchisedech without forebears, whose university training was worthless, who rejected all his teachers had told him, who turned instead to mathematics and experiment as the sole certification of his scientific method, which they claim to be identical with the "hypothetico-deductive method" of twentieth-century science. The fact of the matter is that Galileo was a man of his times who was well acquainted with the thought of progressive Aristotelians such as the Jesuits and who made good use of the methodological canons of the *Posterior Analytics.* Indeed, he attempted to formulate his new *scientia* with the aid of *principia, definitiones, suppositiones,* and *demonstrationes* so as to furnish strict proof of the *proprietates* and *passiones* he attributed to his proper subject. He manifested great originality in devising experiments and developing mathematical techniques, particularly those dealing with proportionalities. But all of this was done in an Aristotelian-Euclidean-Archimedean context that, as it turns out, is quite foreign to the thought of twentieth-century empiricists.

Yet another myth is one that puts Galileo on a white horse and sees him as the champion of truth against benighted and malicious scholastics who refused to consider the facts presented to them. Most of Galileo's biographers unfortunately turn out to be hagiographers: for

---

32. EN, I, 333–34. For the Jesuit references, see *Prelude to Galileo,* pp. 116, 248, 250, and 313.

them Galileo is always on the side of the angels and anyone who opposed him is either stupid or ill-willed. One of the instructive features of the controversies between Galileo and his two celebrated Jesuit adversaries, Scheiner and Grassi, is that they show the pitfalls of this attitude. All three were accomplished mathematicians and experimenters, and all three were using all the resources at their command to determine the nature and motions of two phenomena that are still not yet fully understood: sunspots and comets. The methodologies to which they were committed were basically the same, and that is why they could have such prolonged arguments over the interpretations of their respective results. Galileo's debate with Grassi is particularly illuminating in this regard. Grassi, then teaching astronomy at the Collegio Romano, was convinced that the comets of 1618 were real objects whose parallax measurements showed them to be far above the orb of the moon. Galileo, on the other hand, somewhat fearful that the path claimed by Grassi for the comets might count against the Copernican hypothesis, insisted that they were not real objects but mere optical illusions! Who, one might ask, was in possession of the facts in that particular case?

Of more profound significance is the bearing of these new discoveries on the understanding of the "trial" of 1633 and the work that occasioned it, Galileo's "Dialogue" of 1632. There are many legends that have grown up around the trial and Galileo's disastrous encounter with the Roman Inquisition. In the popular mind, for example, it is thought that Galileo offered conclusive proof of the Copernican system and that he was forced to perjure himself by the Inquisition in swearing that the earth stands still. Before the transcription of the logical questions of MS 27, and the discovery of the source from which they derive, one might have wondered about Galileo's knowledge of demonstration and of the canons of proof that would be required to justify a claim of the earth's motion. Now that this information is available, it is quite clear that he had a sophisticated awareness of the problem. On rereading the "Dialogue" in the light of MS 27, in fact, one is impressed that nowhere in the four days of its discussions does Galileo claim to have *demonstrated* the earth's movement, although in many of his writings leading up to this work he had made other demonstrative claims, and of course the *Two New Sciences* of 1638 is replete with them. A recent analysis of the "Dialogue" serves to strengthen this view, for it portrays this as a rhetorical work aimed at urging the acceptance of the Copernican system in the absence of conclusive proof.[33] If this was Galileo's real

---

33. M. A. Finnochiaro, *Galileo and the Art of Reasoning: Rhetorical Foundations of Logic and Scientific Method* (Dordrecht and Hingham, Mass., D. Reidel Publ. Co., 1980);

intention, and he himself was aware that the truth of the Copernican theory had not yet been established, then he would not have perjured himself when assenting to the interpretation of the scriptural passages that argue against the earth's motion. He was simply accepting on faith that the earth does not move, which he could do in all honesty if his reason had failed to prove the opposite.

These, then, are a few of the common impressions about Galileo that stand to be corrected as the result of recent scholarship. His early connections with the Jesuits, as has been seen, were not "all bad." They were so good, one might say, that the strong adversary relationship between them that developed around 1632 and 1633 may well be seen as an illustration of the ancient adage, *corruptio optimi pessima*. Even at that, as Grassi was later to observe after the trial, it was Galileo's personality, if not his pride and arrogance, that brought about his downfall.[34] This notwithstanding, Galileo was still a man of brilliant intellect and courageous will, and the fact that he owed his early insights to the Collegio Romana takes no credit from him as the key figure who ushered in the age of modern science.

continuation

see also Jean D. Moss, "Galileo's *Letter to Christina*: Some Rhetorical Considerations," forthcoming.

34. See P. M. D'Elia, *Galileo in China* (Harvard University Press, 1960), pp. 57–58.

PART TWO

GALILEO AND THE SCHOLARSHIP
OF HIS TIME

3

Galileo and the Philosophy of his Time

Mario Viganò

Galileo as Mathematician and Philosopher

When he wrote in May 1610 to Belisario Vinta, secretary to Grand Duke Cosimo II of Tuscany, in order to come to agreement on the conditions for his transfer from the University of Padua to the service of the Court of Florence, Galileo, after alluding to his scientific work in connection with his honorarium, added a request:

> Finally, as to the title that indicates the nature of my service, I would wish Your Highness to add to the title of mathematician that of philosopher: I can vouch for having consecrated more years to the study of philosophy than months to the study of pure mathematics.[1]

This request was destined to encounter no difficulty. Thus, on July 10 of the same year, Galileo received from the grand duke a communication informing him of his election as First Mathematician of the University of Pisa and First Mathematician and Philosopher to the Grand Duke.

To conform to his father's wishes, Galileo had commenced medical studies at Pisa in 1581, a course of studies that at that time also included Peripatetic philosophy. He had quickly abandoned these studies, however, in order to take up mathematics, in which he had gained a certain notoriety. He then devoted himself to the study of physics, with which he was to occupy himself for the rest of his life, a subject that, under the title of natural philosophy, formed a branch of philosophy. But he certainly did not imagine that his title of philosopher would be contested during his life and even after his death.

---

1. EN, X, 353.

In his claim to the title of philosopher alongside that of mathematician, we do not know if Galileo was thinking of the already long-established distinction between *mathematical astronomers*, who occupied themselves with constructing geometrical models of the sidereal universe allowing a "saving of appearances," as it was then called (i.e., serving to describe and predict celestial phenomena), without concerning themselves as to the conformity of these models with reality, and *physical astronomers*, philosophers who set out to determine the true nature, the qualities, and properties of celestial bodies.

In any case, if Galileo had heeded the advice of Cardinal Bellarmine and his own friends, and had occupied himself with astronomy, and if he had done this as a mathematician — *ex hypothesi*, in the phrase current then — he would have avoided irritating the Scholastic philosophers and theologians, and the Holy Office would not have concerned itself with him. But to occupy himself with these things as a philosopher and to claim to teach how things really go was to signify an upheaval of the entire world system, to overthrow the Peripatetic philosophy that had been taught in all the schools for centuries, to compromise theology itself, which had continually made use of Aristotelian philosophy, and to put in doubt passages of scripture hitherto taught by the fathers of the church and the theologians. The condemnation of the *Dialogo dei massimi sistemi*, Galileo's abjuration, and his enforced residence at Arcetri were all due to the fact of his not having observed the explicit condition concerning this publication imposed by Urban VIII, to the effect that the question would be treated as one of mathematics and not philosophy.[2]

Fortunately, the theme proposed for my study concerns "Galileo and the philosophy of his time," which accordingly absolves me from concerning myself with Galileo and the philosophy of *our* time. If I had to collate and discuss the writings of contemporary philosophers on the subject of Galileo's philosophy, I would find myself faced with an almost endless task, but from a certain point of view not a task without humor, and the first to be amused by it would, I think, be Galileo himself. As an example of this one can find some indications, incomplete to be sure, in an article by F. Olgiati, *La metafisica di Galileo Galilei*.[3]

---

2. It is impossible to deal with this theme adequately without referring to the historical events of the "Galileo question." Here, I try to restrict myself to certain essential references; for a more ample development of the problem and further documentation, I would refer the reader to previous study published in the publications of *Civiltà Cattolica* in 1969: *Il mancato dialogo tra Galileo e i teologi*. Some of the arguments concerned here have been treated somewhat more fully in another article, "L'aristotelismo di Galileo," *Gregorianum* (1972), 117–44.

3. *Nel terzo centenario della morte di Galileo* (Milan, 1942), pp. 97–163.

There are those who deny that Galileo has the right to the title of philosopher today. Others discover connections with the thought of Pythagoras, or even Plato, or Aristotle, or St. Thomas. Some make him and example of empiricism, others of rationalism. Others find that he goes beyond empiricism and rationalism, and yet others find mechanistic and finalistic thought in him. Kant, in the preface to his *Critique of Pure Reason*, saw in Galileo a forerunner of his own critical system. Idealists and positivists invoke him for the same reason. Olgiati poses the following question:

> Galileo's thought embraces a little of Democritus, of Pythagoras, of Plato, Aristotle, and St. Thomas, a little mechanism and finalism, a little empiricism and rationalism, a good dose of dogmatism and a germ of Kantian criticism. Does he not force us to think that he would have been outraged at any desire to discover a philosophical *system* and an organic totality of metaphysical principles in him? Would it not be in vain to speak of a Galilean philosophy and metaphysics?[4]

Despite this, after a serene contemplation of the works of Galileo, Olgiati arrives at the following conclusion:

> Galileo is the creator, not only of a new science, of a new scientific methodology, and even a gnoseology, but he is also the creator of a metaphysics that evinces a systematization that is made more rigorous than at first seemed, and deserves to be bought to light.[5]

I shall therefore relinquish taking into consideration such contradictory modern interpretations, in order to give a rapid glance over the principal philosophical currents of the 16th and 17th centuries, to the extent that they can be related to Galileo's work. I shall then be able to define Galileo's position with respect to these currents, and I shall consider the role of philosophy alongside theology in the trial of Galileo. I can then suggest a reply to the question of understanding whether Galileo can even today aspire to the title of philosopher.

Philosophy at the Time of Galileo: The "Way of the Ancients" and the "Modern Way"

In Christian Europe until the 11th century, philosophy remained strictly dependent on theology: *fides querens intellectum.* Furthermore, little was known of the works of the philosophers of Greek antiquity, Plato and Aristotle.

Their rediscovery in the second half of the 12th century via Arab commentators — particularly Avicenna and Averroes — and, as a

4. Ibid., p. 103.
5. Ibid., p. 106.

consequence, the direct translation of their works, thus constituted a great event. One was faced with complete philosophical systems, constructed by pagan authors on the basis of reason alone. This was the beginning of a process in the course of which the autonomy of philosophy and human reason grew ever stronger.[6]

These systems contained several theses contrary to Christian revelation, giving rise to the first defensive reactions — ineffective — on the part of the church. Faced with this situation, two currents arose in the 13th century.

Some thinkers, above all in academic circles such as Paris and Padua, readily accepted the Aristotelian philosophy, generally via the interpretation of this or that Arab commentator, and occupied themselves almost exclusively with study of and commentaries on the texts. But because most of these authors wished to remain faithful to the church, they resorted to various astute devices in order to reconcile their loyalty both to Aristotle and to the church. Sometimes they made a distinction between philosophical truth and theological truth; I need not examine exactly the way in which they strove to justify this ambiguous position.

AVERROES

According to Averroes:

> Aristotle founded and completed logic, physics, and metaphysics. I say that he founded them because all works on science prior to him are not worthy of mention and are put in the shade by his writings. I say that he completed them because no one among those who came after him up to the present day — that is to say, for fifteen hundred years — has been able to add anything to his writings or to discover any important error in them.[7]

In our case Averroes is particularly important because his philosophy constituted a powerful current in Paduan Aristotelianism, a current still alive at the time of Galileo, a fact that helps us to understand the kind of Aristotelianism that Galileo described with such astute subtlety in the Simplicio of his "Dialogue," and against which he directed the irony of his polemic.

A typical and even famous representative of this current was Cesare Cremonino, professor of philosophy at the University of Padua at the time when Galileo taught there. Cremonino's fidelity to Aristotle ri-

---

6. For the cultural importance of this fact and a certain analogy with the establishment of modern science in the 17th century, one can consult F. Copleston, *A History of Philosophy* (Image Books, 1962), vol 3.

7. Quoted by P. Duhem, *Le système du monde* (Paris, 1913), vol. 2, pp. 133–34.

valed that of his master Averroes.[8] He never wished to bring his eye to the astronomical telescope because, he said, to look through glasses would have corrupted his head (XI, 165). Despite this, relationship between Galileo and Cremonino remained cordial.

ST. THOMAS AQUINAS

Other 13th-century writers, above all in Scholastic circles, although fully accepting the substance of Aristotle's philosophy, sought to integrate with his thought elements drawn from other philosophers — preeminently Platonist and Neoplatonist elements — with the aim of interpreting, developing, and correcting him in accordance with Christian revelation.

Among these philosophers a particular place belongs to St. Thomas. Drawing a clear distinction between philosophy — a work of human reason — and theology, the study of biblical revelation, St. Thomas not only avoided an absolute separation between the two disciplines, but even sought their fertile integration — so much so that insofar as the speculative sciences are concerned he established criteria for both a clear distinction and a mutual integration, which, in my opinion, can still be of real value.[9] In particular he states explicitly that for us human beings who gain all our knowledge via the senses, metaphysics presupposes physics, and that the latter, if it wishes to avoid errors, should take count of experience. It is also remarkable that in his classification of the sciences St. Thomas recognized the particular place that belongs to mathematical physics, science intermediate between physics and mathematics. It should be added that in fact the physics of St. Thomas, like that of Aristotle, is often found to be mixed with some metaphysical elements. Be that as it may, I think that these criteria could also prove to be useful for evaluating the work of Galileo.

Although St. Thomas's methodological principles themselves appear to be balanced, their application was to lead to lamentable consequences, which exercised a determining influence on the "Galilean question." In fact, St. Thomas's main interest remained theological, and for this reason he did not seek to promote a debate — even if only embryonic — on the experimental science of pure physics, as initiated by some contemporary philosophers such as Roger Bacon, and even

8. For documentation on Cremonino's philosophy, see A. Puppi, "Una riflessione a proposito delle critiche di Galileo all'aristotelismo, *Nel quarto centenario della nascita di Galileo Galilei* (Milan, 1964), pp. 171–90.

9. St. Thomas, *In Boethii de Trinitate*, qq. V and VI. For a summarized treatment, see "L'aristotelismo di Galileo," pp. 130–33.

Thomas's master, St. Albert the Great. In physics and astronomy St. Thomas accepted Aristotle's teaching of the four elements, of proper places and natural motions, of a system of celestial spheres set in motion by directed intelligences, incorporated in a hierarchy dominated by the First Unmoved Mover, upon whom everything depends in a series of subordinate causes. The First Unmoved Mover is clearly identified with the Creator God and Providence of Christian revelation, and the intelligences are identified with the angels. Neither fortuitous events nor free human acts are subject to the universal influence of celestial causes. In order to account for the reaction of Scholastic philosophers and theologians to the new things announced by Galileo, it is important to emphasize the extent to which this doctrine of universal agents subordinated to a hierarchical order appears as deeply integrated in St. Thomas's metaphysics and theology.[10]

It is nevertheless true that the Aristotelian universe — which for its epoch cannot be denied a certain esthetic value and also a certain experimental basis — had for a considerable time begun to show its defects. Immediately after Aristotle's work, account had been taken of the fact that the system of fifty-six concentric spheres around the earth, introduced in the interests of a rational explanation of the motions of the celestial bodies, was incompatible with the increasingly precise observations of the astronomers and did not "save the appearances." As a result the system had to be successively adjusted, until Ptolemy, 150 A.D., proposed his own system, which "saved the appearances" in a satisfactory fashion, but seemed very complicated, and clashed with some of the Aristotelian canons. It is precisely on this point that those thinkers who had hope to be able to return one day, one way or another, to the original Aristotelian system, had originated the distinction between *mathematical astronomers* and *physical astronomers*. St. Albert the Great sought to prove that by means of the Ptolemaic system one could also save the principles of Aristotelian philosophy. St. Thomas was aware of the problem, but does not seem to have attached any importance to it.

At the time of Galileo the philosophers and theologians substantially followed St. Thomas. At the moment when, thanks to the astronomical telescope, Galileo's discoveries began to put in question the whole Aristotelian system and particularly the structure and incorruptibility of the heavens, the majority of them, with more or less conviction and

10. T. Litt, O.C.S.O., *Less corps célestes dans l'univers de Saint Thomas d'Aquin* (Louvain, 1963); M. Beltrami, S.J., "L'universalità dell'azione del corpo celeste nella fisica tomista," *Miscellanea Adriane Gazzana* (Milan, 1960), pp. 137–208; "Il corpo celeste nel fisica tomista," *Scritti filosofici* (Milan, 1961), vol. 1, pp. 67–138.

enthusiasm, still held to the methodological principles of St. Thomas and Aristotle, recognizing the primacy of experience. But when one began to deal with the Copernican system, things did not seem so simple. It was only necessary to apply one's eye to the telescope to convice oneself of the movement of the earth and the immobility of the sun: the most pedestrian experience, however, appeared rather to show the contrary. The distinction between mathematical astronomers and physical astronomers seemed to allow one to dispense with a serious examination of the scientific arguments of Copernicus and Galileo — and, as we shall see, to dispense with a new exegetical examination of those scriptural texts that appeared to support the traditional system. On this point opinions were strongly divided among the Scholastics.

In the 17th century, the *via antica* with its two currents, textual and Scholastic, was still very much alive, but already in the 14th century, philosophy, having become autonomous, had initiated with Ockham the *via moderna*, concerned with detaching itself completely from theology and from the philosophy of Aristotle.

PLATO

Another factor of renewal played its part in that preparation of Renaissance philosophy for which Galileo worked: Platonism, favored by the literary humanism of the 15th century and by the Council of Florence in aid of union with the Greeks, promoting contacts with cultured Byzantines. This in turn entailed the discovery of translations of many of Plato's dialogues hitherto unknown in the West.

A certain tension was thus engendered between Platonists and Aristotelians. The former extolled a greater linguistic refinement in Plato, and a more lively interest in the human being and in religion; the latter appreciated a more profound interest in nature on the part of Aristotle. There were also those who, like Pico della Mirandola, strove for a synthesis of the two systems.

There is, however, a Renaissance current of philosophy that, due above all to the mediation of Nicholas of Cusa, drew its inspiration from Platonism, but which, although energetically contesting Aristotle, interested itself in nature to such a point that it enters into the history of philosophy under the name of *philosophy of nature*. It includes philosophers of very diverse inspiration, but nevertheless with several points in common. The principal interest is the human being — *in the world*, an integral part of the cosmos, a microcosm that reflects the whole universe, the macrocosm. Just as there is a soul in the human being, so also there is a soul of the world by which all beings are animated: this is a panpsychism that sometimes touches on — if not explicitly fuses with — pantheism and nature religion. In this philosophy one also commonly finds an idea of nature as a perfectly autonomous system, an idea that tends to exclude every supernatural element and miracle, although marvels and prodigies largely enter into it via magic. In effect, if nature is animate, it is natural that apart from the influence exerted by the stars it should be possible to exercise a psychic and magical influence. Bodies act on each other by mediating sympathies and antipathies; magnetism is an obvious example.

Scientists also had a part in this current of thought, in which, it must be repeated, representatives differed widely among themselves; such were the doctors of medicine G. Fracastore and Paracelsus, for example, and the celebrated mathematician G. Cardano. Johannes Kepler was also influenced by this current to a certain extent.

B. Telesio is sometimes pointed to as a forerunner of the experimental method, which he inculcated in *De rerum natura iuxta propra principia*, apart from the fact of his being occupied with various natural phenomena: earth tremors, tides, comets, the rainbow, color, sound, respiration, sleep, and the like. The proper principles of all these phenomena were readily discoverable, thanks to experience; the sun is warm, luminous, tenuous, mobile; the earth is cold, dark, dense, and immobile. The two active principles of nature are consequently heat and cold; the first expands things and makes them light and apt for movement; the second condenses them, rendering them heavy and immobile. These two principles are incorporeal; in order to act they require a corporeal mass able to bear their action. It follows naturally that all the phenomena of the universe result from the action of heat and cold on corporeal masses.

To undergo the action of heat and cold, all bodies are endowed with perception; life is a property common to all matter. One would not have had any difficulty in demonstrating the fertility of the experimental method of the natural philosophers.

In addition it should not be forgotten that in the spirit of the naturalists there was no lack of philosophers who carried out authentic experimental research in proper laboratories furnished with scientific instruments: furnaces, retorts, bellows, and so forth, apart from magic formulas and cabalistic symbols for arousing nature. Such were the alchemists in search of the philosopher's stone; it cannot be denied that thanks to favorable stars, or the power of magic, or more simply to chance, they sometimes obtained results of a certain scientific value.

GIORDANO BRUNO

It is well to recall two more well-known philosophers from this current of thought who, in their different ways, entered into particular relationships with Galileo — namely, Giordano Bruno and Tommaso Campanella, both Dominicans, who, having fallen prey to difficulties of doctrinal nature, were both accused of heresy, leading a life which was somewhat errant and spending long years in prison. We leave to historians the details of their lives and doctrine. It is their relationships with Galileo that interest us here.

In connection with Galileo, Bruno is often mentioned as having firmly upheld the Copernican system, and as having encountered the Inquisition, being accused of heresy and then being condemned to be burnt at the stake just sixteen years before the first examination of Galileo.

As to Bruno's trial and condemnation, even if it is thought by some that he was not a pantheist, one cannot deny that he often oscillated between a kind of immanentism, which seemed to identify God with nature, and a kind of transcendence, which seemed to confine God in the domain of the absolutely unknowable, thus removing God from the sphere of philosophical interest. To this is added Bruno's accusing all religion — Catholic as well as Reformed — of superstition, useful at best for common folk who need to be governed. True religiosity, that of "the theologians and scholars," was identified with the philosophy that he understood and expressed. Apart from any judgment that one may wish to make as to the death sentence imposed on him, his condemnation for heresy appears to have been accepted by all, in contradistinction to the declaration of heresy promulgated in 1616 against the Copernican theory, a decision contested even in its day by theologians of standing.

As to Bruno's "Copernicanism" it can be observed that he took no interest in scientific reasoning, but was interested only in the fact that this conception favored the notion of an infinite universe, with countless solar systems, possibly inhabited by intelligent beings, corresponding to the idea of a universally animated nature. It is nevertheless possible that this "Copernicanism" of Bruno contributed to arousing the aversion of theologians, above all Urban VIII, against the Copernican theory.

As we shall see, Campanella showed himself an enthusiastic admirer of Galileo, with whom he maintained what may be called a unilateral relationship. Although Bruno's ideal was that of a nature religion, that of Campanella was a utopian politico-religious conception, which he described in his *Civitas Solis*. In philosophy he took up the ideas of Telesio, though alloting a greater place to magic. It is strange that he seems to have met with a certain degree of favor on the part of Urban

VIII, who was opposed to the Copernican theory, however, and was consequently so severe toward Galileo.

JOHANNES KEPLER

Kepler's case deserves separate consideration. Having been rapidly converted to "Copernicanism," he broke off his theological studies for the Protestant ministry at Tübingen, and turned to teaching mathematics in Graz. He also carried out a statistical analysis of the value of horoscopes, which showed him how little credit could be attached to them. This did not prevent him for following his profession of astrologer, if only to remedy his modest salary. Some good luck with several predictions gained him a certain reputation, which allowed him, despite his "Copernicanism," to be admitted as Tycho-Brahe's assistant. In order not to renounce geocentrism, the latter had devised a hybrid system in which the inner planets revolved around the sun, which in turn, together with the moon, revolved around the earth. But Tycho-Brahe was a skilful observer and he had collected a rich harvest of fairly precise locatings of the planets on diverse dates.

On his death he bequeathed this material to Kepler, who, as a good mathematician, undertook to study it systematically, and arrived at his three famous laws of planetary motion.

It is nevertheless typical of the time in which he lived that into this serious scientific work, based on precise measurements and rigorous calculations, Kepler admixed strange considerations on the relationships between the planetary distances relative to the sun and the dimensions of imaginary regular polyhedra, successively inscribed one inside another, or, even further, the harmonic relationships of music, a field in which the symbolism extolled by the Pythagorean and Neoplatonist schools exerted its influence.

Nevertheless, despite these fantastic ideas and his more or less convinced penchant for astrology, Kepler cannot be classified among the naturalist philosophers. He did not accept magic and he was even obliged to wage a painful batttle to save his mother, who had been accused of withcraft. He did not support the idea of universal animation, but proposed the hypothesis of a universal attractive force between the sun and the planets to explain their movements; the attraction exercised by the moon was the cause of the tides. Acording to Kepler, however, this force was inversely proportional to the distance and not to the square of the distance, as by Newton's law of gravitation.

Philosophy in Search of a Method at the Time of Galileo

Naturalist philosophy had shown that in order to construct a valid science of nature it was not enough to appeal to the authority of Aristotle, or even to experiment, without a precise method — as the alchemists had done. A kind of intuition had been arrived at, which was confirmed in the upshot, but it was largely a matter of affirmations devoid of any serious foundations, and mixed with utterly fantastic notions. Many contemporary writers recognized that the naturalistic philosophy was no better than that of Aristotle. The latter at least saw a certain order in nature, which, by contrast, was thrown into disorder by the naturalist philosophers. As a consequence, if one desired to construct a valid philosophy of nature, it was necessary to solve the problem of method.

Independently engaged in this enterprise, on different lines, were three major philosophers of differing nationalities: Francis Bacon (1596-1626) in England, René Descartes (1596-1650) in France, and Galileo Galilei (1564-1642) in Italy.

FRANCIS BACON

Bacon, a man of politics, was motivated above all by practical intentions. He represented the revolution engendered by printing in the realm of letters, by gunpowder in martial arts, by the mariner's compass in navigation, but these were more or less chance discoveries. He aimed rather at a systematic organization of research, and from this point of view revealed a surprising modernity. In his *Nova Atlantis*, an incomplete work published posthumously, he presents a kind of utopian vision, a prelude to modern research institutes. In these institutes one was to apply oneself to the contemplation of "the works and creatures of God," but the ultimate aim was to push back the boundaries of human knowledge as far as possible. Among the discoveries on the agenda in this book are the submarine and the airplane. In this development of technique Bacon saw an aspect of redemption; in fact he concludes his *Novum Organum* with the following observation:

> Original sin cost man his innocence and his role as master of creation. As far as these two losses are concerned, there can be reparation, at least in part, in this life: for innocence, thanks to religion and faith; for mastery of creation, thanks to art and science, given that the divine curse has not caused the radical rebellion of the creature against man. By virtue of the precept: *in sudore vultus comedes panem tuum*, by means of various processes, and certainly not by disputes or useless magical ceremonies, the

creature — that is to say, the natural being — yields to offer man his bread, that is to say, to be useful for human life.[11]

But technique presupposes knowledge of nature. Bacon had a clear objective, that "knowledge is power," and thus he became the theoretician of the new science.

Aristotelian logic and the syllogism are useful for teaching an already constituted science, but what was now necessary was an *ars inveniendi*. To this end Bacon had conceived a very vast work, the *Instauratio magna*, which was to supply directives for all the sciences. In fact he only published the first part of this work, *De dignitate et augmentis scientiarum*, which looked forward to a classification of all the sciences, and the *Novum Organum* — published in 1620, unfinished — which was to replace the Aristotelian *Organon*.

His criticism of Aristotelian philosophy was not so much directed against Aristotle himself as against Aristotelians who were content merely to repeat their master's doctrines. Bacon was persuaded that nature is inexhaustible and that Aristotelian science was clung to because of laziness, timidity, and a fear of having to revise one's own positions, a state that in Bacon's eyes amounted to a form of skepticism and lack of confidence in human reason. On this point he expressed the opinion — also adopted by a number of writers after him — that we are "antiques" — that is, ancients — relative to the first philosophers; we enjoy greater experience.[12] We should not distrust those who have gone before, but we ourselves should endeavor to advance further.

As to method, Bacon took account of the necessity of avoiding past errors, those of the empiricists who, like ants, are content to accumulate what they can find around them, being curious about these things rather than interpreters of truth. But one should also avoid the error of those who neglect experience in trusting exclusively to reason, like spiders who spin their webs out of their own bodies. The true scientist, on the contrary, imitates the bees who gather matter from the flowers, but fashion it themselves, transforming it into wax and honey.[13]

Bacon did not accuse the Aristotelians of neglecting experience, but of allowing themselves to proceed to generalizations that were too hazardous, and of having neglected the doctrine of scientific induction, which had to be constructed *ex novo*.

This new doctrine, propounded in the *Novum Organum*, is well known in its two parts, negative and positive. Negatively, he was

11. *Novum Organum*, book 3, no. 52.
12. Ibid., book 1, no. 84.
13. Ibid., book 1, no. 95.

concerned to free the human spirit from errors and prejudices represented by idols: *idola tribus*, idols of the tribe (anthropomorphism);
idola specus, idols of the cave (personality cult); *idola fori*, idols of the
marketplace (too great a dependence on language); *idola theatri*, idols
of the theater (tradition). Positively, by means of tables of presence,
absence, and degree, he taught the determination of the nature, "the
form," of the property under study. It is true that this theory of
induction, somewhat complicated, never entered into scientific practice.
Nevertheless Bacon marks an enormous progress in the conception of
science and of nature compared with preceding philosophers, Aristotelians or naturalistic, though he was partially influenced by them.

To explain the reciprocal interactions of bodies he has recourse to the
customary example of the magnet that attracts iron, as a sponge draws
in water: the attracted body pierces the pores into which it inserts itself
and lodges within the body to which it yields. This is literal truth, not
just a metaphor: "In connection with such a fundamental and precise
doctrine, two opposed errors have been committed: that of pushing it to
the extreme, and that of neglecting it." Bacon sought the correct way of
not breaking definitively with tradition.[14]

He accepts the four Aristotelian causes: material, formal, efficient,
and final, but then insists on the fact that only the formal cause is worthy
of attracting the attention of the scientist, even if it is difficult to
determine the true meaning of this term:

> The work and discovery of human science consists in illuminating the form
> of a given nature, or in other words, its true difference or "naturalizing"
> nature, or source of emanation, from the moment that these words maxi-
> mally approximate that which we wish to express.[15]

This concept seemed in some way to be connected with a devaluation
of the use of mathematics in the sciences, and this further sets Bacon in
opposition to Descartes and Galileo. Thus in connection with optics he
writes:

> Much is said about the trajectory of luminous rays, but not a word is said
> about their origins. But the cause of this omission, as in a countless number
> of other cases, is the widespread habit of inserting perspective into the
> mathematical disciplines; in fact one is very rapidly set at a distance from
> physics.[16]

According to Bacon it is necessary to seek what luminous bodies have
in common — that is, the form of light.

---

14. *De dignitate*, book 4, no. 3.
15. *Novum Organum*, book 2, no. 1.
16. *De dignitate*, book 4, no. 3.

Mathematical astronomy also has a tendency to deceive the human intellect, as Prometheus deceived Jupiter with an ox skin stuffed with straw, in the guise of a real ox:

> Mathematical astronomy presents the exterior of celestial phenomena, namely the number, situation, movement, and periods of the stars, all this being like a heavenly skin, a splendid skin, that is beyond discussion, but without entrails, that is to say, without a theory that causes us to know the substance, movement, and influence of the celestrial bodies, in a word, the whole as it really is. . . . A fairly serious research into this nature has never been attempted. One is only occupied with observations and mathematical demonstrations.[17]

As a result Bacon shows indifference and distrust toward the Copernican hypothesis. The latter may be true, but it could also be nothing more than a pure fiction, invented to facilitate and shorten calculations. All the mathematical hypotheses of the astronomers are equivalent; at most they indicate the apparent movements, serving to "save appearances," but they do not indicate the true causes, the reality of things.[18]

There remains the fact that Bacon as the theoretician of experimental method never carried out an experiment and above all made no discovery of importance. R. Lenoble entitles his chapter devoted to Bacon, "Francis Bacon's false start."[19] He promises much but reveals nothing. This is the judgment passed by most of his contemporaries. His glory was to begin with Leibniz, who was to discover in him "a divine genius." Even today opinions are very divided; one can share the observation made by Schuhl:

> It is important not to underestimate how prescientific his universe was. Nevertheless, the contagious spirit that inspired his writings contributed to prompting humankind to the discovery of nature. . . . . As a true man of transition — we could say, like a new Moses — he pointed out the promised land without being able to enter it.[20]

RENÉ DESCARTES

Descartes, the second father of modern science, takes a position that we could consider the antithesis of that adopted by Bacon. If the latter strove to imitate the bee extracting nectar from flowers and transforming it in its interior, Descartes is more like the spider extracting everything from its interior. This different approach is in the first place due to

17. Ibid., book 3, no. 4.
18. Ibid.
19. R. Lenoble, *Le origini del metodo scientifico moderno* (Bari, 1976), p. 65.
20. Ibid., p. 66.

the role allotted to mathematics in the construction of the sciences. In this Bacon saw an obstacle and did all that he could to perfect induction and direct contact with nature. Descartes found in the role of mathematics the one sure foundation of all knowledge and did all that he could to reconstruct a metaphysics *more geometrico*, which led him to the "geometrization" of physics.

Bacon, who maintained that "we are the antiques," recognized the progressive character of science, sought to assure its progress, and condemned the stagnation of the Aristotelians. His ideal was the domination of nature by human nature; he is the prophet of modern technology. Descartes, in subjecting the whole culture of his time to critical examination, demolished everything except mathematics, which retained its certitude, and regretted that nothing of importance had been built on this foundation. By locating the problem of criticism at the base of his system, he marks the beginning of modern philosophy.

Faithful to his mathematical ideal, the force of which rested on the fact that starting from absolutely certain postulates and following a perfectly logical chain of deduction one can set up a construction capable of withstanding any criticism, Descartes sought incontestable principles that could serve as a foundation for the new philosophy. He thus resolved to doubt everything, even the existence of the outside world and the validity of mathematics itself; he wanted to take precautions against the injurious dexterities of some evil spirit. But precisely in this state of doubt he found the basis he had been seaking, *cogito ergo sum*, the existence of the *res cogitans*. Critical examination of his own thought then led him on to the discovery of the idea of God as absolutely perfect Being, an idea that could not spring from finite thought such as ours. Thus the existence of God is assured, and via the truth of God there is assured the objective value of our clear and distinct ideas, among them the idea of the existence of the outside world. But once again, in this case the only clear and distinct idea is that of geometric extension and local motion. Qualitative ideas, in particular those of sensible qualities, are shown to be confused, and the human body itself can only be extension and local motion, a machine pure and simple, though complex.

It is not only that the axioms of geometry are derived *a priori* from the *res extensa*, but the laws of motion, of mechanics, are also deducible *a priori* from the attributes of God. In particular, from God's immutability stems the law of conservation of matter and of quantity of motion, and from the latter in turn comes the law of inertia and the concept of local motion as a state of becoming.

According to many writers this concept of motion is one of the major achievements of Cartesian physics, even if the method used to obtain it leaves us somewhat perplexed. Always *a priori*, basing himself on the attributes of God and on the objectivity of clear and distinct ideas, Descartes in this way also arrived at the deduction of the laws of collision of bodies and the distribution of the quantity of motion, but in this case his results proved to be false and contradicted by experience.

From the moment when there is an identification of matter and extension, the void cannot exist. Furthermore, extension is always divisible, and as a result Descartes rejected the atomism of Democritus. Matter is nevertheless constructed from corpuscles, the interstices between them being filled with a more rarified matter. In the upshot, at a maximal degree of rarefaction, matter becomes light. Again because of the impossibility of the void, movement always appears in the form of a vortex.

On the groundwork of these principles, Descartes composed a "Treatise on the World," the publication of which was suspended, however, following Galileo's condemnation, because in the "Treatise" Descartes upheld the Copernican theory as a consequence of the theory of vortices. Let us note that if the laws of matter are absolutely necessary, flowing from the attributes of God, and the structure of the universe results therefrom, then if God created another universe, it would assume a structure similar to ours.

To understand the mentality of Descartes, it is useful to keep in mind an observation by Koyré.[21] In an earlier phase Descartes had concerned himself with the law of the free fall of heavy bodies and had deduced an erroneous formula: the speed of fall was taken to be proportional not to the time elapsed, but to the distance through which the moving body had fallen. Galileo had also made the same mistake but had retracted. But toward 1630, the epoch of his composition of the *Regulae ad directionem ingenii*, Descartes's thought underwent a profound evolution. He brought his philosophical reflection to maturity and came to a new conception of the world and of the principle of inertia, as stated above. His construction of mathematical physics — that is, the new science customarily attributed to him — nevertheless underwent a halt.

His "Principles of Philosophy" do not comprise mathematically formulated laws, and there is no word about the fall of heavy bodies. Writing to Mersenne he explains why: the preceding law formulated by him presupposed a void, which cannot exist. If one wished to proceed according to these principles, one should determine at the outset what is heaviness, lightness, and hardness. This is what he proposed to do. The

21. Alexandre Koyré, *Etudes Galiléennes* (Paris, Hermann, 1966), pp. 107–35.

"mathematicization" of physics made it a deductive science requiring an ordered procedure by stages, impossible in practice. This concept is of importance for an understanding of Descartes's criticism of Galileo.

Descartes is generally recognized as the father of modern philosophy, perhaps more on account of the problems he raised than the solutions he offered. In mathematics he can claim the privilege of a position of the first rank for having played an important part in the foundation of analytical geometry, and we still use the expression "Cartesian coordinates." In physics, as in the case of Bacon, we may be tempted to speak of a second "false start." Even in his day nobody took seriously his foundation of science on God's truth and immutability, any more than the a priori deductive form. Nevertheless in the foundation of modern science there is attributed to him a role more or less equal to that of Galileo. This is due to the fact that the beginning of modern science is marked by a "mechanistic explosion"[22] considered necessarily related to the application of mathematics in science. It is certain that the "mechanization" together with the "geometrization" of physics has largely contributed to the development of mathematical physics, but this same development soon provoked the crisis of mechanism itself, at least in the metaphysical and absolute form imparted to it by Descartes.

Galileo and the Philosophers of his Time

One argument for contesting Galileo's title of philosopher in the modern sense could be the fact that he had no relationship with the philosophical movements of his time. Galileo is a scientist. He declares himself to be a disciple of Archimedes, of whom he always speaks in very laudatory terms. The latter concerned himself with statics and Galileo carried the work forward into the field of kinematics. He was interested in Copernicus and sought to consolidate and set forth his work; he passionately defended its realist significance against those who wished to see in it a simple mathematical artifice for computational convenience. On the other hand he showed a profound lack of interest for the whole philosophical movement represented by the naturalistic philosophers.

In "The Assayer" Galileo replies simply to Sarsi, who had expressed the opinion that he had taken certain elements from Cardan and Telesio: "What Cardan and Telesio have written, I have never seen" (EN, V, 236).

---

22. Lenoble, *Le origini*, pp. 129–53.

TOMMASO CAMPANELLA

The case of Campanella, passionate admirer of Galileo's work, is particularly significant. On the occassion of the publication of "The Starry Messenger" he wrote a long letter to Galileo, praising him for having "purified the eyes of men by showing them the new heavens and a new earth in the moon," but he offered Galileo some suggestions, something that he repeated on other occassions, with great liberty.

In 1616 he made an offer to Galileo that he would refute a dissertation addressed to the latter by Ingoli, in which the Copernican system had been refuted by mathematical, physical, and logical arguments (EN, XII, 287). In the same year he composed an *Apologia pro Galileo, mathematico florentino, ubi disquiritur utrum ratio philosophandi quam Galileus celebrat faveat Scripturis an adversetur*, which, however, was not published until 1622 in Frankfurt (EN, XIII, 106). In 1630, according to Cesi, Campanella was prepared to uphold the Copernican cause before Urban VIII, from whom he received the following reply: "This was never our intention, and if it depended only on us this decree [of 1616] would never been made" (EN, XIV, 90).

After the publication of Galileo's "Dialogue," in 1632, Campanella complained that he had been neglected, because Galileo had paid homage to much of the world "and not to me who am more devoted to him than the others" (EN, XIV, 255). When he had finally obtained the work and read it, he wrote a letter full of praise and suggestions, expressing a strong wish to be able to collaborate with Galileo:

> I wish to say that if we were together in a villa for one year, great things would come about, and although you are self-sufficient, I know myself to be of use, together with you, for properly removing doubts, either Peripatetic or common, on the subject of the first decrees of philosophy. God does not need to be praised. These novelties of old truths, of new worlds, of new stars, of new systems, of new nations, etc., are the beginning of a new century (EN, XIV, 367).

Confronted with so much good will, Galileo showed himself cold and indifferent. We do not know if he sent a letter to his devoted admirer, but in any case none has been preserved. It seems that in 1614 he offered him, through Adami, financial help, which was politely refused (EN, XII, 93). In Galileo's writings Campanella's name appears once, in a marginal note, unrelated to the argument dealt with in the text: "To Father Campanella: I hold it better to find a truth, however small, than to dispute at length the greatest questions without arriving at any truth" (EN, IV, 738).

A study by R. Amerio, "Galileo et Campanella,"[23] also makes it clear to what extent Galileo and Campanella were on very different planes. Galileo intended to take a modest step on behalf of science, but a sure step, toward a greater knowledge of the physical universe. Campanella, not much interested in the reality of the Copernican system, was above all drawn by the new heavens and the new earths, omens of his utopian politico-religious ideas. In Galileo's new discoveries he hoped to find support for his philosophico-theological speculations, which left Galileo utterly skeptical and indifferent.

Galileo's lack of accord with an image-laden naturalistic philosophy also emerges in his relationships with Kepler. In 1597 the latter had sent Galileo his *Mysterium cosmographicum*, in which he openly declared himself to be a Copernican. As soon as he had read the preface, Galileo replied with a letter enthusiastic at having found such a companion in the search for truth, and which declared that he had embraced the Copernican opinion for many years, but that for the moment he did not wish to make his opinions public, because many had turned Copernicus into an object of derision and had rejected him. He ended by expressing the desire to read the whole book, declaring himself tò be a great friend of Kepler and wishing to receive letters from him (EN, X, 67-68). It seems, however, that his enthusiasm for the *Mysterium cosmographicum* did not extend beyond the pages of the preface. Galileo did not reply to Kepler's pressing requests, desiring to receive a critical judgment of his work — so much so that in the end Galileo did not seem to be greatly interested in Kepler's writings, even though Kepler always showed great esteem for Galileo's astronomical discoveries.

The explanation is perhaps supplied by a comparison between the image-laden and complicated style of the Prague astronomer and the linear clarity of the Florentine astronomer. In fact, toward the end of his life, addressing himself to Fra Miconzio, Galileo passed on Kepler a very severe judgment:

> As to the virtuosity of which you speak, perhaps you will make it understood, as occasion offers, that I have always held Kepler in esteem for his free (perhaps too free) and subtle ingenuity, but my way of philosophizing is very different from his, and it can be the case that while writing on the same subjects, it is only in connection with celestial motions that we have encountered — though rarely — some similar idea; we have thus attributed the same true reason to the same true effect, but that does not even amount to one percent of my thoughts (EN, XVI, 163).

---

23. *Nel quarto centenario della nascita di Galileo Galilei*, pp. 299–325.

In sum, not only do Galileo and the naturalistic philosophers have nothing in common, but Kepler's manner of philosophizing, completely different, prevented Galileo from recognizing, amidst Kepler's Pythagorean meanderings, that scientifically valid element destined to advance Copernicus's and his own work and to prepare Newton's great leap forward.

It is futile to try to find greater agreement between Galileo's philosophy and that of the two other forerunners of modern science: Bacon and Descartes.

FRANCIS BACON

Galileo was in agreement with Bacon in the sense that both adopted the beelike tactic of associating experience and intellectual reflection, while always giving primacy to experience. But as for other matters we can say that they advanced along different roads.

In the refashioning of scientific method, Bacon strove to trace out a truly precise and complex theory of that method. Galileo worked at science on every possible occasion without bothering to compose a theoretical treatise. Bacon looked to the form, in the interior of things, neglecting the exterior, the skin. Galileo renounced the determination of essence, though not denying its existence, relegating knowledge of it to the future life, to the state of beatitude, contenting himself with phenomena in this life below (EN, V, 187–88), going on to advance some more general hypothesis on the nature of sensible qualities, particularly heat (EN, VI, 347–52).

The contrast between the method of Galileo and that of Bacon emerges more clearly, however, in connection with the role attributed to mathematics in the practice of science. Bacon not only neglected it but saw in it a departure from physics. Galileo on the contrary, in a celebrated passage (EN, VI, 232) maintained that philosophy is written in the great book that is the universe, in mathematical language, without which it is impossible to understand a single word of it. As a consequence Bacon attributed to the theory of Copernicus a purely hypothetical, instrumental value. Galileo passionately upheld its realist significance throughout his whole life.

This does not mean that Galileo would have known of Bacon's work, or vice versa. We have only two letters from Tobias Matthew to Bacon, who sent him an extract from the letter to Castelli and spoke of Galileo's work. It seems that neither of them had occasion to pronounce on the work of the other.

RENÉ DESCARTES

Things are different in the matter of relationships between Descartes and Galileo.

Mersenne, an active intermediary between the two scientists, made sure that Galileo had access to Descartes's "Discourse on Method," offering to convey to its author any observations that Galileo might care to make (EN, XVII, 226).But in Galileo's writings we find no allusion to Descartes. It should be noted that during these years Galileo was confined at Arcetri, suffering from incipient blindness and occupied in writing his treatises on mechanics; furthermore Descartes's problematics could hardly have interested him.

Descartes, on the other hand, had Galileo's works in his hands, and writing to Mersenne on several occasions he expressed his judgment.

In 1634 he was lent the *Dialogo dei massimi sistemi* for thirty hours. He observed that Galileo made good enough philosophical sense on motion, but, he added, few things were entirely true. The argument about the tides seemed to be dragged along by the scruff of the neck; its proper explanation, also derived from the motion of the earth, was completely different. The reasons given for the earth's movement were very good, but not very effective, because of continual digressions. He added that for him it was impossible to resolve some questions of physics before having explained all its principles, and that could not be done without the "Treatise on the World," which he had decided to suppress (EN, XVI, 124–25). In previous writings he had explained the reason for this decision, while fully recognizing that the condemnation of Galileo was not definitive, because it had not been confirmed by the pope or by a council; but in no way did he wish to oppose the church. On this occasion he announced his maxim: *bene vixit qui bene latūit*, but at the same time he recognized that if there were in his own philosophy a single erroneous proposition, then the whole system would be deprived of its force.

In 1638 Descartes was able to have in his hands the *Discorsi e dimonstrazioni matematiche intorno a due nuove scienze*. On April 23, after having turned over the pages for two hours, he remarked that they presented nothing of interest (EN, XVII, 369). But on October 11 he sent Mersenne a somewhat longer letter, with many observations. Galileo, according to Descartes, philosophizes very much better than is usually the case. He avoids the errors of the schools and treats the arguments of physics mathematically. In this respect Galileo agrees with him but Descartes again complains about Galileo's continual digressions, that he does not get to the bottom of arguments, that he proceeds without order and without taking the first causes of nature into consideration, and that he seeks the reasons only for a particular effect. He has thus built without foundation. But his way of philosophizing, nearer to the truth, allows his errors to be better understood. There follows a long list of criticisms of particular points.

Descartes concludes by recommending Mersenne to keep these observations to himself, because he refuses to correct the errors of others. Apart from this he has never met Galileo, has taken nothing from him, and finds in him nothing that arouses his envy or that he would wish to recognize as his own. The best part is that in which Galileo deals with music, but this had been written by himself (Descartes) nineteen years earlier. What Galileo had said about the force of percussion, and which he had found difficult, had been easily explained in his (Descartes's) own "Principles" (EN, XVII, 387–91).

Finally, in December 1638, on the subject of tables calculated by Galileo dealing with the ranges of cannon, Descartes observes: "Having disapproved of all the reasons on which he bases himself, it does not seem worthwhile to speak about it" (EN, XVII, 416).

In essence, Descartes's judgments, abstracting from his tone of distrustful superiority, illuminate the divergences existing between the two scientists, divergences much deeper than their points of convergence. Descartes is above all a metaphysician, who wants to deduce physics from his metaphysics. Galileo is first and foremost a physicist who nevertheless, on occasion, rises to metaphysical considerations.

Descartes accuses Galileo of building without a foundation. In reality, the foundation is very different. Whereas Descartes, in a very summary procedure, totally rejects the entire traditional doctrine, Galileo starts out from a realist position, which is nevertheless not devoid of a critical spirit. As Favaro notes in the foreword of the edition of the writings of Galileo's youth:

> The battles waged by Galileo against Aristotelian physics are known to all; but until now there have not been made public those authentic documents that would have revealed how he had studied it in depth before attacking it.

In fact, against Simplicius — who recalls the reproach addressed to Plato by Aristotle, to the effect that he had departed from sound philosophy by studying too much geometry — Galileo proposes the mathematical philosophers — an obvious allusion to himself, "who deal more willingly with those who are well instructed in the common Peripatetic philosophy than with those who do not possess such instruction, and who as a consequence cannot draw parallels between doctrine and doctrine" (EN, VII, 423).

Galileo demolishes Aristotelian physics piece by piece, basing himself on a diligent and critical examination, as appears from the dialogues with Simplicius, which Descartes calls useless digressions.

Nevertheless, he does not reject the whole Aristotelian metaphysics a priori, even though he is convinced that it should be revised in depth. In a note on the occasion of the composing of the *Dialogo dei massimi sistemi* he wrote:

> For those who are troubled at having to change the whole of philosophy, I want to show that this is not the case, and that the doctrine of the soul, of generations, meteors, and animals remains unchanged (EN, VII, 541).

It is true that Galileo frequently followed Descartes in the domain of mechanistic philosophy, and it cannot be denied that he had in him an extraordinarily mechanistic tendency. Nevertheless the two men are on essentially different planes.

Descartes is a metaphysician and himself admits that if one of his propositions fails to stand, then the whole system is gravely compromised. Galileo is a physicist; he advances propositions for mechanistic explanations of particular phenomena, but makes no categorical affirmations.

In a passage often quoted in favor of Galileo's mechanistic outlook, in connection with the generation of insects during the evaporation of cider, he writes:

> I have never really understood substantial transformation (always keeping within purely natural terms), thanks to which a matter is totally transformed, to the point where one has to say of necessity that it is completely destroyed, that nothing of its first state of being persists, and that another body very different from the first matter has been made of it. If a body is presented to me, under one aspect, and then soon afterward under another, fairly different, I do not exclude that this can be due to a simple transposition of its parts, without anything being destroyed or engendered. We observe metamorphoses of this kind all the day long (EN, VII, 64–65).

In this case, Galileo certainly does not intend to give an explanation of generation; he speaks of a simple possibility, of a hypothesis, all the more so because a few lines above he has declared that he does not understand anything of these matters and that he consequently recognizes the mystery contained in generation:

> Between the fashioning of a statue and the formation of a living person, and even of a very lowly worm, there is an infinite distance (EN, VII, 128).

The difficulty in accepting generation expressed here comes, on the one hand, from the false conception formulated of it, as if it were a question of the annihilation and creation of substances; hence the parenthesis "always keeping within purely natural terms." On the other hand the difficulty is understandable because of the inadequacy of the Aristotelian explanation proposed by Simplicius, on the basis of the opposed properties of the elements and the incorruptibility of the heavens, against which is directed the whole discourse developed over several pages.

One can make the same observation on the subject of the passage in "The Assayer" that concerns sensible qualities. Here again a hypothesis is proposed: "I think that. . . ." " I do not think that it can have any more existence than a titillation." The purely hypothetical and uncategorical character of this explanation of sensible qualities becomes even clearer if we take into account the relationship here proposed between the four elements and the four senses — touch, taste, smell, hearing — although he states that he knows very little about light, and elsewhere (EN, XVIII, 233–34) asserts that he knows absolutely nothing about it.

The mechanistic nature, of a Cartesian type, of Galileo's philosophy often appears through the very character of mathematical physics, on the ground of the distinction between qualitative science and quantitative science. To clarify this, it is useful to compare two well-known texts by Galileo in which he eulogizes mathematicians. At the end of the first day of the "Dialogue," in connection with knowledge of mathematics, Galileo draws a distinction:

> There are two modes of knowing, *extensive* and *intensive*. As far as the *extensive* is concerned — that is to say, the mode that refers to the infinite multitude of intelligible things — human knowledge is as nothing, even when it embraces a thousand propositions, because a thousand relative to infinity is as zero. But if one considers *intensive* knowledge, to the extent that this term comprises in an intensive manner — that is, perfectly — certain propositions, then I say that human intelligence can know some of these perfectly enough and about these has a certitude as absolute as nature itself. This is what the *pure* mathematical sciences are [24] — that is, geometry and arithmetic — about which the divine intellect knows many more infinite propositions, because it knows them all. But as to those, few in number, that the human intellect can know, I believe that cognition of them, in objective certainty, equals the divine, because it comes to understand that necessity beyond which, it appears, there cannot be greater certitude (EN, VII, 128).

In "The Assayer" we read a further eulogy of mathematics:

> Philosophy is written in the great book that is continually open before our eyes (I mean the universe), but nothing of which can be understood unless one first learns to understand the language and recognize the characters.

---

24. The word "pure" is stressed by Galileo.

This book is written in mathematical language and the characters are triangles, circles, and other geometrical figures, without which it is humanly impossible to understand a word; without these one would find oneself lost in an obsure labyrinth" (EN, VI, 32).

Galileo makes a clear distinction between *pure* mathematics — geometry and arithmetic — in which our intensive knowledge seeks to equal the divine knowledge, and natural philosophy written *in mathematical characters*, about which we can never say that our knowledge equals the divine knowledge. We have already seen the hypothetical, possibilist way in which he speaks about generation and sensible qualities; their essence is inaccessible to us and knowledge of them is reserved to the beatific vision (EN, V, 187–88).

For Galileo, mathematics constitutes the language in which the great book of nature is written, but not its content. In order to read Homer's poems, I should know the characters of the alphabet and the Greek language, but this will not suffice; I should in fact have concern for the reading and interpretation of the text. To read the book of nature it is not enough to know mathematics; I should apply myself to observe nature attentively and interpret it.

As to the quantitative character attributed to mathematical physics, we must deny it if by quantitative is understand geometric, pure extension in the Cartesian sense, excluding all qualitative aspects. The thinkers of antiquity had already mathematically treated time and weight, which are not simply geometrical magnitudes. In modern physics, measurements and mathematical calculations involving forces, energies, temperatures, electric and magnetic fields, and a thousand other magnitudes are introduced, magnitudes that are not simply a "quantity" in the geometrical sense. The qualitative aspect enters into calculations through the units of the measurements, which constitute an integral part of the measurements themselves.

Furthermore, as early as Newton, who introduced the idea of force, Cartesian physics entered a crisis, whereas the more open Galilean physics began its ascent without experiencing interruption.

We can accept the distinction between qualitative science and quantitative science if by the former is understood a science of "the fairly close": of large and small, of much and little, of warm and cold, of heavy and light, and if by the latter is understood an "exact" science, of precise measurements based on preestablished units, whether it be a matter of geometrical or physical magnitudes. Such is Galilean science, through which the observation made in "The Assayer" comes to be more valid now than ever before.

To sum up, as a methodologist of science, Galileo is perfectly original; he stands out clearly from — one could even say that he is in opposition to — all his philosophical contemporaries, but he is indeed the true father of modern science.

Galileo and the Philosophers of Antiquity

If Galileo seems completely independent and disinterested as far as the "modern" philosophers are concerned, the same cannot be said of the philosophers of antiquity.

In his biography, Viviani states that when Galileo was at Padua he studied "medicine and philosophy, after the style of the lectures; but at the same time he examined with great diligence the works of Aristotle, Plato, and other philosophers of antiquity, striving to grasp properly their dogmas and opinions in order to examine them and in the first place to satisfy his own intellect" (XIX, 603). In the same biography we further read:

> It is certainly not true that he spoke of the philosophers of antiquity, and especially Aristotle, with little esteem and with distrust, as is stupidly said by some who claim to be his disciples. He only said that the manner of philosophizing of this great man did not satisfy him and that in it he had found delusions and errors . . . .He exalted Plato highly for his truly golden eloquence and for his manner of writing and composing dialogues, and above all he praised Pythagoras for his way of philosophizing; but, said he. it is the ingenious Archimedes who surpasses them all and whom he called his master (EN, XIX, 645).

Nevertheless, if we examine Galileo's works, we can find some surprises.

Certainly, let us observe, Galileo had a mechanistic tendency without being a mechanistic philosopher, and in fact, in the hypothesis that he advanced on the nature of heat, he clearly has an atomistic conception. For all that, he very rarely evokes Democritus, and then without much enthusiasm.

PYTHAGORAS

From Viviani we have learned that Galileo particualy appreciated Pythagoras, and this is not surprising, because among the disciples of Pythagoras we find the first partisans of the heliocentric system. Pythagoras had dealt with the theory of music, with which Galileo and his father were concerned. Above all, in his philosophy Pythogoras had placed mathematics in the first rank.

But when Simplicius evokes the authority of the Pythagoreans, "who say that all things are determined by three: principle, middle, and end, and that three is the number of everything," Galileo declares that he is not satisfied, and observes:

> I do not understand or believe that for legs, for example, three should be more perfect than four or two, nor, it seems to me, that four should be imperfect for the elements, and that they would be more perfect if they were three. It was therefore better to leave inexactitudes to orators and to prove one's intention by necessary demonstrations, as it is appropriate to do in the demonstrative sciences.

In reply to Simplicius's astonishment that Galileo, a mathematician and Pythagorean philosopher, could distrust the Pythagorean mysteries, Galileo explains the reasons for his admiration of Pythagoras and Plato:

> That the Pythagoreans held the science of numbers in high esteem, and that Plato himself admired the human intellect and considered it as participating in the divine intellect only because it knew the nature of numbers, I very well know, and I would not be far from passing the same judgment, but in no way do I believe that the mysteries for which Pythagoras and his sect held so much veneration in their science of numbers are the stupidities found in the words and writings of the vulgar (EN, VII, 35).

Galileo thus thought that the hidden meaning which the Pythagoreans attributed to numbers was a simple artifice to guard the secret of their real mathematical discoveries. In addition I have already alluded to the unfavorable impression made on Galileo by Kepler's Pythagoreanism.

PLATO

We have likewise seen that Viviani attributed Galileo's enthusiasm for Plato to the latter's literary qualities. In the last quotation above — to which others could be added — Galileo appreciated Plato for the esteem in which he held mathematics. In Galileo we can find other Platonic reminiscences, in particular the maieutic method (EN, VII, 183, 217).

Alexandre Koyré has upheld the Platonism of Galileo with particular insistence,[25] but he does not seem to meet with much approbation. In the conclusion of his essay he draws a line of demarcation between Platonism and Aristotelianism:

> If one proclaims the *superior value* of mathematics and if one further attributes to it a real value and a predominant role in and for physics, one is a Platonist; if, on the other hand, one sees in mathematics an "abstract" science and consequently a science of *inferior value* relative to the physical sciences and to metaphysics which are concerned with the real — and if, in

25. Koyré, *Etudes*, passim.

particular, one claims to base physics *directly on experience*, allotting to mathematics a subsidiary role, then one is an Aristotelian.[26]

We shall see that in fact Galileo declares himself to be an Aristotelian, precisely because he puts experience at the base of physics.

ARISTOTLE

It is important to pay special attention to the relationships between Galileo and Aristotle, because the latter is the philosopher in whom Galileo is particularly interested, if only in order to criticize him. In the analytical index of the Edizione Nazionale of the works of Galileo, Aristotle's name occupies more than seven columns, whereas Archimedes and Plato occupy little more than one column, and Pythagoras and Democritus about half a column. Furthermore, the fact of having so carefully reconstructed the reasoning of the Peripatetics, which he places on Simplicius's lips, is sufficient in itself to show an uncommon interest on Galileo's part.

Viviani observes that Galileo did not mistrust Aristotle, but that he only said that he found the latter's mode of philosophizing unsatisfactory and that it contained delusions and errors. Consequently it may be of interest to determine in what way Aristotle's manner of philosophizing is distinct from that of Galileo.

But it is above all necessary to dispel a frequently observed misunderstanding on the subject of Aristotle's science. R. Lenoble seems to introduce an absolute opposition between the science of Aristotle and that of Galileo: Aristotelian science was founded on concepts that express essences, and was deductive, necessary, static, and qualitative, whereas 17th-century science, especially that of Galileo, was "*phénoménique*," dynamic, always ready to be revised, quantitative, and mechanistic.[27]

Similarly, E. Agazzi in a work that is otherwise worthy of the highest consideration by all who are interested in the philosophy of science, maintains that:

> The authentic change of perspective from which modern science stems took place with Galileo. This is not because he practically perfected the experimental method and integrated the essential mathematical element with it, as is often affirmed, so as to gain an adequate scientific method (an achievement of enormous weight). It is rather on account of the much more important and truly decisive reason that he had understood that a more adequate knowledge of nature could not be gained by a simple change of

26. Ibid., p. 279.
27. Ibid., passim.

philosophy, but by recourse to a different category of research — that is, *nonphilosophical research*. The frontier between the old and new type of research is formed by the renunciation of an inquiry into the *essence*, which, as has been seen, had been one of the pivots of the problematization of experience and the stimulus for philosophical research ever since the classical age. . . . [28]

Over the centuries the problem of grasping the essence (that is to say, of replying to the question: What is a certain reality?) had been considered a task of "pure reason," entrusted to the capacity of our intellect for abstracting from objects exactly their essential characteristics, via a synthetic act able to grasp underneath the "accidental" particularities the *unicum* that characterizes them relative to objects of different species. [29]

In other words, by means of an act of abstraction, one should have been able to arrive directly at the essential definition through genus and specific difference, whence by the road of deduction and syllogism, one would have derived the properties. The Galilean methodological reversal would then have consisted in a renunciation of the penetration of essences, a vain and fruitless undertaking, in order to limit oneself to "appearances" (EN, V, 187–88).

The notion of a deductive Aristotelian science, certain and absolute, starting from definitions in order to arrive at properties *more mathematico*, has in fact a firm basis if we restrict ourselves to consulting Aristotle *the theoretician of science*, in the first book of the *Posterior Analytics*. But if, on the other hand, we consult Aristotle when he is *constructing science* in physics, and particularly in his works on specialist physics — *De Caelo, De Generatione et Corruptione, Meteorologica* — and in his works on biology, we find that Aristotle himself has mitigated methodological rigor, that he is much less categorical, and that he cedes the first place to experience. This has been particularly brought to light by J.M. Le Blond,[30] among others, who goes so far as to affirm that Aristotle's metaphysics is an "experimental metaphysics" in contradistinction to that of Plato.[31]

The explanation of the apparent contradiction is clear enough: in elaborating his theory of science, Aristotle is thinking of the model offered by the mathematicians, the only science then formed into a doctrinal system. When he is working in natural science and following unexplored paths, he has to create a new method, naturally giving first place to experience and leaving a large number of questions open.

28. E. Agazzi, *Temi e problemi della filosofia della fisica* (Milan, 1969), p. 9; see also his "Fisica galileiana contemporanea," in *Nel quarto centenario*, pp. 2–11.
29. Agazzi, *Temi e problemi*, p. 12.
30. J.M. Le Blond, *Logique`et méthode chez Aristotle* (Paris, 1970).
31. Ibid., p. 441.

I consider it opportune here to give voice to Sir David Ross, eminent authority in Aristotelian studies:

> Aristotle is neither an empiricist nor a rationalist, but he recognises that sense and intellect are complementary. . . . According to his theory sensible perception has the task of providing the scientist with data: the ὅτι (thing) should be known before the search for the διστι (reason) is begun, and the αποδει ξις (demonstration) is not conceived as a way of arriving at a knowledge of particular facts by reasoning, but as an explanation, via reasoning, of facts already known through sense perception. Without doubt that is the correct theory.[32]

We know that in fact Aristotle devoted himself personally to biological research and that he obtained appreciable results in this domain. In physics he was less fortunate. He held to the scientific data of his time — Eudoxus and Calippus in astronomy, Empedocles for the doctrine of the four elements — elaborating the whole into a theoretical system as imposing as it was fragile, because it was based on superficial and uncritical experience. It should also be observed that in contradistinction to Socrates and Plato, Aristotle never found a disciple of his own stature, who could have followed up and completed his work.

It is undeniable that disciples are not always faithful to their master. This cannot, however, be leveled as a reproach against St. Thomas, who explicitly stated:

> In sensible things we are ignorant of the true essential differences; for this reasoñ we express ourselves by means of the accidental differences that derive from the essentials, as a cause expresses itself through its effect and as "biped" shows itself different from "human being."[33]

In fact Galileo holds rather to the Aristotelians than to Aristotle, in remarking that:

> A dispute is carried on concerning the interpretation of some words in the testament of someone who is dead. If he were alive, it would be folly to address oneself to others rather than to him in order to establish the meaning of what he had written. Equally, it would be simplistic to go off searching for the meaning of the things of nature, when nature itself, always alive, is at work and present before our eyes, veridical and immutable in all its ways (EN, XVI, 338).

Consequently Galileo departs from the Aristotelian doctrine, which he has Simplicius expound, and submits it to a more rigorous confrontation with nature. This critical examination causes the crumbling of the whole edifice of Aristotelian physics, bit by bit, like a house of cards.

---

32. W.D. Ross, *Aristotle's Prior and Posterior Analytics*, p. 86.
33. *De ente et essentia*, chap. 4. See P.J. Rohellec, "Utrum iuxta S. Thomae doctrinam essentiae rerum sensibilium in simplici apprehensione statim percipiantur," in *Xenia Thomistica* (Rome, 1925), vol. 1, pp. 288–318.

Despite this, if we were to ask Galileo, he would not hesitate to call himself an Aristotelian, more so than his Peripatetic adversaries. Toward the end of his life, in 1640, writing to Liceti, he again asserts with insistence:

> I am accused of putting into question the Peripatetic, or rather the Aristotelian teachings, at the same time as I myself profess and am certain that I observe them with more devotion than many others, who, with indignation, make me appear as an adversary of sound Peripatetic philosophy (EN, XVIII, 234).

To the astonishment of Liceti, he makes his own point of view clear:

> I consider (and believe that you also hold this point of view) that to be truly a Peripatetic — that is, an Aristotelian philosopher, consists above all in philosophizing according to the teachings of Aristotle, proceeding by means of those methods and those true suppositions on which scientific discourse is based, and presupposing that general information from which one cannot depart without committing a grave mistake.

> One sure way to reach truth is to prefer experience [experiment] to any discourse whatsoever, from the moment that we are convinced that such discourse contains delusions at least in a concealed fashion, and that it is possible that an experience of the senses could have been contrary to truth: this is also a precept highly regarded by Aristotle and very much preferred to the value and force of the authority of all in the world.

This extremely sure principle is contravened by those who "wish that to philosophize well is to accept and maintain any expression and proposition whatsoever written by Aristotle, to whose absolute authority they submit." And Galileo concludes:

> For the moment I wish to add only this: I am convinced that if Aristotle were to return to this world, he would receive me among his disciples in virtue of my few, but quite conclusive, contradictions — much more than many others who, in order to maintain the truth of all that he has said, go and search in his texts for ideas of which he would never have thought. And if Aristotle were to see the new discoveries recently [made] in the heavens, whose immobility he had asserted, because no alteration had previously been seen in them, he would now without doubt state the contrary; this is readily understood, because if he declared the heavens to be unalterable because nobody had seen any alteration in them, he would now declare them to be alterable because alterations are seen in them [V, 138–40, 235; V, 136, 348; VIII, 639].

There is no lack of trustworthy Galileo specialists who substantially share his profession of Aristotelianism. A. Carugo and L. Geymonat quote and support a judgment by E. Garin:

> Scientific research, the framework of science, remained Aristotelian, at least to a considerable extent. If the new science was to be built, it had to take account of Aristotelianism; it should criticize that system, but not in a

violent or negative fashion. Rather it should carry out a fruitful revision that uses what has been criticized in order to build further. In this respect Galileo can be called a true Aristotelian.[34]

To assert that Galileo can be called a "true Aristotelian" does not imply that he did not perfect the Aristotelian method by substantial contributions, above all by a deeply critical sense in the analysis of experience, often by using *ad hoc* instruments or by "thought experiments," always based on a profound sense of observation. This he achieved without resting content with summary observations, but by seeking to refine them on the basis of measurements and calculations, as far as possible.

What particularly characterizes the Galilean spirit is an awareness of the limits of our science, an awareness expressed on a number of occasions. Thus we read in "The Assayer":

Signor Sarsi, the herd of senseless folk, those who know nothing, is infinite; those who know a little philosophy are fairly numerous; those who know part of it are few in number, and only one, God, knows all of it [EN, VI, 236].

But at the same time, Galileo showed himself very sure as to that small segment that he judged himself to understand, and this brought him into collision with the theologians.

Philosophy in the Charges Brought against Galileo

It might be of interest, I think, to reconstruct the two trials exactly, in order to take into account the philosophical environment in which Galileo lived. But I leave the care of this work to others, since it is neither useful or necessary to undertake it here. In any case I have already concerned myself with this question in the volume cited at the outset.

Here I wish only to recall some of the circumstances that I consider to be of interest in clarifying the part played by philosophy in the "Galilean question."

The document serving as a foundation for the condemnation of the Copernican theory in 1616 and the "Dialogue on the Two Principal Systems" in 1633 consists of the unanimous judgment passed in 1616 by the commission of eleven theologian-consulters of the Holy Office, entrusted with examination of the two Copernican propositions:

That the sun is the center of the world [universe] and consequently immobile as far as local motion is concerned.

34. A. Carugo and L. Geymonat, *Galilei, Discorsi e dimostrazioni matematiche intorno a due nuove scienze* (Turin, 1958), p. xv.

That the earth is not the center of the world, or immobile, but turns upon itself [spins], wholly, by a diurnal motion [EN, XIV, 20].

The opinion of the consulters was:

As to the first proposition: all concur that this proposition is stupid and absurd, and false in philosophy, and formally heretical, for it explicitly, and in many paragraphs, contradicts the sentences of holy scripture, read according to the proper sense and the common interpretation of the holy fathers and of theologians.

As to the second proposition: all concur that this proposition is equally absurd and false in philosophy; and as far as theology is concerned, it is considered as *ad minus erronea in fide* [EN, XIX, 320–21].

It is true that this was only an internal and consultative document of the Holy Office, with no official value, but it is also true that all the subsequent juridical measures were based on this opinion.

The only thing that interests us here is to know how this "trial" was brought about, and what could have been the meaning of the censure of "absurd and false in philosophy" as a premise to the theological censure of both propositions.

It is noteworthy that although Galileo was very early converted to the Copernican system, nevertheless in his academic teaching and his writings he maintained considerable reserve and prudence. But in 1609 the situation changes: the telescope allows the first staggering astronomical discoveries: the lunar mountains, the satellites of Jupiter, the numberless stars invisible to the naked eye. Galileo hastens to spread the news in *Sidereus nuncius magna longeque admirabilia spectacula pandens, suspiciendaque proponens unicuique, praesertim vero philosophis atque astronomis*, which clearly stirred up much clamor, all the more so if one takes into account the discoveries made soon after: the phases of Venus, sunspots and the rotation of the sun, and the peculiar shape of Saturn.

Apropos of the *Sidereus nuncius* Armellini has written:

It was a matter of a *total reversal* of the ideas possessed by humanity for thousands of years as to the nature and constitution of the heavenly bodies. It can be said that in this little book there perished the world of dreams about the stars that had nourished human fantasy for thousands of years, and that true, modern astrophysics came into the world.[35]

Peripatetics of the strict observance, on the other hand, rose up against this in various writings, striving to deny the authenticity of the discoveries, attributing them to flaws in the astronomical telescope, or distorting their meaning. Ludivico dalle Colombe in addition questioned the movement of the earth, adding theological reasons to philo-

35. G. Armellini, "Galileo e l'astronomia," in *Nel terzo centenario*, pp. 79–80.

sophical reasons. Galileo paid no attention to his writings beyond adding a marginal note. It is noteworthy that in the writings of these years he still maintained a very reserved position on the subject of the Copernican theory and made only a brief allusion to it: if actually speaking about it, he would have had to be more explicit.

Alongside his critics, however, he was greatly eulogized by writers who were more competent than his detractors; in the first place Kepler, in Germany, and also the Jesuit mathematicians of the Roman College led by Fr. Clavius, who, after initial hesitations due to the difficulty of verifying his observations on account of the imperfections of available instruments, were even able to give an extensive confirmation. On the occasion of a visit to Rome by Galileo, they gave him a warm welcome, even organizing a solemn academic session in the presence of many cardinals and prelates.

That did not prevent a certain ill humor from worming its way in, even among ecclesiastic circles. Fr. Grégoire de Saint-Vincent, who had been present at the above-mentioned academic session, returning to the argument many years later, recalls the sullen growls of the philosophers (EN, XI, 162–63). In a letter addressed to Galileo in 1611, Cigoli reports the clamor of hostile meetings, grouped round the archbishop of Florence.

As long as it was only a matter of rumors, Galileo did not concern himself. But when he learned in 1615 that the Copernican opinion had been discussed at the court of the grand duke, and that the grand duchess was impressed by several passages of scripture cited against the theory, he wrote a private letter to Castelli: *Circa il portare la Scrittura Sacra in dispute di conclusioni naturali* (EN, V, 279–88).

Ecclesiastical authority nevertheless continued to show itself favorable to Galileo. Furthermore, when in 1614 Fra Tommaso Caccini fulminated against the Copernicans and all mathematicians from the pulpit of New St. Mary's, disapproval was general, even among the Dominican authorities.

If the Holy Office began to be interested in Galileo in 1615, it did not become so on its own initiative, but as a consequence of an accusation lodged by two Florentine Dominicans. The first intervention ended in favor of Galileo: in February 1615 a Fr. Lorini had forwarded to the prefect of the Sacred Congregation of the Index for examination a copy of the letter to Castelli. The judgment of this tribunal was that Galileo "even if sometimes using improper expressions, does not transgress against an orthodox manner of speaking" (EN, XIX, 305).

The second intervention, in March of the same year, was provoked by a formal accusation on the part of Fr. Caccini, the same who had preached in New St. Mary's. He attributed a number of heretical propositions to Galileo. After a careful examination, it was found that the majority of the accusations were the fruit of the fervent fantasy of this particular religious. Out of the whole accusation there remained only the two above-mentioned Copernican propositions, and on February 13, 1616, these were transmitted to the commission of theologian-consulters, which gave its own judgment on February 23.

Unfortunately, in the trial documents the reason for the judgment has not been preserved. It would be interesting to know why the theologian-consulters considered it opportune to subject the two propositions to philosophical censure prior to the theological censure, and on what grounds they based the drastic condemnation.

We can observe that in their recourse to the Holy Office the two Dominicans alleged a philosophical reason alongside a reasoning based on holy scripture. Fr. Lorini justified his allegation by basing himself on the fact that the public admonition imparted by his colleague had remained in vain, the letter to Castelli continuing to circulate on all sides, and that his superiors hardly seemed to be concerned. Thus, in his opinion, everyone continued to expound holy scripture in his own way, to speak of the fathers of the church and St. Thomas with little esteem, and to distrust the entire philosophy of Aristotle used by Scholastic theology. He therefore considered it his duty, as a Christian and a son of St. Dominic, theologian and preacher, to intervene more energetically (EN, XIX, 297–98). It was a matter of saving not only traditional exegesis, but also traditional philosophy, which seemed to be closely bound to Scholastic philosophy.

As to the basis of the philosophical censure, Paschini cites reflections contained in the *Argomento fisico-matematico del Padre Giovanni Battista Riccioli d.C.d.G contro il moto diurno della terra*, published in Bologna in 1668:

> The reasons that led the Sacred Congregation to condemn the opinion of the earth's motion and the immobility of the sun as absurd and false, are unknown to us. But if it is permissible to form hypotheses in this connection, the reasons were that conclusions that can be drawn from sensory evidence relative to the natural movement or immobility of a body should be founded physically and not by philosophizing according to the caprices of mathematical or metaphysical possibilities. By the universal and continued experience of the senses, the whole human race is one in affirming that the sun moves and that the earth remains immobile.[36]

This evident "philosophical absurdity" of the Copernican theory seems to have dispensed the consulters of the Holy Office from a serious

---

36. P. Paschini, *Vita e opere di Galileo* (Rome, 1965), p. 339.

examination of the passages of holy scripture customarily cited in opposition to the theory. If the theory being opposed is taken as absurd, it is clear that the passages of scripture in question have been interpreted literally. On the other hand, the theological censure was necessary as the basis for a judgment by an ecclesiastical tribunal, even if this censure seemed debatable to many minds.

In fact, not only was it the case that the exegetical criteria expressed by Galileo to Castelli had been judged orthodox barely a year before, but also in the intervening period between the two inquiries a number of renowned theologians had expressed doubts as to the validity, or at least the opportuneness, of the judgment of heresy inflicted on the Copernican theory.

Examination of this whole affair gives the impression that the nub of the Galilean question was philosophical in nature rather than theological, insofar as concerns the validity of the proofs in favor of the Galilean theory offered by Galileo, or even the capability of that theory for being demonstrated.

It is true that in his letter to Foscarini (EN, XII, 272), Cardinal Bellarmine conceded that if authentic proofs were offered, it could be necessary to search for another interpretation of scripture, or that scripture had not been understood. He nevertheless added that as long as these proofs could not be presented, it was not proper to abandon the traditional interpretation. According to the theologians, these proofs did not exist. The fact that the theory saved appearances proved nothing; it did not exclude the possibility that other theories could do the same.

Urban VIII, who played such an important part in the second trial and condemnation of Galileo, had his argument ready to prove that the Copernican theory could never have been demonstrated to be true: God, who is omnipotent, could cause the celestial phenomena in a way unthinkable to us. He was so convinced as to the correctness of his argument that he demanded that Galileo insert it into his *Dialogo dei massimi sistemi*; in fact this argument concludes the discussion developed throughout the whole of the *Dialogo*. The argument was nevertheless put into the mouth of Simplicius, apparently without malice, but certainly with little prudence, even if the two interlocutors approved in a rather overexuberant manner.

Others speak about Galilean epistemology, so much discussed and so complex. Here I will report only the replies given by Galileo to his adversaries.

To Cardinal Bellarmine he objected:

> The former [Ptolemaic] system is without doubt false, just as it is clear that

that which adjusts itself very well can be true; and one cannot or should not seek a greater truth in a proposition than that which corresponds to all the particular appearances [EN, V, 369].

To the argument of Urban VIII he does not reply directly, but to Morino, who had raised the same difficulty based on the omnipotence of God, he gave the following response:

> This is a domain of great discussions. We do not seek what God could have done, but what God has done. . . . Thus, if one seeks what God has done in domains hidden from us, seeing that in those known to us God always operates in the easiest and simplest fashion — while in the more difficult cases his power is better discovered — we who know that, moving some celestial bodies whose movement is for us a certainty, he brings about in a longer delay major circuits, should we not say that an infinitely larger circuit is accomplished in a much shorter delay? Signor Morino, God could have made birds with bones of massive gold, with veins full of molten silver, with flesh heavier than lead and with tiny wings, and in this way he would more effectively have shown his power. He could have made fish heavier than lead, and thus twelve times heavier than water, but he has willed to make the former of bone, flesh, and feathers that are light enough, and the latter as heavier than water, to teach us that he rejoices in simplicity and facility [EN, XVII, 565–66].

Does Galileo Still Have a Right to the Title of Philosopher?

The reason why Galileo always showed himself so obstinate, against the advice of his friends, in not considering the Copernican theory purely and simply as a mathematician, but wanting to keep himself always on a physical and realist plane, was because for him, as he wrote to Vinta in 1610, the work that he intended to publish, *De systemate seu constitutione universi*, was "full of philosophy, astronomy, and geometry" (EN, X, 53).

But he did not take into account that it was he himself who, in founding a "new science," had created a gulf between philosophy and science, and that for this reason, subsequent generations who accorded him the title of "father of science," refused him the title of philosopher. Thus G. Gentile writes in the preface to *Frammenti di lettere di Galileo Galilei*:

> Galileo was not a philosopher properly speaking, but a mathematician and a naturalist, who, in contradistinction to our greater Renaissance philosophers — Telesio, Bruno, Campanella — and the more celebrated thinkers and scientists who opened the modern age — Bacon, Descartes, and Kepler — saw for the first time, with the greatest clarity, that a science of nature can be constructed provided that it is rigorously separated from metaphysics and that one keeps within its proper character of direct cognition of facts. These facts are not to be produced, but are to be considered as

already accomplished and indecipherable in their intrinsic being, in their way of appearing and in their qualitative differences, and consequently can be observed and measured only in their quantitative proportions.[37]

It has already been remarked that this distinction and opposition between quantitative and qualitative knowledge involves a serious equivocation, which reveals a lack of reflection on scientific praxis.

As early as 1612 Galileo himself was prepared for the opposition between mathematics and philosophy. He gave a reply to those who leveled the reproach, "it is one thing to treat questions from the point of view of physics and another thing to treat them from the point of view of mathematics: geometers should not leave their subtleties nor seek to draw philosophical matters into their confraternity, because the truths of philosophy are different from those of mathematics." After recounting the example of the medical doctor Acquapendente, who could not be a good physician because he knew surgery, he concluded:

> Let my adversaries see if I treat matters in the same way as Aristotle, and whether he himself introduced, where necessary, geometrical demonstrations. And may it be given to them to cease being so hostile to geometry. It amazes me, because I believe that one cannot be the enemy of an unknown person [EN, IV, 49–50].

We can also ask who has more right to the title of philosopher: the one who writes a treatise on the method of science, rapidly contradicted by scientific practice, or the one who, practising science without writing a systematic treatise, teaches a method that shows itself to be extremely effective in use. A language first forms itself and then the grammar is written; the artificially composed Esperanto texts have so far not enjoyed much credit. Here once more, Galileo follows Aristotle's praxis.

I nevertheless believe that what Galileo never saw clearly — and never would have accepted — is that a science of nature should be rigorously separated from metaphysics in order to remain at the direct cognition of facts.

Galileo was certainly against a science of nature founded on a preconstituted metaphysics, be it Peripatetic, Cartesian, or Hegelian, closed to experimentation and facts, but it is for this very reason that he was opposed to a rigorous separation between natural science and metaphysics; he thought in fact that the latter had something to learn from the former. In connection with the discovery of sunspots he expressed the hope "that these new things may serve me admirably to match several pipes of the great discordant organ of our philosophy, on which I have the impression of many organists vainly wearying themselves in

37. Cited by F. Olgiati, *Nel terzo centenario*, p. 100.

trying to give it a perfect temperament, and this is because they leave and sustain discords between three or four of the principal pipes, to which the others absolutely cannot respond with perfect harmony" (EN, V, 113).

But he more readily accepts a physics that, following Bacon's "ant policy," remains with its proper cognition of the facts, and for this reason often passes to arguments in the metaphysical domain.

Thus, to restrict ourselves to one example among many others, Galileo has recently been accused of not having confronted the problem of criticism in the manner of Descartes, who (it is considered) justly reproached him for building without a foundation. In reality Galileo speaks of this at the end of the first day of the "Dialogue," on the concrete basis of facts, and following his own method. He sets in mutual opposition those who think they know everything because they have grasped nothing, and those who, having understood something, confess to knowing little, if anything at all, by comparison with that which they admit they do not know. He writes:

> I therefore conclude, that our knowledge — as to its mode and the multitude of things understood — is separated from the divine knowledge by an infinite interval; but I do not, however, distrust it to the point of considering it as infinitesimal: quite the contrary, when I reflect on so many profoundly marvelous things that persons have grasped, sought, and done, I recognize even more clearly that human intelligence is a work of God, and one of the most excellent [EN, VII, 130].

Galileo himself probably did not perfectly evaluate the powerful instrument with which his "new quantitative science" had perfected human ingenuity. Thus, the "mysteries so profound and the concepts so subtle, which the continual efforts and studies of a great number of ingenious persons have succeeded in penetrating thanks to research continued over thousands and thousands of years" (EN, V, 229–30) are small in stature relative to what has subsequently been discovered in a few hundred years.

The qualitative distinction of colors into red, yellow, green, and so forth, has been replaced by a quantitative distinction based on wavelength. The spectrum is greatly extended toward the ultra-violet, X, and gamma rays on the one hand, and infra-red and radio waves on the other hand, even if these "colors" are not perceived by our eyes but by photographic emulsions or other detectors. Telescopes for X and gamma rays have been created as well as radio-telescopes that have revealed and incessantly continue to reveal new marvels of the cosmos.

With all this, one still does not arrive at the end of the mystery of the sidereal universe or of color; quite the contrary, this mystery is revealed as being much more profound and marvelous than one could have imagined.

Continuing to study the phenomena of water quantitatively, one has not concluded with a definition by genus and specific difference; rather it has been discovered that water is not one of the four elements, but a "compound," which has been given a scientific definition (H_2O). Evidently, the whole theory of elements and compounds has been transformed; physical chemistry has been born, widely applied also in the study of living organisms.

In particular, it has been discovered that the generation of fruit flies (cider flies), which in the intervening period have been given the scientific name Drosophila, takes place via a "transposition of parts," and more precisely, "four small characters," A,G,C,T (adenine, guanine, cytosine, thymine), with which nature composes the program of each living being, just as humans communicate with their own kind by means of varied groupings of twenty-six "small characters on a sheet of paper" (EN, VII, 130–31). It is obviously not a question of a "simple transposition of parts"; the mystery remains even more impenetrable and marvelous.

In any case, if Aristotle's observation remains true — namely, that wonder is the beginning of philosophy — then we must conclude that Galileo, even without having written a treatise on metaphysics, possessed a profoundly philosophical spirit. This is shown when he went to the Venetian arsenal to admire and learn more than to teach, or again when he concerned himself with demonstrating to the senators of Venice the astronomical telescope in order to gain an economic advantage that would allow him to continue his research, but then turned it to the heavens *magna longeque admirabilia spectacula pandens, suspiciendaque propenens unicuique, praesertim vero philosophis et astronomis.*

4

Galileo and the Theology of his Time

François Russo

I. INTRODUCTION

I cannot attempt to treat the subject allotted to me in this collective work without a certain number of preliminary observations concerning its exact nature and the way in which I have come to conceive its treatment.

I do not think that I will jeopardize the aim of the present work, as defined by those responsible for it, by identifying the phrase *'culture théologique'* with the phrase *'pensée théologique.'* Nor will I jeopardize it by considering this latter expression as constituting a formulation equivalent to the term "theology," with this single difference that, apart from systematic writings bearing on theology, though including these in addition, my work envisages writings that also concern theology but are of somewhat diverse types. These latter are notably writings by nonspecialists in theology, particularly scientists, a situation that is often the case here, because I shall have to take into account the theological writings of Galileo who in fact was not a professional theologian.

Even with this qualification, the title of my article, though doubtless "theoretically" accurate insofar as I will be giving an account of the relationships of Galileo with the theology of his time, will in fact be both wider and narrower.

Wider, because in a general way the theology of an epoch always relates to the theology of the past, above all to that of the fathers of the church, a fact particularly important for Galileo's time.

Narrower, because the only theology with which Galileo was concerned and to which he devoted his writings was exclusively scriptural exegesis, and further exclusively exegesis bearing on those passages of scripture that concern astronomy. But this exegesis led him to give a treatment of general principles of interpretation of scripture, at least of the Old Testament, and above all of Genesis, a point to which I shall later return.

On the relationships of Galileo's theology with other aspects of theology, there is nothing to be said, because Galileo was not concerned with these aspects, contenting himself with being a good Christian, taking care to remain faithful to the teaching of the church.

Certainly his struggle for a large measure of autonomy for science with respect to theology and to the magisterium of the church constitutes a theme that goes beyond exegesis. But it was with exegesis that he was concerned.

Even with this restriction, my study will not entirely correspond to what it should be, because a thorough treatment of this subject would necessitate a good knowledge of the state of exegesis in the Galilean epoch. Now, astonishing as it may seem, there are no comprehensive studies of the exegesis of that time, of the type of those very developed works devoted to patristic and medieval exegesis. In addition there are very few truly satisfactory monographs dealing with a large part of the authors connected with the history I am treating.

The numerous and often very valuable works dealing with theological aspects of Galileo's work — that is, essentially his conflict with church authorities and with a certain number of theologians of his time, a conflict referred to as the "Galileo affair" — with rare exceptions study predominantly the two sentencings of 1616 and 1633. It is only on this occasion and then marginally that they touch upon my topic — that is, Galileo's exegesis and his relationships with the exegesis of his time.

That is why this study turns out to be somewhat novel, with one reservation that will be explained in the next section of this chapter.

The full understanding of the relationships between Galileo's exegesis and the exegesis of his time presupposes an examination of the validity of the proofs of the earth's mobility given by Galileo. This is because in his argument Galileo often interpolates the view that the Copernican theory has been proven beyond doubt. Nonetheless, his theses are valid in the framework of the ideal case of scientific propositions that are certain, whatever may have been the case in connection with the Copernican theory, for which it is known that Galileo did not offer an entirely satisfactory proof.

Here I will deal only with Catholic exegesis, and not at all with Protestant reactions to the Copernican theory, reactions known to have been very lively.

Principal Aspects of the Subject

The subject with which I am concerned presents the following principal features, some "formal," others "substantial."

Without doubt Galileo was interested in holy scripture to the extent that it raised problems for the affirmation of the earth's motion and the immobility of the sun and stars. But apart from some passages of scripture — principally the arresting of the sun by Joshua — Galileo very quickly grasped that interpretation of texts of scripture dealing with astronomy was governed by a *general conception* of scriptural interpretation. In addition, it is predominantly to this general conception that he devoted his writings on exegesis. Nevertheless it is a fact that the views that he developed principally concern the Old Testament and mainly Genesis.

The texts in which Galileo presents his views on the principles of interpretation of scripture constitute one of the most developed expositions of the question up to his time.

More particularly, with reference to the passages of scripture that concern astronomy, Galileo's writings constitute the richest repertoire of patristic texts, then and even today, on scriptural interpretation, above all where St. Augustine is involved. Similarly, they constitute a repertoire, though to a lesser degree, of the texts of medieval and 16th- and 17th-century theologians, with this reservation, however, that Galileo has mainly gathered together texts that serve his thesis. But today we recognize that with few exceptions they manifest a proper conception of scripture.

In the sum total of Galileo's work, the writings in which he deals with problems that the Copernican theory poses for exegesis occupy only a minimal place. Essentially it is a question of the letter to the grand duchess of Tuscany — the earlier letter to Castelli is much more summary — and their writing covers only a brief space of time: the three years prior to the decree of March 1616, which did not allude to Galileo, at least directly; it only involved the placing of Copernicus's *De revolutionibus* on the Index, together with the writings of two theologians, Foscarini and Zuñiga. Between 1616 and 1633, the date of Galileo's trial, I have not found any document by Galileo or by any other author dealing with this problem. But this point remains to be verified.

It should be noted in addition that if the letter to Castelli played a major part in the decision taken in the decree of 1616, it is not known, on the contrary, if his letter to the grand duchess of Tuscany, a text of much greater importance for exegesis, the writing of which was completed less than a year before the 1616 decree, was known by those charged with preparing the decree. Furthermore, even in the trial of 1633 it is possible that this letter was not taken into account, because of its very limited circulation. It was not published until 1636.

Galileo's theses on exegesis, as well as the texts cited by him in support, are presented in a not very orderly fashion and are badly distinguished from each other. In addition the exposition includes a certain number of repetitions. Thus it is opportune to identify them exactly, and to place them in mutual relationship. I shall endeavor to do this.

Mode of Treatment of the Subject

How I shall deal with the subject depends on its characteristics, just outlined, and at the same time on the works that have been devoted to it.

To clarify and justify this procedure I must cite two essential texts at the outset; detailed references will be the subject matter of the Bibliography, below.

To my knowledge there are only two publications that directly treat this subject:

1) Translations with introduction and notes of the letter to the grand duchess of Tuscany — one (my own) in French, in the collective work *Galilée, aspects de sa vie et de son oeuvre* (1968), the other by Prof. Stillman Drake in English.

2) The article by Fr. André Dubarle, "Les Principes exégétiques et théologiques de Galilée concernant la science et la nature" in the *Revue des sciences philosophiques et théologiques* (1966). Fr. André Dubarle, O.P., exegete, is the brother of Fr. Dominique Dubarle, himself a specialist in Galilean questions.

The two translations being widely accessible, this study will not repeat them in matters concerning the circumstances that surround the publication of this letter or concerning the text itself. I will give extracts from the most characteristic passages of Galileo's texts but, with rare exceptions, I will not reproduce long citations. In this way for a reader at an introductory level, this study will not need recourse to the above translations. But as a deeper level it is necessary to have them at one's disposal.

This study has seemed to me an opportune occasion to go beyond the phase of translation and do a thematic study. This will essentially consist in an identification and an exact analysis, together with an organic presentation (which neither I nor Professor Stillman Drake have so far attempted), of the exegetical theses concerning the Copernican theory, be it a matter of Galileo's theses or those of the authors cited by him, or of certain authors whom he does not cite but who adopted a position relative to his viewpoints and who have seemed to me opportune to mention.

An identification and analysis of these theses have already been done by Fr. Dubarle in the above-quoted article, based on my translation. But Fr. Dubarle has not proceeded to give an organic presentation of these arguments allowing one to get a good grasp of their specificity and to distinguish them clearly. As I have said, it is precisely such a presentation that I propose to give here. It will thus serve at the same time to extend the two translations and Fr. Dubarle's study. The latter, to which I owe much, is therefore almost entirely integrated into my study. In addition I have thought it opportune, because of Galileo's numerous citations, to present them in a more explicit and detailed fashion than in Fr. Dubarle's study, and also to complete his study by notices concerning little-known authors quoted by Galileo.

After section II devoted to bibliographic considerations, there are two sections forming as it were a diptych. Section III presents the major exegetical problems raised by the advent of Copernican astronomy. Section IV comprises notices arranged in chronological order. These are devoted to principal authors who, either prior to Galileo's positions, or at the time of the Galilean controversies (but not after), have dealt with these theses. Apart from indications concerning the persons involved (when they are not well known), each of these notices contains references to the publications in which the theses are developed, as well as to the exact passages in which they are to be found. This above all concerns St. Augustine, and essentially his *De Genesi ad litteram*, which Galileo quotes fourteen times.

The bonding of these two sections is ensured by including in each of the theses presented in section II a reference to corresponding texts in section IV.

Let me add that in this study I have also profited from several important recent works, which although going beyond our subject, nevertheless contain elements relevant to it, mainly the little work by Fr. F. Soccorsi (quoted below, sec. II).

II. BIBLIOGRAPHY

Here it is exclusively a question of publications that entirely or in part concern exegetical questions in their relationships with the Copernican theory.

I have reserved to section IV bibliographical references involving authors other than Galileo and St. Augustine.

Galileo's Writings

Although it is to be found only in major libraries, I must in the first place cite the complete modern edition of Galileo's works which are in their original language, Italian, except for rare instances: *Edizione Nazionale delle Opere di Galileo Galilei* (EN), 21 tomes in 20 volumes (vol. 3 contains 2 tomes; vol. 20 has the tables), Florence, 1st edition 1890–1909; 2nd edition 1929–1939; reprinted 1966. Pagination is the same in all three editions.

• Letter to Benedetto Castelli, December 21, 1613 (EN, V, 280–88). French translation by P.H. Michel in *Galilée, Dialogues et Lettres choisies* (Paris, Hermann, 1966), pp. 384–93. This letter, which briefly expounds the views on the relationships of scripture with the Copernican system that were to be developed in the letter to the grand duchess of Tuscany, rapidly gained a wide circulation. It was communicated to the Holy Office by the Dominican Lorini, who added the comment that "according to the judgment of all the fathers of the Friary of St. Mark [in Florence], there are to be found herein many propositions that seem suspect and rash."

• Letter of Galileo to Monsignor Pietro Dini, February 16, 1615 (EN, V, 291–95). This letter deals with problems of interpretation of scripture raised by the theory of Copernicus.

• Letter of Galileo to Monsignor Pietro Dini, March 23, 1615 (EN, V, 297–305). Galileo replies to a letter from Dini, who in response to Galileo's letter of February 16, gives him to understand that he has seen Cardinal Bellarmine. The latter did not think that the Copernican theory should be condemned, but he desired that Galileo would moderate his positions and make it clear that the Copernican doctrine only spoke "according to appearances." Galileo replies that the Copernican doctrine should not be weakened; it should be accepted or rejected in its entirety.

• Letter to Christine of Lorraine, grand duchess of Tuscany, ca. May 1615 (EN, V, 309–48). French translation with commentary and notes by François Russo, in *Galilée, aspects de se vie et de son oeuvre* (PUF, 1968); introduction, pp. 324–31; text, pp. 331–59. This translation will be cited by the acronym LCL. It was initially published in the *Revue d'Histoire des Sciences* (1964, pp. 330–66). The publication of 1968 is a much improved version, thanks, notably, to observations by Fr. Dubarle, who cites the first version in his above-quoted article. It has been reprinted in the review *Athéisme et Dialogue*, Secretariat for Non-Believers, Vatican City, 1980, pp. 162–76. English translation by Stillman Drake, in *Discoveries and Opinions of Galileo* (New York, Doubleday, 1957), p. 302. As has been said, the circulation of this letter was for a long time restricted. It is not known whether Bellarmine knew of it. It can even be queried whether it was known to the judges of the 1633 trial. In any case, I know no text of the Galilean epoch that takes account of it. It was published for the first time in 1636. There is here an important point of history that it would be good to clarify.

De Genesi ad litteram

It is from this work of St. Augustine that Galileo borrows the greatest number of quotations from the fathers of the church — fifteen, of which fourteen are taken from the Commentary on Genesis, out of a total of twenty-one. It is also important to add a certain number of clarifications on this subject.

These quotations are all found in the letter to the grand duchess of Tuscany. Furthermore, because this text is available in the French and English translations referred to above, I will not reproduce it in this study. In section III there is given only: (1) the initial phrase of a citation; (2) the reference in *De Genesi* (book and chapter) — references given by Galileo himself — but I add the number of the continuous-number reference of each book found in more recent editions of *De Genesi*, which will better allow location of citations; (3) reference to the texts in the *Edizione Nazionale* (EN).

The most recent and best edition of *De Genesi ad litteram* is found in the Latin-French edition of the works of St. Augustine in the *Bibliothèque augustinienne*, nos. 48 and 49 (Desclée de Brouwer, 1972). The French translation, the introduction, and the notes are by the Jesuits P. Agaësse and A. Solignac. The very extensive notes are precious for our subject. My French translation (in the original, French, edition of *Galileo Galilei*) was made from the Italian version of a Latin text that was doubtless less sure than that of the *Bibliothèque augustinienne*. One should not be surprised at the quite numerous differences in the two French translations. But it appears that there are no appreciable differences, at least as to the fundamental meaning.

Studies on Galileo and his Work

GENERAL STUDIES

• *Bibliographie galiléenne*, in the quarterly bulletin *Athéisme et Dialogue* published by the Secretariat for Non-Believers, Vatican City, June 1980.

• Fr. P. Paschini, *Vita e opere di Galileo Galilei* (Vatican City, Pontifical Academy of Sciences, 1964), 2 vols., 721 pages. Reprinted, Rome, Herder, 1965. A French preface by Fr. Lamalle, S.J., is omitted in certain volumes of these two editions. This preface contains reservations as to the *Vita*. This is a very rich work, which doubtless constitutes the most complete overall view of Galileo. But inasmuch as it was written in the years 1942–1944, it is not up to date on a number of points and the judgments on Galileo call for reservations.

• E. Vacandard, article "Galilée" (136 columns) in the *Dictionnaire de Théologie catholique*. Although old (1920), this article remains fundamental from the theological point of view.

A Publication Essential for this Study

• Fr. André Dubarle, O.P., "Les Principes exégétiques et théologiques de Galilée concernant les sciences de la nature," *Revue des sciences philosophiques et théologiques*, (January 1966), pp. 67–87. As I have said in section I, this article, together with my translation of the letter to the grand duchess, forms the basis of the present study.

OTHER PUBLICATIONS

• Walter Brandmüller, "Der Fall Galilee — Konflikt Naturwissenschaft und Kirche?" *Stimmen der Zeit* (Munich, 1968). French translation under the title "Le cas Galilée, vérité et légende — Origine et consequences," in *Athéisme et Dialogue*, Secretariat for Non-Believers, Vatican City, September 1980.

• *Galilei und die Kirche oder das Recht auf Irrtum* (Regensburg, F. Pustet, 1982), 174 pages.

• Ostwald Loretze, *Galilei und der Irrtum der Inquisition* (Kevelaer, Buxton, 1966), 220 pages. This book, which visualizes Galileo's work from the point of view of problems in interpreting scripture, has brought precious elements to my study, though I do not follow it on a certain number of points.

• G. Morpurgo Tagliabue, *I processi di Galileo e l'epistemologia* (Milan, 1963). Favorably commented on and critiqued by Fr. A. Dubarle ("Les Principes," p. 83) and by Mario Viganò (see chap. 3, above). Revised edition, with four appendixes (Rome, Armando, 1981), 204 pages. Reviewed in *Osservatore Romano*, April 30, 1981.

• Emile Namer, *L'affaire Galilée* (Paris, Gallimard-Julliard, 1975), 260 pages. Clear, precise, well informed, but its views on the opposition of the church to science are debatable.

• G. Santillana, *The Crime of Galileo* (University of Chicago Press, 1955). French translation, *Le Procès de Galilée* (Paris, Club du meilleur livre, 1955), 460 pages. See my critique in *Etudes* (Paris, 1956), pp. 96–105.

• F. Soccorsi, *Il processo di Galileo* (Rome, Edizioni "La Civiltà cattolica," 1947), 108 pp. Reprint of two articles published in *La Civiltà cattolica*, 98 (1946) 175–84 and 429–38. This work contains data and original reflections that have been valuable for my study.

• M. Viganò, S.J., "Fede e scienza in Galileo," *Civiltà cattolica* (1965), vol. 1, pp. 36–47, 226–39; vol. 2, pp. 35–47, 226–39, 448–55. Also published in book form, *Il mancato dialogo tra Galileo e i teologi* (Rome, Edizioni "La Civiltà cattolica," 1969).

III. THE THESES

As has been indicated, the third and fourth sections of this study are presented as the two wings of a diptych.

Section III is made up of the formulation of those theses concerning the interpretation of scripture that are found above all in texts written or quoted by Galileo, as also in passages not quoted by Galileo but coming from authors whom he cites in other extracts — particularly in matters which concern St. Augustine.

These theses are grouped in two main divisions: general theses and particular theses.

At the outset I formulate these theses briefly. Then to this formulation I will add: (1) citations from the most significant passages of Galileo's texts; (2) some comments; (3) mention of citations in one of the following forms: (a) simple reference followed by the opening phrase for texts that are found in the translation of the letter to the grand duchess, with the exception that very brief texts or particularly significant passages of a text that is developed in content will be quoted in their entirety; (b) integral quotation of other texts; (c) summary of a text — most often from Galileo — the reference being given in parentheses.

Basic Perspectives

1. THE TWO BOOKS

God speaks to us in two ways; scripture and the creation. This viewpoint is expressed through the classic image of the two books. Galileo employs this form, speaking of "The Book of Nature (the Heavens), which is open before our eyes" (EN, V, 329; LCL, 345).

He emphasizes this thesis:

> The Bible is not our only means of knowing. God has endowed us with sense and intelligence and he has not wished us to neglect the use of these faculties, nor has he visualized giving us by another name the knowledge that we can gain by their employment in questions of nature. We ought not to deny our senses or our reason by rejecting the conclusions that we can come to thanks to them (EN, V, 317; LCL, 337).

Galileo supports these views notably by a text from Tertullian (see below).

2. TWO TRUTHS — IN THIS CASE, THE TRUTHS OF SCRIPTURE AND OF SCIENCE — CANNOT CONTRADICT EACH OTHER

Galileo advances this principle on many occasions (notably EN, V, 330; LCL, 346) and supports it by the authority of St. Augustine (ibid.) and also by that of Peyreyra (EN, V, 320; LCL, 330; see below, "Peyreyra," 4th rule). This view is also to be found in Bellarmine in 1571 (see below, "Bellarmine," text no. 4).

General Rules of Exegesis

The theses of Galileo and of the authors he quotes, who will be reported here, show a general characteristic in the sense that they do not relate only to scriptural texts dealing with celestial motions. But in the thought of Galileo, and of certain authors quoted by him, they are intended to clarify particular texts.

1. GREAT PRUDENCE IS REQUIRED IN THE INTERPRETATION OF SCRIPTURE

Notably, one should take care not to be influenced by philosophical and scientific ideas of the moment. One should not reject something that science could later demonstrate to be true (EN, V, 310). Galileo quotes St. Augustine in support of this thesis (see below, citation no. 1). It is especially expedient to hold to this rule when the same text has occasioned different interpretations by the fathers, as St. Augustine insists (EN, V, 329; LCL, 352; citations of St. Augustine nos. 9, 11, 12), or again when an author hesitates over the interpretation of a text (citation of St. Augustine no. 10).

Furthermore, interpreters of the scriptures can be mistaken, not grasping the significance imparted to them by their Author (EN, V, 322; LCL, 340-41). It often happens that they trust in their own opinion, or become victims of prejudice, or of their own ignorance, or of their own lack of intelligence (EN, V, 338; LCL, 353; citations of St. Jerome no. 3, and St. Augustine no. 15).

This was already noted by Copernicus in the preface to his book addressed to Paul III: "Mathematics is for mathematicians" (EN, V, 314; LCL, 334-35; and EN, V, 345; LCL, 354).

2. CASES IN WHICH THE PROPOSITIONS OF SCIENCE AND SCRIPTURE SEEM TO BE OPPOSED

If a scientific proposition is true, it is necessary to correct an interpretation of scripture that seems to oppose it:

> Having obtained a certain scientific knowledge, which is also a gift of God, one must apply oneself to search out the exact meaning of the scriptures in passages that seemingly appear not to be in agreement with natural knowledge (EN, V, 332; LCL, 347).

Galileo supports this view by a citation from St. Augustine (citation no. 4, the end of which is resumed in no. 6). An imprudent exegesis should not mar the respect due to the human search for natural causes, and the value that should be recognized in that search:

> Who could pretend to put a limit to the powers of the human spirit . . . . If we have it from the mouth of the Holy Spirit that God has abandoned the world to the disputes of men (*Deus tradidit mundum disputationi eorum; Ecclesiastes 3:11*), why, in distrust of this sentence, prohibit them to philosophize freely on the things of the world and of nature? (EN, V, 320; LCL, 339-40).

In addition, adds Galileo (EN, V, 340; LCL, 353-54), if one refuses to correct an interpretation of scripture that is in opposition to a proven scientific proposition, one inflicts the greatest damage on the Christian faith. One should not, then, be astonished when men of science turn away from the faith. In the context of this observation Galileo quotes a long text from St. Augustine (citation no. 13).

In the same sense Bellarmine himself declares that "if it happens that an as yet unproved scientific theory should (come to) be recognized as true, then it is necessary to correct the interpretation of scripture" (citations of Bellarmine nos. 1 and 3).

But because for Galileo science had demonstrated that the Copernican theory is true, it was necessary to correct without delay the interpretations of scripture opposed to it (EN, V, 338-44; LCL, 352-57).

In any case, he states precisely that it is imprudent to declare new theories of science contrary to scripture and thus heretical, without having shown them to be certainly false, and without having very attentively examined the necessary demonstrations that they claim to supply (EN, V, 312-14; LCL, 333-34; and EN, V, 342-43; LCL, 355; citation of St. Augustine no. 9).

Even more precisely, Galileo declares that in the matter of "natural conclusions truly demonstrated, before condemning them it is necessary to bring forth a proof that they have not been demonstrated in a necessary fashion. And this task belongs not to those who hold them to be true, but to those who consider them false" (EN, V, 327; LCL, 344).

Particular Rules

There are other norms of interpretation that are undoubtedly general in that they apply to the totality of scripture, but less general than the preceding ones. They occupy a place in the arguments not only of Galileo but also of the exegetes of his epoch, whether they uphold them as did Galileo, or whether they oppose them. These three norms are: the norm of the meaning (of a passage) commonly admitted by the fathers of the church; the affirmation that scripture essentially aims to teach on the subject of our salvation; the necessity of not interpreting certain texts by enslavement to the letter.

1. THE CONSENSUS OF THE FATHERS

A decree of the Council of Trent (see below) declares that scripture should be interpreted by following the consensus of the fathers — but only in matters of faith and morals.

In many instances Galileo bases himself on this decree, for he correctly considers that astronomical questions do not touch on the faith, so that what the fathers said could not have supervened upon the issue.

But in his letter to Foscarini (see below, no. 3), Bellarmine adopts a curious attitude with regard to the decree of the Council of Trent. The movement of the sun and the immobility of the earth do not concern the faith with regard to the subject matter (*ex parte objecti*) but they do with regard to the person speaking (*ex parte dicentis*). Furthermore, earlier in his "Controversies" (below, citation no. 2), Bellarmine was not concerned to stress this restriction of the Council of Trent solely to matters of faith and morals.

In his violent attack on Galileo in 1614, the Dominican Caccini had entirely passed over in silence this matter of the decree of the Council of Trent.

In his arguments Galileo did not content himself with simply a reference to the decree of the Council of Trent. He brought out its limited scope by two observations:

1) One is not bound to follow the teaching of the fathers on questions that they have not seriously considered:

> The agreement of the fathers binds us to the extent that it corresponds to a proper judgment on their part and not simply to an unstudied conviction that they share in common with their epoch. In questions about nature, it must not only be considered whether they are in agreement on certain formulations, but also whether they had really put to themselves a question to which they had subsequently given a reply. Thence one would have a proof in the case where, after a careful discussion of the arguments on both sides, they had expressed a concordant opinion (EN, V, 335-36; LCL, 349-50).

2) On a number of questions one does not observe a consensus among the fathers, so that one is not constrained to follow them. It is this that Galileo shows at length in the case of the interpretation of the text relating that Joshua stopped the sun (EN, V, 335–37 and 344; LCL, 349–51 and 356).

2. SCRIPTURE HAS AS ITS ESSENTIAL AIM TO TEACH US THE WAY TO SALVATION

This thesis, vigorously upheld by Galileo, to prevent the intervention of the magisterium of the church in questions of astronomy, had been expressed by Baronius in a famous saying (see below), which Galileo quotes: "The intention of the Holy Spirit is to teach us how to go to heaven and not how the heavens go." But Galileo also appealed to patristic texts: to St. Jerome (citations no. 2 and 3), and to St. Augustine (citations no. 2, 3, and 7).

Galileo had already upheld this thesis in his letter to Castelli of December 21, 1613 (see above, translation by P.H. Michel, p. 387). He develops it in a long passage on theology and the way in which one should understand its preeminence, notably declaring:

> Theology does not have to lower itself to the humble speculations of the inferior sciences, and it does not have to concern itself with these, because they have not dealt with beatitude (EN, V, 325; LCL, 343).

Galileo sees a supplementary proof of this thesis in the fact that scripture only summarily deals with astronomical questions, Thus it is that "in them the planets are not even named, with the exception of the sun, the moon, and Venus" (EN, V, 318; LCL, 337).

3. LITERAL EXEGESIS DOES NOT APPLY TO CERTAIN TEXTS OF SCRIPTURE

Referring above all to the Old Testament, particularly Genesis, at least in the part that deals with creation, Galileo, following several fathers, notably St. Jerome (citations no. 2 and 3), and also St. Thomas Aquinas (citations no. 1 and 2) maintains that one is dealing with texts that should not be understood literally:

> To adapt themselves to the understanding of the multitudes, the scriptures state things that differ greatly from abosolute truth, in their expression and in the bare meaning of the words (EN, V, 315-16; LCL, 335-36).

Galileo developed this thesis at length in another passage in his letter to the grand duchess (EN, V, 332-34; LCL, 348-49), emphasizing that scripture ought not to "trouble the feeble capacity of the people." And he had already expressed this in the letter to Castelli of December 21, 1613 (Michel translation, pp. 385-86).

In the fact that scripture sometimes expresses the same reality by different images, Galileo saw a confirmation of the thesis that certain passages of scripture should not be understood literally. Thus, quoting St. Augustine (citation no. 5), Galileo notes that scripture speaks of the heavens as stretched like a skin, and soon afterward as suspended like a vault.

There are certain texts of scripture where modern exegesis does not hesitate to depart from a literal interpretation, but Galileo understands some of them "in servitude to the letter," succumbing to an imprudent concordism. This concerns the passage of the book of Joshua referring to the arrest of the sun by Joshua. Galileo claims that the Copernican theory yields an explanation of the immobilization of the sun not assured by the theory of Aristotle and Ptolemy (EN, V, 343-45; LCL, 356-57). This concordism is also to be found in the letter to Castelli of December 13, 1613 (Michel translation, pp. 388-89).

Galileo also shows concordism concerning the sun, at the close of the letter to the grand duchess. He exalts its nobility and its beneficial influence throughout the universe, seeing in this an argument in favor of heliocentrism. He supports these views by a text of Denis the Areopagite (EN, V, 346-48; LCL, 357-59).

The exegetical theses concerning the problem of the compatibility of Copernican theory with scripture raise a question of coherence. Let us concern ourselves with this one case: as soon as one has supposed that scripture contents itself with "telling us how we go to heaven and not how the heavens go" — to refer to Baronius's celebrated phrase — it seems to be established that we then do not have to ask ourselves if the Copernican theory, which only tells us "how the heavens go," is compatible with what is written in scripture about the nature and movements of the stars. Consequently, the debate about the literal or nonliteral meaning of certain texts would appear useless. In fact, this debate is internalized in the same author — be it St. Augustine or Galileo — with the thesis that scripture deals only with that which concerns salvation.

IV. AUTHORS AND TEXTS

As I have already stated, this section catalogues texts concerning exegesis raised by the theory of Copernicus, most of them quoted by Galileo, the majority favoring the compatibility of Copernican theory with scripture. In addition it gives some indications about less well-known authors. Authors are cited in chronological order, and each author's texts likewise, except in the case of St. Augustine where citation is made in the order in which the texts appear in the letter to the grand duchess of Tuscany.

The numerous quotations by Galileo found in this collection do not come from his own personal reading. Galileo was not a professional theologian. These texts were provided for him by his friends, as Castelli informs us in a letter to Galileo of January 6, 1615:

> I am in contact with a Barnabite priest who is greatly attached to your ideas and who has promised me certain passages of St. Augustine and other doctors in confirmation of your opinions about Joshua (EN, XIII, 126).

And in a letter to Piero Dini of May 2, 1615 (EN, V, 185), Galileo alludes to what he had learned about St. Augustine and other fathers of the church from his friends.

We do not have any more precise indications about these friends; we are ignorant of the name of the Barnabite priest who was so well intentioned toward Galileo.

Fathers of the Church

TERTULLIAN (ca. 155-220)
"We declare that God . . .," *Adversus Marcionem*, lib. 1, cap. 18 (EN, V, 317; LCL, 337).

SAINT JEROME (331-420)

1. "This art (of the Scriptures), the elderly lady . . .," *Epistola ad Paulinum*, 4111 (EN, V, 323; LCL, 341).
2. "There are many passages of Scripture . . .," Commentary on chap. 8 of Jeremiah (EN, V, 323, LCL, 348).
3. "In the Holy Scriptures it is usual . . .," Commentary on chap. 14 of St. Matthew (EN, V, 333; LCL, 349).

ST. AUGUSTINE (354-430)

De Genesi ad litteram, passages cited by Galileo:

1. "For the moment we will content ourselves with observing . . .," 1.2, chap. 18, no. 38 (EN, V, 310; LCL, 332). This passage is identical with the end of no.6.
2. "One usually asks under what form . . .," 1.2, chap. 9, no. 20 (EN, V, 318; LCL, 338).
3. "Some of the brethren also ask . . .," 1.2, chap. 10, no. 23 (EN, V, 319; LCL, 338).
4. "We ought to take it as beyond doubt . . .," 1.1, chap. 9, no. 21 (EN, V, 327; LCL, 344).
5. "But, it will be said, is this not to contradict . . .," 1.2, chap. 9, no. 21 (EN, V, 331; LCL, 346).
6. "Although, as far as the present . . .," 1.2, chap. 18, no. 38 (EN, V, 331; LCL, 347).
7. "I will reply that the question of knowledge . . .," 1.2, chap. 10, no. 23, (EN, V, 337; LCL, 351). This passage is identical with the end of no. 4.
8. "If in obscure matters . . .," 1.1, chap. 18, no. 37 (EN, V, 339; LCL, 352).
9. "It cannot be considered . . .," 1.1, chap. 19, no. 38 (EN,V, 339; LCL, 352).
10. "If a certain reason . . .," 1.1, chap. 19, no. 38 (EN, V, 339; LCL, 353). Peyreyra also quotes this text (see below).
11. "If the context does not offend . . .," 1.1, chap. 19, no. 38 (EN, V, 340; LCL, 353).
12. "And if we find . . ., 1.1, chap. 19, no. 38 (EN, V, 340, LCL, 353).
13. "In fact if often happens . . .," 1.1, chap. 19, no. 38 (EN, V, 340; LCL 353).
14. "One cannot speak often enough of the pain and sadness . . .," 1.1, chap. 19, no. 39 (EN, V, 341; LCL, 352).

Epistula septima ad Marcellinum, quoted by Galileo:

15. "Should it happen that the authority of the Scriptures . . .," (EN, V, 320; LCL, 339).

De Genesi ad litteram, not quoted by Galileo:

16. "*Narratio Moysi* . . .," 1.8, chap. 1, no. 2. Text cited by Peyreyra (see below; first rule).

DENIS THE AREOPAGITE (6th century)

1. "Light resembles . . .," *De Divinis nominibus* (EN, V, 346; LCL, 357).
2. "If in fact this Sun . . .," *De Divinis nominibus* (EN,V, 346; LCL, 357).

The Middle Ages

I will be very brief as to the exegetical positions of this epoch that could bear upon the hypothesis of the earth's mobility. Nevertheless, the general exegetical principles of this period deserve mention. For if they had been followed, the crisis leading to Galileo's condemnation could have been avoided.

Let us note only that in several places St. Thomas Aquinas taught that certain passages of scripture should not be interpreted literally, but should be considered as adapted to the ways of thinking of the time in which they were written.

This is the case in a passage in chap. 27 of his "Commentary on the Book of Job" (*Sancti Thomae Opera Omnia*, Leonine Edition [Rome, Santa Sabina], vol. 26, chap. 27, 1, 11, 12-15) and in passages in his *Summa Theologiae*, I, q. 9, a. 1, ad 3; I-II, q. 98, a. 3, ad 2). The text from the "Commentary on Job" is cited by Galileo (EN, V, 334; LCL, 349) but he does not cite the two texts from the *Summa*.

Exegesis in the 15th, 16th, and 17th Centuries (up to ca. 1616)

NICHOLAS COPERNICUS (1473–1543)

His novel views on the universe (immobile stars and the sun, the earth spins on its own axis and goes around the sun) are expounded in the *De revolutionibus orbium caelestium* (1543). If they did not arouse opposition on the part of church authorities until the time of Galileo, this is because, unknown to Copernicus, the work was endowed with a preface by Osiander explaining that Copernicus did not speak about reality but about appearances. On the other hand, the preface addressed to Pope Paul III, by Copernicus himself, states the contrary, in the very passage that was invoked to place the work on the Index in 1616.

One can only remain astonished that this agreement between the two prefaces was not referred to earlier. It was precisely on this passage in Copernicus's preface that Galileo insisted when arguing in the letter to the grand duchess, a year before Copernicus's book was placed on the Index, to the effect that because this passage had not been condemned by the magisterium of the church, the Copernican theory must be compatible with scripture.

THE COUNCIL OF TRENT

In a decree of April 8, 1546, the council declares:

> Nobody has the right, basing himself on his own prudence, in matters of faith and morals that concern the edification of Christian doctrine, to violently divert the Holy Scripture toward his own opinion and to interpret it contrary to the sense that Holy Mother the Church holds and has held, to whom it belongs to judge the true meaning and the interpretation of the Holy Scriptures, or even contrary to the unanimous agreement of the Fathers.

Galileo insists on the importance of this text, stressing that, because "the mobility or immobility of the earth is not *de fide*" and does not concern morals, this question falls outside the norm of conformity to the consensus of the fathers (EN, V, 337; LCL, 351).

DIDACUS STUNICA (IN SPANISH, DIEGO DE ZUÑIGA, 1536-1589)

Zuñiga, a Spanish Augustinian, was the first defender of the Copernican system in Spain, especially in his "Commentary on the Book of Job," " . . . in Job commentarii" (Toledo, 1584, 589 pages [Paris, Bibliothèque Nationale, A 3060]; 2nd edition, Rome, no date, 580 pages).

This book was placed on the Index in March 1616 together with Copernicus's *De revolutionibus* and the long letter by Foscarini (see below). These works were not withdrawn from the Index until 1835.

Without quoting it, Galileo mentions a passage from Zuñiga's "Commentary on Job," chap. 9, 6: "in which there is presented a long discussion on Copernicus's position and in which it is concluded that the mobility of the earth is not contrary to scripture" (EN, V, 336; LCL 350).

Galileo again invokes Zuñiga in a letter to Curzio Picchena of March 6, 1616 (see above, P.H. Michel, p. 396), signaling the very recent placing of Zuñiga's "Commentary on Job" on the Index.

Bibliography: H. Hurter, *Nomenclatura litteraria theologica* (Innsbrück, Lanteri, 3rd edition, 1907); *Illustrissimi viri augustinenses*, vol. 2 (Toledo, 1859); *Bibliotheca hispanica nova* (1773); Jordan Gallego,

O.P., "La metafísica de Diego y la Reforma tridentina de los Estudios Eclesiásticos," *Estudio Augustiniano*, 9/1 (1974) 3-60.

CARDINAL BARONIUS (1538–1607)

Baronius, an Oratorian, was the second superior general of his order. Galileo quotes his famous formula: "The intention of the Holy Spirit is to teach us how to go to heaven, not how the heavens go" (EN, V, 319; LCL, 339). Baronius and Bellarmine went to Padua in 1598, when Galileo was teaching there (EN, V, 319).

BENEDICT PEYREYRA (1535–1610)

A Spanish Jesuit, he taught rhetoric, philosophy, and theology at the Roman College. Galileo knew his treatise on natural philosophy, *De communibus omnium rerum naturalium principiis et affectionibus* (Rome, 1576). His chief work is a commentary on Genesis, *In Genesis commentarium et disputationes* (Rome, 1591). This book underwent several editions in Rome and elsewhere, notably in Lyons (1595), Cologne (1601), and Mainz (1612). The Mainz edition is a folio of 1006 pages. This very diffuse commentary is not of high quality but it is headed by four "rules." The first, reproduced here, is in favor of the literal interpretation of the Bible. Galileo does not quote it; he quotes the fourth, which shows more nuances (EN, V, 320; LCL, 339):

> As the true always coincides with the true, the truth of Holy Scripture cannot be contrary to truths and teachings furnished by human disciplines.

And in support of these views he conjoins a text of St. Augustine (citation no. 10, above).

Here is the text of the first rule, not quoted by Galileo:

> The doctrine of Moses on the creation of the world is fully historical. In fact Moses reports that the world began to be created at a certain instant, but that this creation unfolded in stages, over six days. This is confirmed by St. Augustine when he writes: "In these books, in fact, the account does not involve that literary genre in which things are stated figuratively, as is the case in the Song of Songs, but from beginning to end relates data that have really happened, as in the Book of Kings and other historical books. These books speak of things in the domain of everyday life: they are understood without difficulty, even at first sight, in a literal sense, free for subsequent speculation on how real facts are equally a figure of the future. Genesis, on the other hand, relates facts that are extraordinary for those who observe the ordinary course of nature. One does not seek to understand them in the literal sense but only in the figurative sense; one sees that history — that is to say, the narration of facts properly speaking — begins only at the moment when Adam and Eve, chased out of paradise, cleave together and

bear children. As if it were an everyday occurence among us that men lived so many years, that Enoch was transported from this world to other regions, that an aged and barren woman bore a child, and other marvels of this kind! (1.8, chap. 1, no. 2).

Bibliography: Sommervogel, *Bibliothèque de la Compagnie de Jésus*; *Dictionnaire de la Bible*, article "Peyreyra"; H. Hurter, *Nomenclatura litteraria theologiae catholicae* (Innsbrück, 3rd edition, 1907), part 3, p. 471; H. de Lubac, *Exégèse médiévale*, vol. 4, pp. 161-62.

Paolo Antonio Foscarini (1580–1616)

A Neopolitan Carmelite, he played an important role in the controversy over the Copernican theory by publishing in 1615 a letter to the father general of his order, Sebastiano Fantone, a letter that is in fact a small work, *Lettera sopra l'opinione dei Pittagorici e del Copernico della mobilità della terra e stabilità del sole e del nuovo Pittagorico sistema del mondo* (Naples, 1615, 65 pages; Bibliothèque nationale de Paris, R. 12953). This letter is an apologia for the heliocentric doctrine and its compatability with scripture (summarized in Paschini, *Vita e opere* (see above), chap. 2, pp. 304-8). It was placed on the Index in 1616, together with the books of Copernicus and Zuñiga.

Bibliography: *Dictionnaire de thèologie catholique*, article. "Paolo Antonio."

CARDINAL ROBERT BELLARMINE (1564-1621)

Bellarmine was not the head of the Holy Office, but a member. Nevertheless he played a major part in the placing of the three works on the Index on March 5, 1616.

Bellarmine's attitude toward the exegetical problems posed by the Copernican theory evolves noticeably in the course of his theological "career." It is punctuated by three writings: (1) the unpublished notes of 1571, which are rather open in nature; (2) passages of his *De Controversiis*, which are much less open; and (3) the letter to Fr. Foscarini in 1615, which reveals a certain degree of openness.

1. *Unpublished notes of 1571*. The following text is notable:

If in the future it should be demonstrated with evidence that the stars move with the movement of the sky and not by themselves, it would then be necessary to see how the scriptures should be understood, in order that they might not be in opposition to any other acquired truth. It is certain that the true meaning of scripture cannot be opposed to any other truth, whether philosophical or astronomical [Italian text is cited by Fr. Soccorsi, *Il processo* (see above), chap. 2, p. 29].

2. *De Controversiis Fidei adversus hujus temporis haereticos*, tome I, *De Verbo Dei* (1586), book 3, chap. 3, and chap. 10, argumentum 1.

Bellarmine shows at length that the church is the supreme judge, not of scripture, but of controversies that may arise among Christians as to the meaning of scripture.

In tome II, chap. 12, Bellarmine writes:

> In Scripture not only the thought, but the words, in their totality and taken singly, concern the faith, for we believe that in scripture there is not one word that is useless or incorrectly used [text referred to by Fr. André Dubarle in his article cited above, chap. 2, p. 77].

This, Bellarmine's major work, underwent several editions, the second in 1599.

3. *Letter to Fr. Paolo Foscarini, April 12, 1615 (EN, XII, 171-72).*

Here is the essential part:

> It seems to me that Your Reverence and Signor Galileo acted prudently in contenting yourselves with speaking by hypothesis (*ex suppositione*) and not absolutely, for it is thus that I have always understood Copernicus to have spoken. In effect, to say that by supposing the earth to be mobile and the sun immobile, one can save celestial appearances much better than can be done with eccentrics and epicycles, is to speak very soundly; this does not present any danger, and this manner of speaking is sufficient for the mathematician. But to wish to affirm that the sun is in reality at the center of the universe and only turns upon its axis, without moving from east to west, and that the earth is in the third heaven [sphere] and rotates around the sun with great speed, is a very dangerous thing, not only liable to arouse all the Scholastic theologians and philosophers, but also liable to injure our faith by making holy scripture false. Your Reverence has clearly demonstrated that there are many ways of interpreting holy scripture, but you have not applied these methods to any particular passage, and if you had wished to expound all the texts you have quoted, you would doubtless have encountered the gravest difficulties.
>
> You will be aware that the Council of Trent forbids the interpretation of the scriptures in a sense contrary to the common opinion of the fathers. . . . It is of no use to reply that this is not a matter of faith, because if it cannot be a matter of faith with regard to the subject matter (*ex parte objecti*), nevertheless it is so with regard to the speaker (*ex parte discentis*). . . .
>
> If there were a real proof that the sun is at the center of the universe, that the earth is in the third heaven [sphere], and that the sun does not go around the earth but the earth goes around the sun, then we would have to proceed very circumspectly in order to explain those passages of scripture that seem to teach the contrary, and we should rather admit that we have not understood them than declare as false an opinion that has been

demonstrated to be true. But, for my part, I will not believe that there are any such proofs until they have been demonstrated to me. And it is not the same thing to prove that "if the sun is supposed to be at the center and the earth in the heavens, the celestial appearances are saved," as to prove that the sun is really at the center and the earth in the heavens. One may, I believe, find the first kind of proof, but as to the second kind I have the gravest doubts, and in case of doubt one should not abandon the holy text as interpreted by the fathers of the church.

Bibliography: J. Brodrick, *Robert Bellarmine, Saint and Scholar* (1916). This work is a corrected and much abbreviated rewrite (in which Galileo is favorably judged) of his work *Blessed Robert Bellarmine, S.J.* (1928).

V. CONCLUSION

My treatment of this topic has been abstract, in the sense that I have in no way evoked the human, social, and scientific environment surrounding the exegetical debate engendered by the Galileo affair. Nevertheless, this abstraction has been necessary in order to make this question appear in its essential structure and in the diversity of its aspects, a question that up to now has been considered in a somewhat marginal fashion, and rarely in itself.

What strikes me in the history I have endeavored to retrace is that it shows three phases. First, a time of peace, when the Copernican theory in no way disturbs Catholic theologians. This was not the case among Protestants. Then, rather suddenly, in the course of four or five years, following on Galileo's discoveries with the astronomical telescope, a lively controversy engendering many writings, principally Galileo's letter to the grand duchess of Tuscany, completed ca. May 1615. This controversy was to lead to the placing of three works on the Index in 1616. Finally, a period in which no trace of this exegetical controversy can be found in writings, letters, or books. And the trial of 1633 does not engender any document that discusses exegetical theses in relation to the Copernican theory. It seems that at the trial there was a contentment with the state of controversy and with the works that preceded the 1616 Index condemnations.

Here it can only be a matter of provisional conclusions. Perhaps subsequent works will be able to bring out the nuances involved.

My study bears on a subject that has not hitherto been directly probed in depth, at least not satisfactorily. Thus it seems to me to constitute on the one hand a contribution, as limited as it may be, toward the knowledge of Galileo's thought and the reactions aroused by it, and on the other hand a contribution to the history of exegesis in his time.

PART THREE

GALILEO: FROM THE ENLIGHTENMENT
TO THE PRESENT

5

The Church and Galileo During the Century of the Enlightenment

Bernard Jacqueline

In the 18th century it is above all Isaac Newton who stands out in the study of nature; the role of Galileo was then less and his renown was somewhat limited to Italy, even if some influence on Newton is attributed to him.[1] The writers of the 18th century in fact tend to interpret Galileo in the light of the post-Newtonian epoch.

Nevertheless, works devoted to Galileo were not lacking in the 18th century. Antonio Favaro counts 236 volumes devoted to Galileo for that century[2] and G. Boffito adds a further 18;[3] in this respect works by Italian authors are particulary numerous.[4]

The fundamental work for the knowledge of Galileo in the 18th

---

1. On Galileo in the 18th century, see A. Rupert Hall, "Galileo nel XVIII° secolo," *Rivista di Filosofia*, 15 (Oct. 1979) 367–90.

2. A. Favaro, "Bibliografia galileiana di Antonio Favaro," in *Atti del R. Istituto veneto di scienze, lettere e arti*, in collaboration with A. Carli, 1896; it covers the years 1586 to 1895. The Barnabite G. Boffito has completed it by a *Supplemento alla bibliografia Galileiana di A. Favoro (1896–1940)* (Rome, 1942).

3. For the bibliography of Galileo, see also S. Vismara, "Bibliografia Galileiana" in *Nel terzo centenario della morte di Galileo Galilei* (Milan 1942), pp. 407–28, and E. Gentili, "Bibliografia Galileiana fra i due centenari (1942–1964)", *Scuola cattolica*, 92 (1964) 267–308, and 93 (1965) 82–86. On the current state of knowledge on the case of Galileo, see R. Aubert, "L'état actuel de l'affaire Galilée" in *Colloques d'histoire des sciences I et II*, University of Louvain; *Recueil des travaux d'histoire et de philology*, 6/9 (Louvain, 1976) 151–63; and the article "Galilée" in *Dictionnaire d'histoire et de géographie ecclésiastique*, fasc. 111 (Paris, 1980), col. 780–81.

4. Apart from works examined later, one can quote for the second quarter of the 18th century, G. Andres, *Saggio sulla filosofia del Galileo* (Mantua, 1776), and L. Brenno, *Vitae Italorum doctrina excellentium qui saeculis XVII et XVIII floruerunt* (Pisa, 1778), vol. 1, pp. 1–230.

century is the life of Galileo by his disciple Vincenzo Viviani, *Racconto istorico della vita di Galileo*. It is probable that Viviani wrote this biography in April 1654 — that is, approximately twelve years after the death of Galileo, at the request of Prince Leopoldo de' Medici. In 1674 an attempt was made to correct his work by Michelangelo Ricci, who found it boring.[5] This work was edited by Salvino Salvini in *Fasti consolari dell'Academia Fiorentina*, a work that appeared in Florence in 1717. Viviani's life of Galileo is particularly important; he was Galileo's last student and copyist. He not only refers to the writings and correspondence of his master, but also to conversations with him and to discussions with his students and with others who had known him. Because the notes taken by Viviani during the life of his master have disappeared, one can query if he has always properly understood and transmitted what he had heard.[6]

In 1633, in his "Observations on the Prophecies of Daniel and the Apocalypse of St. John" (Landrer, 1733), Newton had conducted a polemic against the church. But it is at the end of the 17th century that the critics of church doctrine became more lively in France with the "Conversations on the Plurality of Worlds," in which Fontanelle[7] took up the ideas of Copernicus, and with the "Historical and Critical Dictionary" of Pierre Bayle (1647-1706), which opposed reason to faith. The French philosophers of the 18th century drew inspiration from these two authors in the criticism of religion, in particular Voltaire.[8] The latter preferred Galileo to Descartes; he wrote to Der Alleurs, on November 26, 1738:

> There was, in his time, a certain Galileo, who was a true discoverer, who fought Aristotle with geometry and experiments . . . Descartes was a lucky charlatan, but Galileo was a great philosopher.

In his "Philosophical Dictionary" (1764) he says:

> Those who placed Galileo under penance were even more mistaken. Every inquisitor should blush to the roots of his soul at the sight of one single

5. G. C. Nelli, *Saggio di Storia Letteraria Fiorentina del secolo* XVII (Lucca, 1759), p. 4; A. Favaro "Sulla veridicità del 'Racconto istorico della vita di Galileo' dettato da Vicenzo Viviani," Archivio Storico Italiano, 73/1 (1915) 324.

6. Rupert Hall, *Galileo*, pp. 317–72.

7. Bernard Le Bouyer de Fontenelle (1657–1757) was a member and permanent secretary of the *Académie des Sciences*, and his thought inspired Cartesian thought. His *Entretiens sur la pluralité des mondes* were republished in 1761 in tome IX of his works; see Thierry Moulnier, *Les Entretiens de Fontenelle* (Lausanne, 1946), pp. 173–89.

8. Apart from the remarkable work of Paul Hazard, *La crise de la conscience européenne, 1680–1715* (Paris, 1935), republished 1961, one may consult on this subject J. S. Spinh, *La libre pensée francaise de Gassendi à Voltaire* (Paris, 1966), and the work of J. Delumeau, *Le catholicisme entre Luther et Voltaire* (Paris, 1971).

Copernican sphere. However, if Newton had been born in Portugal, and if a Dominican had seen a heresy in the law of the inverse square of the distance, Sir Newton would have been dressed in the sanbenito of an auto-da-fé.[9]

In Germany, Jacob Brucker, in his *Historia critica philosophiae* (1744) attributes the condemnation of Galileo to the Peripatetics.[10]

In England, Guiseppe Baretti, in *The Italian Library*, attributed Galileo's condemnation to the jealousy of the Jesuits, in particular to Fr. Christopher Scheiner, S. J. (1575–1650).[11] G. Targioni Tozzetti, in his *Notizie degli aggrandimenti delle scienze fisiche*, published in Florence in 1780, attributed the troubles of Galileo to members of religious orders and the darkening of his memory to obscurantism.[12] These accusations were renewed by Girolamo Tiraboschi in his *Storia della letteratura italiana* (Modena, 1780). The responsibility of religious in this affair became a common theme, still echoed by G. C. Nelli in his *Vita et commercio litterario di Galileo Galilei*, which appeared in Protestant circles in Lausanne in 1793:[13]

> Who will deny that in the great host of regular religious and ecclesiastics, all of whom should have been scholars and true fathers in spirit and in charity, there was not one who was enlightened and a good person.

One can see that in the Protestant countries, criticism of the church in connection with the Galileo affair began with the *Historia critica philosophiae* of Brüchner (Leipzig, 1744 and 1756) and *The Italian Library* (London, 1757). One should also draw attention to the appearance of the first English translation of the sentence and recantation of Galileo in the *Historia Inquisitionis* (1692) made by Samuel Chaudler (London, 1731).[14] This version was reprinted in the *Gentleman's Magazine*[15] in 1745 and inserted into an article aimed at arousing hatred of Rome at the time of the second Scottish rebellion in favor of the Stuart dynasty. In this article the cardinals who opposed Galileo appeared as enemies of true knowledge and of the benefits of science.[16]

What was the reaction of Catholic circles? Guido Grandi, O. S. B., in his *Risposta apologetica alle opposizioni (di) A(llessandro) M(archetti)*,

---

9. Voltaire, article "Newton," in *Dictionnaire philosophique* (in *Oeuvres complètes de Voltaire* [Paris, 1869], vol. 14, pp. 234–35); P. Cassini, "Briaric et miniature: Voltaire et Newton," in *Studies on Voltaire in the 18th century* (Oxford, 1979).
10. Vol. 4, part 2 (Leipzig, 1756), pp. 634–39; the first edition was in 1744.
11. This text is taken up in *Les Querelles littéraires* (Paris, 1761), vol. 3, p. 49.
12. Vol. 1, p. 58.
13. Two volumes; the dedication date is June 9, 1790.
14. Vol. 2, pp. 228–34.
15. 15 Nov., pp. 584–86; and also in Westminster Journal.
16. Rupert Hall, *Galileo*, p. 318.

published in Lucca in 1712, had come to the defense of Galileo and Viviani, as is shown by the subtitle of his book, "On this occasion Galileo and Viviani are defended." As to the Jesuits, they were still hostile to Copernicùs at the beginning of the century. In 1704, the *Mémoires de Trévoux* give an account of a work proving the falsity of the Copernican hypothesis,[17] and in 1730 the same publication takes up a position against a work claiming that the majority of scientists are Copernicans.[18] But in the second half of the 18th century voices favorable to Copernicus and Galileo were raised in Belgium. In 1772 Fr. Semmes fully admitted the doctrine of Copernicus, and in 1774 Professor Van Lemenpoel declared that Galileo's system should be accepted unconditionally.[19]

Finally, what was the position of the Roman Congregations in connection with Galileo in the century of the Enlightenment? Measures were taken on two occasions in the 18th century on the subject of Galileo: in 1734 the cardinals of the Holy Office authorized the erection of a mausoleum to Galileo in the church of Santa Croce in Florence, and in 1757 books teaching the mobility of the earth were withdrawn from the Index.[20]

When Galileo died, at the age of seventy-seven, on January 8, 1642, "his body was transfered from the villa of Arcetri to Florence and, on the instructions of His Sacred Highness the Grand Duke of Tuscany, laid to rest in a separate place in the church of Santa Croce, where there was an ancient sepulchre of the noble Galileo family."[21] But the Medicis could not render Galileo the homage they intended, because Cardinal Francesco Barberini, nephew of Urban VIII in whose pontificate Galileo had been condemned, had written to Fr. Masellis, inquisitor of Florence:

> Mgr. the Assessor has read before His Holiness [Urban VIII] Your Reverence's letter announcing the death of Galileo Galilei and alluding to projects envisaged for his sepulchre and for his obsequies. And His Holiness, together with the opinion of their Eminences [the cardinals], has decided that, with your customary competence, you should whisper in the ear of the grand duke that it is not right to raise mausolea for the body of one who has been placed under sanction by the tribunal of the Holy

17. *Mémoires de Trévoux*, April 30, 1704.
18. Ibid., Nov. 1730, art. 106; see J. Ehrard, *L'idée de nature en France dans la première moitié du XVIII siécle* (1963).
19. G. Monchamp, *Galilée et la Belgique, Essai sur les vicissitudes du système de Copernic en Belgique* (1892) (review by Fr. V. Schaffer in *Revue des questions scientifiques* [1892], p. 221).
20. Grisar, *Galileistudien, Historische theologische Untersuchungen über die Urtheile der römischen Congregationen* (1882).
21. Galileo, *Opere* (ed. Antonio Favaro), vol XIX, doc. XLV.

Inquisition and who has died during the time of his penance, for good persons could be scandalized by this and adversely judge the piety of His Highness. But if this project cannot be averted, [Your Reverence] should take care that in the epitaph or inscription affixed to the sepulchre there cannot be read words that would offend the reputation of this tribunal. It is needful to have the same care with regard to the person who gives the funeral oration, arranging to see and examine it before it is delivered or printed. His Holiness trusts to the known sagacity of Your Reverence to supply a remedy in this affair.[22]

It was not until 1734, under the Florentine Pope Clement XII, that permission would be given by the tribunal of the Inquisition for the raising of a funeral monument to Galileo.

Following a request addressed to the inquisitor of Florence, the consultors of the tribunal of the Inquisition, on June 14, 1734, were in accord to reply to the Florentine inquisitor instructing him not to hinder the construction of a mausoleum to Galileo.[23] This favorable opinion of the consultors was approved on June 16, 1734, by the cardinals of the Holy Office,[24] and the reply was sent by Cardinal Ottoboni on June 29, 1734.

The bequest of Vicenzo Viviani could thus be carried out by the inheritor Giovanni Nelli, who spent 7,269 scudi instead of 4,000 for the erection of the monument, still visible in the church of Santa Croce in Florence. The design of the monument is by Giulio Foggini,[25] the sculpture in honor of geometry is by Girolamo Ticciati, and that in honor of astronomy is by Biondo Simone Peruzzi.

Thus it was that the memory of Galileo was rehabilitated in 1734 by Pope Clement XII, who was the first pope to condemn freemasonry by his two bulls of April 28, 1739, and who entrusted to the Florentine architect Alessandro Galilei the construction of the romanesque facades of St. John Lateran (1730–1735) and St. John of the Florentines.

Galileo's memory having thus been rehabilitated, his writings re-

22. EN, XVIII, 379–80. Bibliography: A. Favaro, *Galileo e l'Inquisizione, Documenti del processo Galileiano esistenti nell'Archivio del S. Uffizio e nell'Archivio Segreto Vaticano* (Florence, 1907); I. Cioni, *I documenti galileiani del S. Uffizio di Firenze* (1908); G. Pagani, *Le persecuzioni postume mosse a Galileo Galilei con un cenno della loro cause* (1889).

23. *DD.CC fuerunt in voto rescribendum P. Inquisitori quod constructionem depositi Galilei non impediat, sed curet sollicite sibi communicari inscriptionem super dicto deposito faciendum illaque ad S. Congregationem transmittat ad effectum circa illam dandi ordines opportunos antequam fiat.* See notes 21 and 22, above.

24. *Feria 4, die 16 junii, E.mi supradictum votum D.D. consultorum approbaverunt* (EN, XIX, 399).

25. Gian Battista Foggini (1652–1725), Florentine sculptor and architect, had two sons: Giulio, who was an architect, and Vicenzo, who was a sculptor; a bust of Galileo had been executed by Gian Battista himself, intended for the ornamentation of the mausoleum.

mained engulfed in the condemnation of 1615, which had placed on the Index books following the Copernican doctrine.

It was Nicholas Copernicus (1473–1543), and not at all Galileo, who revolutionized astronomy by his *De revolutionibus orbium caelestium libri IV* (1543), published at the instigation of Cardinal N. Schönberg and Bishop Tiedemann Giese. Not only was it the case that Copernicus's work was not placed on the Index, but Pope Gregory XIII (1572–1585) took account of his conclusions in his Gregorian reform of the calendar.

It was not until March 5, 1616, that *De revolutionibus* was condemned by the Congregation of the Index; at the same time there were also condemned a work of Diego Zuñiga and the *Epistula ad Fantonium* (1615) of the Carmelite Paolo Antonio Foscarini on the opinions of the disciples of Pythagorus and Copernicus.[26] The decree of the Congregation of the Index "proscribed all books that presented the Copernican system as conforming to cosmic reality, not therefore as only a working hypothesis, *donec corrigantur* — that is, as long as corrections had not been made on the subject of his affirmation. No personal work of Galileo was explicity placed on the Index,[27] even though he had proposed the phenomenon of the tides as a decisive proof in favor of the Copernican system. In January 1616 Galileo wrote the "Discourse on the Ebb and Flow of the Sea," which was not published while he was alive; it is reproduced on the fourth day of the "Dialogue."

The condemnation did not prevent the Barnabite, Redento Baranzo, friend of St. Francis de Sales, and a zealot for the theories of Copernicus, from publishing in 1617 his *Uranoscopia seu de Coelo*, republished in 1619, the year of publication of his *Novae opiniones physicae.*[28]

In 1630 Galileo completed his *Dialogo sopra i due massimi sistemi del*

---

26. Galileo, *Opere*, XII, n. 1185.

27. Walter Brandmüller, "Le cas de Galilée: verité et légende — origine et conséquences," in *Athéisme et Dialogue*, 15/3 (Sept. 1980) 130 (French trans. of *Der Fall Galilei. Wirklichkeit und Legende — Hintergründe und Folgen* [Karlsruhe, 1970]). Earlier Prof. Brandmüller had published, in *Stimmen der Zeit* (Munich, 1968, pp. 11–12), a study entitled: "Der Fall Galilei — Konflikt Naturwissenschaft und Kirche?" The decree of the Index contained the list of phrases to be improved; it was required, for example, that the title "Proof of the threefold movement of the earth" become "On the hypothesis of the threefold movement of the earth and its proof." See Grisar, *Galileistudien* (note 20, above).

28. The Florimontana Academy (1607–1610), founded by St. Francis de Sales and Antoine Favre, was continued by the Barnabites. One of the young professors of their college, Don Redento Giovanni Antonio Baranzano, corresponded with Galileo. After the publication of Baranzano's *Uranoscopia seu de Coelo* (1617), without the authorization of his superiors, the general of the Barnabites demanded a retraction, which appeared in 1618. St. Francis de Sales defended Baranzano, asked his general not to withdraw him from Annecy, and praised his *Novae opiniones physicae*. See J. Garin, article "Baranzano

mondo, and, in 1633, the book was incriminated for presenting the Copernican system as certain, causing it to fall under the condemnation of 1616.

In 1754, the article "Copernicus" that appeared in the *Encyclopédie*[29] invited Italy to recognize in Galileo's condemnation "an error prejudicial to the sciences" and added for the attention of Benedict XIV:

> Such a change would be very worthy of the enlightened pontiff who today governs the church, friend of the sciences and himself a scholar.[30]

In 1757 books teaching the movement of the earth were withdrawn from the Index by Benedict XIV (1740–1758).[31]

Tome IV, appearing in 1754, of the *Encyclopédie ou Dictionnarie raisonné des sciences, des arts, et des métiers*, published by Diderot and d'Alembert in Paris from 1751 to 1772, contained articles on Bacon, Campanella, and Descartes, and benefited from the collaboration of several priests: Mallet, de Prades, Yvon, Pestré, but also of an atheist, such as the grammarian du Marsais, and, after 1572, thinkers of the French Enlightenment such as Voltaire and Montesquieu[32] The first edition devoted no article to Galileo and there is no allusion to him in the article "Inquisition"; but in return one finds in the article "Copernicus" a long passage on Galileo, and I have thought it important to reproduce it in its entirety:

> The great Galileo was formally indicted before the Inquisition, and his opinion as to the movement of the earth was condemned as heretical. In the decree which they returned against him, the Inquisitors did not spare the

continuation

(Jean Antoine)" in the *Dictionnaire d'histoire et de géographie ecclésiastique*, col. 565–66; St. Francis de Sales, *Oeuvres* (Paris, Ed. de la Pleiade), p. xlix.It is known that in France the Gallicans did not consider the decrees of the Inquisition obligatory.

29. Diderot and d'Alembert, *Encyclopédie raisonné des sciences, des arts et des métiers* (Paris, 1751–1772), tom. IV (1754), col. 173ff. (bibliography in *Encyclopedia cattolica* [Rome, 1950], vol. 5, col. 337–40).

30. Ibid., col. 174.

31. It was in this same year that there appeared the book by the Italian Guiseppe Baretti, *The Italian Library*, published in London. This book gained a large circulation from its publication in French in *Querelles litéraires* (Paris, 1761). In it we read on p. 49 in connection with Galileo: "At the moment when he was set free, we are assured, remorse seized him. He raised his eyes towards the ground [*sic*], and said, kicking it with his foot: 'And still it moves'" (cited by Rupert Hall, *Galileo*, p. 375). As Stillman Drake has shown in *Galileo at Work* (Chicago and London), pp. 356–57 (see the article by Favaro in *Il giornale d'Italia* (Rome, July 12, 1911, p. 3), Galileo could have made a gesture of this kind at the moment of leaving Sienna, because even though he was then under surveillance as to his place of residence, he was the guest of the archbishop of Sienna before going to his villa at Arcetri.

32. John Lough, *The Contribution to the Encyclopedia* (London, 1973), and *Essays on the Encyclopedia* (London, 1968).

name of Copernicus who had renewed it after the Cardinal of Cusa; nor that of Diego de Zuñiga who had taught the Copernican system in his commentaries on Job, nor that of Fr. Foscarini, Italian Carmelite, who had just proved in a scholarly letter addressed to his superior that this opinion was in no way contrary to Scripture. Galileo, having continued to dogmatize on the movement of the earth, despite this censure, was condemned afresh, obliged to recant in public, and to abjure his alleged errors of speech and writing, which he did on June 22, 1633. Having promised on his knees, his hand on the Gospels, that he would not say or write anything contrary to this injunction, he was led to the prisons of the Inquisition, whence he was soon released. This event so powerfully terrified Descartes, who was very submissive to the Holy See, that he delayed the publication of his treatise on the world, which was ready to appear. You can find all these details in the life of Descartes by Baillet.[33]

Since then the most enlightened philosophers and astronomers of Italy have not dared to uphold the Copernican system; or if perchance they seem to adopt it, they take great care to make it clear that they regard it only as a hypothesis, and that they are furthermore very submissive to the decrees of the sovereign pontiffs on this subject.

It would be highly desirable that a country as full of spirit and knowledge as Italy would wish to recognize an error so prejudicial to the progress of the sciences, and that it would think about this matter as we do in France![34] Such a change would be very worthy of the enlightened pontiff who governs the church today: a friend of the sciences, and himself a scholar, it is for him to lay down the law to the inquisitors, as he has already done in other more important matters. As a famous author says, there is not a single inquisitor who should not blush at the sight of a Copernican sphere. This inquisitorial fury against the movement of the earth is even harmful to religion. In fact, what will weak and simple folk think about the dogmas that the faith obliges us to believe if they find that doubtful or false opinions are mixed in these dogmas? Would it not be better to say that in matters of faith Scripture speaks according to the Holy Spirit, and in physical matters it should speak as the people speak, whose language it should speak well so as to be within reach. With this distinction there is an answer to everything; physics and faith are equally secure. One of the main causes of decrying the system of Copernicus in Spain and Italy is that there one is persuaded that several foreign pontiffs have decided that the earth does not go round, and that in these places one believes the papal judgment to be infallible, even in matters which do not at all concern Christianity. In France only the church is considered infallible, and here one finds it better to believe astronomical observations on the system of the world rather than the decrees of the Inquisition on the subject; for the same reason, according to Pascal, the king of Spain would find it better to believe Christopher Columbus on the existence of the antipodes, because he had come from there, than Pope Zechariah who had never been there. . . .

---

33. Adrien Baillet was the author of "Vie de M. Descartes," which appeared in 1691. His *Vies des Saints pour les mois de janvier-août* was placed on the Index in 1709, doubtless because of his rationalism and his Jansenist sympathies.
34. The Gallicans did not observe the Index.

In the life of Descartes, which we have just quoted, Baillet accuses the Jesuit Fr. Scheiner of having denounced Galileo to the Inquisition for his opinion on the movement of the earth. In fact this father was jealous of Galileo or displeased with him on the matter of the discovery of the sunspots, which Galileo disputed with him. But if it is true that Fr. Scheiner exacted this vengeance from his adversary, such a step does more damage to his memory than the honor which the true or pretended discovery of sunspots could have accorded him. . . .

In France the Copernican system is upheld without the slightest fear, and people are persuaded by the reasons we have given that this system is in no way contrary to the faith, even if Joshua had said, *sta sol*; thus one replies in a sound and satisfactory fashion to all difficulties of nonbelievers as to certain parts of Scripture, where they claim without reason to find gross physical or astronomical errors.

Benedict XIV, who had been archbishop of Bologna, interested himself in the Academy of Sciences at his archepiscopal villa, where he founded a museum and a chair of anatomy.[35] After becoming pope he reformed the Lincean Academy, which became the "New Lincean," and established chairs of chemistry and mathematics at the Roman University de Sapientia. He was in contact with the Newtonian Pierre Louis Horace de Maupertius, member of the French Academy of Sciences and author of *Discours sur la figure des astres*.

Benedict XIV, who had been a consulter of the Congregation of the Holy Office, did not wait for the suggestions of the *Encyclopédie* in order to think about reform of the Congregation of the Index. As early as July 9, 1753, he laid down in the constitution *Sollicita ac provida* that alongside theologians there are persons who are remarkable for their erudition in the profane sciences (*sacra et profana eruditione praestantes*)[36] to guarantee the defense of incriminated authors.[37] These improvements effected under Benedict XIV had been prepared by Fr. Ricchini, who had been secretary of the Congregation of the Index since 1741.[38]

Already in the pontificate of the Tuscan Pope Alexander VII (1655–1667) the decreee of 1616 against works that followed Copernicus had been withdrawn from the Index and replaced by the simple mention: *Libri omnes docentes mobilitatem terrae et immobilitatem solis.*

35. L. Hammermeier, *Akademiebegegnung und Wissenschaftsorganisation während der zweiten Hälfte des 18. Jahrhunderts* (Berlin, 1976), p. 45, note 20 (bibliography); J. Oliger, article "Benedetto XIV" in *Enciclopedia Cattolica* (1940), vol. 2, col. 1281–85.

36. Benedict XIV, *Bullarium*, III, 2, Prato, 1847, pp. 109–16, § 13; L. Pastor, *Storia dei Papi* (Rome, 1933), XVI, 1, pp. 265–66.

37. *Dizionario di Bibliografia italiana*, vol. 8, pp. 1966 ff.

38. Bibliography of the S.C. of the Index; see N. De Re, *La Curia Romana. Lineamenti storico-giuridici* (Rome, 1970), pp. 607–8; A. Van Hove, *Prolegomena, Commentarium Lovaniense in Codicem juris canonici* (Malines and Rome, 1945), vol. I, t.l, p. 399, no. 2.

The definitive decision as to the withdrawal of books teaching the immobility of the sun and mobility of the earth from the Index list was taken by Pope Benedict XIV on April 16, 1757.[39]

Although the Bull introducing the new catalogue of the Index was dated December 23, 1757, its publication was not effectuated until 1758. According to the astronomer Lalande, who had spoken about the matter with the cardinal prefect of the Congregation of the Index in 1765, this delay was due only to external and formal difficulties.[40]

Thus Galileo's books did not remain on the Index until 1818, as believed by Professor A. Rupert Hall,[41] according to whom nevertheless the edition of Galileo's works that appeared in Padua in 1744 would have been the first to print his *Dialoghi sopra i due massimi sistemi del mondo* with the approval of the church.

Paolo Frisi (1728–1784), a secular priest who had formerly been a Barnabite, professor at Milan and Pisa, was a versatile author on

39. See Favaro, *Galileo e l'Inquisizione*, p. 159; *Archivio della S. C. dell' Indice, Acto ab anno 1749 ad annum 1763*, p. 129; EN, XIX, 419.

40. Lalande was a diligent observer; he had catalogued 47,000 stars, and in 1769, from Cité du Cap, had observed the passage of Venus across the sun. He wrote *Mémoire sur la parallaxe lunaire et sur la distance de la Terre* (1752–1787) and *Mémoires sur les équations séculaires* (1757).

41. See Grisar, *Galileistudien*, note 20, above. On September 11, 1822 the Congregation of the Index authorized the publication of books teaching the mobility of the earth and the immobility of the sun: "*Decreverunt non esse a praesenti et futuris pro tempore Magistris Sacri Palatii Apostolici recusandam licentiam pro impressione et publicatione operum tractantium de mobilitate terrae et immobilitate solis juxta communem modernorum astronomorum opinionem dummodo nihil aliud obstet.*" This decree was approved by Pius VII on September 25, 1822, and seemed to have been provoked by the refusal imposed on Canon Settele, professor at the University de Sapientia, to have his book *Eléments d'optique et d'astronomie* published. The refusal was imposed by the Dominican Filippo Anfossi, Master of the Sacred Palace. The decision was taken without opportunity to consult the acts of the Galileo trial, which only returned from Paris to Rome in 1843, as a result of the negotiation of the Treaty of Vienna (A. Mercati, *Come e quando ritornò a Rome il codice del processo di Galileo*, extract from the *Atti della Pontificia Academia delle Scienze "Novi Lincei,"* LXXX, Session 1 of December 19, 1926 (Rome, 1927, pp. 58–63). The decree of December 25, 1822, further makes no reference to the decree of April 16, 1757. In his *Principes de Géologie*, published in English in 1830 (vol. I, 1843, pp. 162–63), Charles Lyell wrote: "In 1828 Professor Scarpellini assured me that Pope Pius VII, a pontiff distinguished for the sciences, had brought about the repeal of the edicts published against Galileo and the Copernican system. In the Assembly of the Congregation convoked for this purpose by the pope, the late Cardinal Toriozzi, assessor of the Sacred College, put forward the proposal to purge the church of the scandal occasioned by the upholding of these edicts. With the single exception of one of its members, a Dominican, the entire assembly hastened to adhere to this idea. . . . Long before the decision of the Sacred College, the Newtonian theory had been taught at the Wisdom University , as well as in all the Catholic Universities of Europe (except, I have heard, in the case of Salamanca); but out of respect for the decrees of the church, the professors restricted themselves to using the word 'hypothesis' instead of 'theory.' Today one speaks of 'the theory of Copernicus.'"

mathematical and physical questions. In his *Elogio di Galileo Galilei*, he passed over the melodramatic and controversial aspects of Galileo's life in silence.[42]

In addition, it was to Fr. Paolo Frisi that the Encyclopedists had recourse in order to publish in 1777 an article on Galileo, which concentrated on the scientific aspects of Galileo's work and kept clear of polemic.[43]

As early as the end of the 17th century the anti-Christian polemic of the Enlightenment used the theses of the Copernican revolution, at first with Cyrano de Bergerac, author of *Historie cosmique, contenant les Etats et Empires de la Lune et du Soleil* (Paris, 1657), and with Fontenelle, author of *Entretiens sur la pluralité des mondes* (Paris, 1686). The Galileo affair was to be exploited in the polemic against religion; a fair number of writings tending in this direction had been published in England, and Voltaire, a great admirer of Newton, took arms against the church on the question. On the other hand, the *Encyclopédie* showed moderation, suggesting to Benedict XIV, in its article "Copernic," that he should resolve the matter, and entrusting the editing of the article on Galileo to the ex-Barnabite, Paolo Frisi.

On the other side of the church, religious circles little by little showed themselves more favorable to Galileo, if we think of Fr. Grandi (1712), Fr. Frisi (1767), or Fr. Semmes (1774).

Insofar as it was concerned, the papacy in the 17th and 18th centuries took three measures in favor of Galileo: authorization of the erection of a mausoleum to him in the Florentine church of Santa Croce (1734), tacit withdrawal of the Decree of 1616 from the Catalogue of the Index (1664), and an explicit withdrawal of books teaching the movement of the earth and the immobility of the sun from this catalogue (1757).

Although the documentation concerning these three measures has been published in its entirety, it is usually passed over in silence, and even the decision of 1882 authorizing the teaching of the Copernican systems makes no reference to the above positions adopted by the Holy See during the 18th century, nor to the acts of the trial of Galileo, which had not yet been reintegrated into the Vatican archives.[44]

---

42. *Elogio di Galileo Galilei* (Leghorn and Milan, 1775).

43. *Encyclopédie-Supplément III* (Amsterdam, 1777), article "Galilée (Philosophie de)," pp. 172–76. Paolo Frisi cites a eulogy of Galileo by the Academicians of Dijon in their *Mémoires*, vol. 1, *Contenant les mémoires d'Expériences physiques de l'Académie del Cimento de Florence* (Dijon-Auxerre, 1776). The *Discours préliminaire* is undoubtedly by Philibert Guéneau de Montbéliard (1720–1785). See Rupert Hall, *Galileo*, p. 381, n.1. On the Academy of Dijon at this period, see R. Tisserant, *Au temps de L'Encyclopédie. L'Académie de Dijon de 1740 à 1793* (Paris, 1936).

44. From time to time someone turns up claiming the communication by the Holy

continuation

Office of the documentation concerning Galileo. In fact, according to the late Fr. N. Kowalski, formerly archivist to the Sacred Congregation *de Propaganda Fide*, the trial of Galileo was in the archives of this latter dicastery prior to the transfer of the archives to Paris in 1810 under Napoleon I. This could have been because Mgr. Francesco Ingoli, Secretary of *Propagand Fide*, was very close to Pope Urban VIII, and was interested in astronomical questions and particularly in the Galileo case (see Josef Metzler, "Der erste Sekretär der Kongregation (1578–1649)" in *S.C. de Propaganda Fide, Memoria rerum, 350 ans au service des Missions, 1622–1972*, vol I/1, 1622–1700 [Rome, Freiburg, and Vienna, 1971], pp. 197–243; bibliography, p. 201 and n. 14). A book on Urban VIII and Galileo was printed by the Tipografia poliglotta della S.C. di Propaganda Fide: *Urbano VIII e Galileo Galilei* (Rome, 1875). It was also on the presses of this dicastery that there was printed the work by Mgr. Mario Mareni, *Galileo e l'Inquisizione, Memorie Storico-Critiche* (Rome, 1850). It contains the history of the manuscript record of Galileo's trial. The acts of the trial of Galileo are kept in the Archivio Segreto Vaticano (see Mercati, *Come e quando* [note 41, above], no. 50, and the documents of the Galileo affair have been published by A. Favaro in EN, vol. X and XVIII); the acts of the trial are published in vol. XIX with the *Racconto Istorico* of Viviani and the *Vita* written by Canon Gherardini; one can also consult M. Cioni, *I documenti galileiani del S. Uffizio di Firenze* (Florence, 1908). On the Vatican archives in Paris, see Jean Mauzaize, "Les Archives du Vatican demeurées a Paris," in *Les Archives religieuses et la vie del l'Eglise aujourd'hui, Actes du Ve Congrès national de l'Association des Archivistes de l'Eglise de France* (Paris, 1982).

6

Galileo Yesterday and Today

Pierre Costabel

O n the 350th anniversary of the trial of Galileo, it should be observed that already for just over a century the person and the scientist, his work and the censure imposed on him, have stimulated a literature of considerable abundance. The bibliography is difficult to master and is ceaselessly enlarged, as a consequence of the fact that Italian specialists in the history of science have not ceased to draw their colleagues in other countries into searching studies occasioned by seminars, colloquia, or international congresses. Since 1980 the organ of the Vatican Secretariat for Non-Believers, *Atheism and Dialogue*, has attempted to disseminate references to the more characteristic books and articles. Even if the intention is not fully realizable, because of countless new publications all the time, it is important that it has at least been attempted, and it is clear that the above-mentioned review puts at the disposal of the public a very extensive and useful selection of works to which a reader can refer.

A VAST LITERATURE

Here there cannot be any question of attempting to give a critical review of what is in fact a vast literature. But with an awareness of the efforts of historians, theologians, philosophers, and scientists who have done so much to advance the Galileo case, centered around the very remarkable publication of the Italian Edizione Nazionale (1929–1939), the necessity of pointing out general perspectives even if restricted to a few major features, makes itself felt.

At the outset it is doubtless not pointless to recall that the proofs of the movement of the earth were not given a wide public until the period

1830–1850. If the discovery of stellar aberration, furnishing a geometrical argument for the movement of the earth around the sun, dates back to James Bradley a century earlier, these findings were not published until 1797–1805. They did not give rise to the important complementary work of Herschel and Bessel until publication dating ca. 1820, and these required several years for a wide and thorough circulation. On the other hand, it was Foucault's experiment of 1851 on the rotation of the plane of oscillation of a pendulum relative to the earth that marked the first crucial evidence of the earth's spin. It is also not without value to recall that the works of Copernicus were removed from the Index in 1757, and those of Galileo in 1822. If it is true that scientific discoveries have had an influence in Vatican decisions, it can be pointed out that such decisions sometimes occurred when discussions in the scientific world had not been concluded by the appearance of definitive argumentation. And we can congratulate ourselves that the church did not wait for the progress of these discussions to lift condemnations that, at their time, caused much regret to many religious minds. But to the extent that, on the one hand, it was a matter of a gesture that could not be publicized, under pain of once again falling into the error of canonizing scientific concepts prior to a rigorous and complete investigation, and in which, on the other hand, opinions had been profoundly strengthened in the direction of a condemned cosmology, it was inevitable that the first half of the 19th century would witness crisis conditions in thought about the Galileo case.

Auguste Comte

It is beyond question that the founder of positivist philosophy, Auguste Comte, played a major part in this respect, and that the image of Galileo, positive scientist victimized by dogmatism, owes much to the whole philosophical stream issuing in France from this master of thought functioning as a prophet. This image has served as a symbol for the anticlericalism that presided over the educational reforms of the Third Republic. If it is impossible here to give more than a fleeting mention of a complex situation — itself requiring a long study for its analysis — it is important to note clearly the point of departure of the general perspective that I have in view. This is, namely, that in the second half of the 19th century there is simultaneously an almost universal consensus as to the truth of the earth's movement and the injustice of Galileo's condemnation, and a commencement of scholarly studies of the works of this scientist and of his trial. The consensus extends to the church, as witnessed by certain remarks recorded at the time of Vatican I, and the earth's movement is taught everywhere, but scholarly studies do not radiate beyond a restricted milieu, and the purely scientific difficulties of experimental proofs also remain the concern of specialists.

"Galileo today," therefore, on the one hand is an image that feeds anticlerical animosity and causes uneasiness for a large number of Catholics and, on the other hand, is the object of research in very diverse directions, but without a real and effective circulation of knowledge. In short, this is a situation that is readily explicable by its historical context and by circumstances of all kinds, but is disastrous in terms of general knowledge.

Is the situation different today? It certainly is in the intellectual world, but much less so on the level of the general public. I propose to explicate what is involved in this curt reply.

First I shall concern myself with the intellectual world. It is true that the considerable development of all intellectual disciplines today makes universality of knowledge impossible and favors the cloistering of specializations, but it is nevertheless true that for about thirty years the Galileo case has represented a privileged meeting ground where the necessity of mastering the fractionation of information has forced itself on all who claim to put forward an opinion or defend a thesis. The publication of the works mentioned at the outset represents a joint and highly significant undertaking. The more the deepening of the various aspects of Galileo's work and history appears indispensable, the more it has been necessary to multiply colloquia, and the less has it been possible for individual researchers to enclose themselves in peace and quiet within the framework of their basic speciality. Certainly this is not a unique phenomenon, but it is in practice rare to meet one like it, and perhaps the Galileo case derives it specialness from the far-distant ecclesiastical trial that puts so many things under examination and resists facile simplifications.

There is therefore a considerable change with respect to the end of the last century in the fact of a circulation of knowledge, and of the results of research concerning Galileo, and an intellectual milieu of great diversity of origin and nationality, a milieu, moreover, much enlarged in number and refined in quality in only fifty years, and still growing.

Is this to say that divergences in interpretation and judgment are tending to fade away in favor of a general consensus? Evidently not, but to the extent that at least a consensus as to the facts makes itself felt — either facts concerning Galileo's history and its context, or facts concerning the analysis of his work — to that extent it is no longer possible to uphold inadequately supported theses and there has been a strengthening of several routes for pursuing analysis. To speak about Galileo today makes sense only in relation to the bifurcations that arise in minds that, in mutual respect, have started out walking a common road.

Pierre Duhem

To do this, as lucidly as possible, it is not without value to compare, in this or that respect, the present situation with the past. It is a fact that at the end of the 19th century there was in France an eminent Catholic physicist, Pierre Duhem, who, to the detriment of his university career, applied himself to the rehabilitation of the Middle Ages and to combating the then very common idea that that period was an extension of the Dark Ages. It is also a fact that by his ten volumes consecrated to the *Système du monde* (up to the dawn of classic science) and elaborated alongside current scientific work, this scientist proved that he was equally a remarkable historian and philosopher as well as an established scientist. Accordingly one should not be astonished to find numerous references to Galileo from his pen.

The characteristic feature of his references to Galileo is the conjunction of two concerns that dovetail perfectly with each other: the concern — natural in a Catholic of that time — to make it understood that the ecclesiastical censure of Galileo was not without serious motivation (contrary to the caricaturing of Duhem's time) and the concern to show clearly the excess of confidence that Galileo had in the absolute truth of his own speculations.

In his *Théorie physique* (1914) Duhem stated that if the judges of the Holy Office had believed Galileo sincere when he distinguished between astronomy, a science of hypotheses, and natural philosophy, a science of the real, they would not have censured him. In his *Essai sur la notion de théorie physique de Platon à Galilée* (1908), the violence of the clash between the two "realisms" in 1633 is related to the fact that, in the half century after the reform of the calendar (1582), the partisans of Copernicus had relegated to oblivion the opinion that astronomical hypotheses are artifices to "save appearances" — that is, able to furnish credible representations of celestial movements such as they are seen by a terrestrial observer. Duhem forcibly expressed the idea that logic — and not only wisdom — was on the side of those who, like Cardinal Bellarmine and Pope Urban VIII, urged Galileo to prudence: the fact in favor of the Copernican theory, that it "saved appearances" better than did the Ptolemaic system, could be an absolute truth only if it were shown that the observed appearances could not be explained otherwise without contradiction. Galileo had believed in the validity of crucial experiments, and Duhem discovered that, at the end of the 19th century and the beginning of the present century, science had refuted this naive belief. Hence a new light was thrown on the debate of former times.

And it is indeed a step forward for the philosophy of science to learn that in physics there is no *experimentum crucis*. In the *Théorie physique* Duhem states:

> The physicist can never submit an isolated hypothesis to experimental check, but only a whole group of hypotheses. When the experiment is in disagreement with his predictions, it teaches him that at least one of the hypotheses making up this group is unacceptable and should be modified, but it does not identify the one that should be changed (p. 284).

Thanks to what the development of science had made evident, Duhem did not hesitate to hold, almost a priori, that the reasons that Galileo could have had for believing in the truth of Copernican cosmology had little value. But, curiously, he maintained that the obstinacy of the scientist in following the path that led to his condemnation had a good result — namely, a regrouping of the explanations of diverse, physical phenomena "with the aid of the same group of postulates formulated in the language of mathematics." He concludes his *Essai*:

> Despite Kepler and Galileo we nowadays believe, with Osiander and Bellarmine, that physical hypotheses are only mathematical artifices designed to save appearances but, thanks to Kepler and Galileo, we demand at the same time that they explain all the phenomena of the inanimate Universe.

Pierre Duhem deserves special mention. At the dawn of our century he renewed investigation of the Galileo case, and did so more seriously than the mathematician Henri Poincaré. In a famous passage in his *La science et l'hypothèse* (1906, p. 141), Poincaré was content to present the choosing of Copernican cosmology as resulting from a judgment of congruence (*convenientia*) between equivalent hypotheses, and because neither the notion of congruence nor that of equivalence was subjected to precise criteria, their application to the debate at the beginning of the 17th century remained very superficial. By comparison, the merit of Duhem's works is clearly that of having put the questionings aroused by the Galileo case into relationship with a skillful analysis of the scientific process. To the extent that these works are today experiencing a return to favor, through various reeditions in the United States and in France, it is no exaggeration to say that their influence is greater after the lapse of half a century. In their time these works did not arouse the curiosity that should have resulted for what concerns us here, as to both the historical sources brought into play and reclarification available from contemporary science.

Alexandre Koyré

This curiosity was aroused in decade preceding World War II. Commenting on the work of Duhem, Alexandre Koyré provoked passionate reactions by minimizing to an extreme the appeal to experimentation, properly so called, that could have been made by Galileo. Partisan defenses of "Galileo, father of experimental science" quickly appeared. Some of them were hardly factual and others only underlined the risk involved in judging the past in the light of present knowledge. This debate is not closed, but one can observe that Duhem saw things in a correct light in attacking the simplistic notion of science based on experimentation in which Galileo had found his confidence in the acquisition of truth. And today many works have shown — better than Duhem suggested — that theory, observation, and experiment were confused in Galileo's work, but that in the matter of measurements and numerical data he used orders of magnitude considered to be significant. This is the hallmark of a sound physics, which modern scientists cannot repudiate. Nevertheless it hardly corresponds to the naive, but still widespread conception among the general public, that science is constructed only on the precise numerical results of investigations of nature.

Pierre Thuillier

In a lengthy and extensively documented study, "Galilée et l'expérimentation," in the French journal *La Recherche* (no. 143, April 1983), Pierre Thuillier emphasizes that study of the Galilean manuscripts kept in Florence has considerably altered the Galilean *status questionis* in the last twenty years, but that the relationship of Galileo with "heuristic" observation as also with "confirmatory" experiments still retains its share of mystery, and that it is impossible to give anything other than a nuanced reply to the question, Did Galileo truly and always engage in experimentation properly so called? Recognition of the necessity of nuances, of limits to our judgments, and this through the very progress of information about Galileo, is certainly a considerable step forward in scholarship.

It is in any case not sufficient to say that the door has been opened to more pertinent research; one shoud also grasp in what way this opening is really new.

Maurice Clavelin

Criticizing Duhem, the historian and philosopher Maurice Clavelin, in his study "Galilée et le refus de l'équivalence des hypothèses," published in 1965, has thought it possible to maintain that Galileo's reasons for rejecting equivalence should be researched within a framework of global and universal physics, whereas the geometric equivalence of the heliocentric and geocentric systems certainly appeared to him to be "unexceptionable." More recently it has been observed that this latter equivalence, far from being "unexceptionable," had already been contradicted by Kepler, and for very positive reasons, the most compelling of them coming from observations of the movements of Venus and Mercury. Doubtless there is here a proof of the precautions that Kepler thought himself obliged to adopt, in the fact that he, inverting the positions of Mercury and Venus relative to that which prevailed in the Ptolemaic system, refrained from comment and left to illustrative figures the task of informing his readers. But it is clear that this inversion was ruinous for the equivalence of these systems, and that up to now one has too easily admitted this equivalence on the pure and simple level of "saving appearances." There is certainly room for researching to what extent Galileo could have been sensitive to the purely mathematical argument of nonequivalence.

In his study, Maurice Clavelin has had the merit of giving a translation of a text of Galileo's published for the first time by Favaro, and which can be dated to 1615 or 1616 (EN, V, 351–63). From the very rigorous discussion concerning the comparison of the cosmological systems to which Galileo restricted himself, there emerges a characteristic phrase:

> In nature all truths *taken together* form a harmonious whole, whereas a resounding dissonance makes itself apparent between false hypotheses and true effects.

The first part of this dictum follows the sense of those interpretations to which Duhem has given the final blow. Science forms itself in the search for an overall harmony, and Galileo would have sufficiently foreseen this to take sides in favor of the Copernican system without possessing sufficient proofs. But it is disastrous to neglect the second part, which leaves all its validity to this or that duly observed partial or local "dissonance." And we still lack a serious and clear inventory of information about Galileo in this respect.

Galileo and Baliani

How can one also fail to recall the correspondence, a little earlier

(January 1614), that Galileo had with the Genoese Gianbattista Baliani (EN, XII, 15–19)? Galileo had sent his works to Baliani, simply saying: "We are studying the same book with the same bases," and it is Baliani who commented significantly in his reply. In the transmitted documents he had found "very beautiful and new opinions proved by very subtle geometric demonstrations without which philosophy does not merit the name of science, but rather that of opinion." And he continued:

> Truly I have always laughed at all philosophical conclusions that do not depend — apart from what we know to be true in the light of faith — either on mathematical demonstrations or infallible experiments. If up to now there have been few who have philosophized in this fashion, this has perhaps happened because there have been few who have a full knowledge of the two sciences in question. Knowing them to be refined in your person, I can do no less than hold you in very high esteem.

Galileo was probably reassured — prior to the 1616 censure of Copernicus — by the agreement of certain thinkers as to the major role of the conjunction of the two disciplines, and surely also by flattering remarks made to him, which is not negligible for the course of history. It is in any case certain that when he wrote, a little later, in "The Assayer" (1624), that the book of nature is written in mathematical characters, this famous declaration had been in preparation for over a decade and does not allow the facile interpretations that have been given up to the present time. There is still much to be done to elucidate what Galileo understood by the book of nature and by the notion of the "characters" in which it is written. It is probable that he distinguished, more than is believed, what is *given* in nature to human reflection and what he, writer and reader at the same time, tried to understand.

The problem thus posed, in view of a serious deepening, would permit a clearer location of the upshot of Duhem's suggestions concerning Galileo's modernism, and the hidden but profound reason for his condemnation. He would have been too ahead of his time in placing all his trust as a scientist in the role of mathematical artifices for the *global* "saving of appearances." Whatever progress can be made in this direction, it is already clear that — contrary to Duhem and other recent commentators — restricting artifices to *local* demonstrations had considerable value for Galileo.

It can be seen how far the case of Galileo has evolved in scholarly circles of our time. But, as I suggested at the outset, there is still the question, What is the impact of this evolution on the general public?

GALILEO AND THE NONSPECIALISTS

The Astonishing Survival of Myths

Echec à la science — *la survivance des mythes chez les Français* (Paris, Nouvelles Editions Rationalistes, 1981) gives the results of a poll conducted by a very well-known public opinion survey institute, with the cooperation of a center for space studies. To the question, "Does the sun go around the earth?," 37% of respondents answered "true." After analysis of groupings according to ages, professions, and the like, pollsters concluded that more than a third of the population of France is still living with a pre-Copernican vision. Doubtless such an opinion survey must be accepted with many reservations, because of how exactly the question was put to the respondents, and there is always the possibility that answers were sometimes misunderstood. Nevertheless the results square with other findings that reveal profound ignorance in the general public with regard to elementary matters of science and astronomy. It seems safe to estimate that 25% of our contemporaries have not reflected on the distinction between appearances and reality in connection with the movement of the sun, which everyone observes daily; and what is more serious, the rating is still 10–20% for those who have received secondary or higher education ("scientists" or "technicians" being happily the least guilty of the error). Profession or not of a religion, taken into account by the pollsters, had no overall effect on the results. It is certain that this poll gives food for thought for dispassionate reflection. Depite the abundance of information — especially on the theme of space conquest, which, as is well known is "page-one" news for the media — and despite obligatory education, myths survive.

IGNORANCE AT THE UNIVERSITY LEVEL

For my part I once composed and analyzed the results of a limited survey, which one of my colleagues, a university professor of mathematics, was kind enough to carry out among his students. They were asked to fill in a questionnaire centered on the Galileo case, and they were requested to complete it on the spot, in a short time, and without communicating between themselves — all of which are useful precautions for sincerity, and were gracefully accepted by the students. Although it concerned a sample not conforming to the customary norms of public opinion institutes, this very limited survey confirmed that 15% were not able to say why Galileo had been condemned; 30% did not know which movement of the earth (rotation about the sun, or spin on its own axis) had been leveled as a reproach against Galileo, and more to the point, did not connect the question with preceding debates (Copernicus). Some thought that Galileo had been burnt at the stake; 20% thought that he had ended his days in a prison of the Inquisition, and the great majority were of the opinion that this old piece of history had no interest today.

These are facts that, at the end of an essay on "Galileo Today," can only arouse uneasiness. The chasm between expert knowledge and general knowledge in this matter is particularly large. It is a chasm that does not affect only the church. It calls for a uniting of effort to dispel what the authors of the poll published by Nouvelles Editions Rational-istes do not hesitate to call "the perverse effect" of the technical development of our modern society.

PART FOUR

GALILEO AND SCIENTIFIC SCHOLARSHIP

TODAY

7

Galileo and Modern Science

Ian Campbell

The purpose of this paper is to trace out some of the enduring influences of Galileo on the activity of contemporary science.

On the one hand we find that Galileo is often called the "father of physics," and less frequently the "first modern physicist."[1] On the other hand, despite intense research on the subject and the admitted greatness of Galileo, it has been said that "on the question of what precisely his contribution was, and wherein essentially his greatness lay, there seems to be no unanimity."[2]

One reason for the differing opinions is that with Galileo a coherent physical science and its general methods largely began. It is still difficult for physics to define its nature or the essence of its methods, and therefore equally difficult for the philosopher-historian to discuss the birth of these things in the work of their greatest originator. In addition it is not easy to sort out the relationships of Galileo with the physics and philosophy that preceded and surrounded him, and thus equally difficult to assess his originality.

At the outset let me put down a series of propositions about the most outstanding contributions of Galileo to modern physics, propositions among those which have most often met with general assent. Then I can proceed to discuss some of them.

Galileo's method was most extensively displayed in his work in

1. G. Bernardini, "Galileo's Influence in Modern Society," in *Homage to Galileo*, M. F. Kaplon, ed. (Cambridge, Mass., M.I.T. Press, 1965).
2. E. J. Dijksterhuis, "La mécanisation de l'image du monde," cited by E. W. Strong, "Metaphysics and the Scientific Method in Galileo's Work," in *Galileo: Man of Science*, E. McMullin, ed. (New York, Basic Books, 1967), pp. 333–34.

dynamics. In part he replaced the Aristotelian concept of movement by one that could be cast in mathematical terms so as to be open to rigorous development and experimental investigation. In this approach he showed masterful examples of abstraction, coupled with subsequent return to the world of real things through experiment. In so doing he provided modern physics with one of its most distinctive methods.

Galileo was unafraid to pass beyond the realm of "common sense" and everyday observations so familiar to Aristotelian and Scholastic thought. Since his time physics has strengthened its trust in a methodology that follows his path. This has allowed contemporary physics to pass confidently from the "common sense" macro-world to the realms of micro-events, singularities, and curved space-time, and to conjectures about higher dimensions, and similar ideas.

In his work Galileo gave many examples of the correct formulation of a problem as the first step in a physical advance. In him the formulation has a certain remarkable intuitive quality, which allows the transition from a perception of a thing or event to a representation of it capable of being mathematically phrased. In his work in mechanics the initial "moment of experience" of a phenomenon came to have a different meaning from that which it had in Aristotelian science.

The great advances in physics made by Galileo came about partly because he had a keen conception of the unity of physical truth throughout the universe. For him cosmological physics and terrestrial physics rested on the same foundation, even though he could not fully unify his methods over the two domains. Furthermore he partly replaced certain *qualitative* differentiations of Aristotelian-Scholastic space by more *quantitative* differentiations. As a result Galilean space lent itself more readily to mathematical concepts of local motion. In the work of Galileo there is a greater uniformity in the idea of movement because space largely ceases to be made up of "natural" and "unnatural" places for bodies, and because the qualitative differences between celestial and terrestrial spaces have been abolished. With a more general view of movement it becomes possible to distinguish with greater precision the factors that affect local motion.

All these things endure in the general texture of modern physics. They are only a few aspects of the greatness of Galileo. If his achievements were limited only to his actual physical and astronomical discoveries, then great though these discoveries are, his stature would be much reduced.

The Mathematics Needed for Galileo's Physics

Some of Galileo's predecessors were well aware of the cardinal importance of mathematics for physics.[3] Behind much of this awareness lay a kind of Neoplatonist form-emanation theory, in which species in the real world were multiplied from mathematical forms and the "first form" was the "common corporeity" of things. Kepler had a view of ascending perfections of numbers and shapes that colored his earlier thinking. Again and again he sought to explain the relationships between the radii of planetary orbits, first by fitting equilateral triangles inside circles, then by fitting squares and hexagons, and finally by fitting the so-called regular solids of the mathematicians. When he finally obtained a fairly workable scheme, it was only by chance, and he had to make many adjustments to the "perfections" to fit the facts. Toward the end of his career, however, Kepler began to move away from a "mathematics of perfections" to a more useful mathematics.

Galileo's approach to the mathematics he needed for mechanics differed radically from a mathematical method based on a scale of nobility. He consciously dispensed with mathematical perfections:

> For my own part, never having read the pedigrees and patents of nobility of shapes, I do not know which of them are more and which are less noble, nor do I know their rank in perfection. I believe that in a way all shapes are ancient and noble; or, to put it better, that none of them are noble and perfect, or ignoble and imperfect, except in so far as for building walls the square shape is more perfect than the circular, and for wagon wheels the circle is more perfect than the triangle.[4]

Perfection of mathematical forms based on a supposed ascent to the divine, or on an emanation of species multiplying forms, is here replaced by *fitness* for the solution of problems in circumscribed areas of the world. The thing that Galileo was after was to gain the *rigor* of mathematics for mechanics. This is of course a seminal thought for the whole of modern theoretical physics. It carries forward the kind of joy felt in mathematics by Leonardo da Vinci, who found mathematics of inestimable value in the works of military and other technology.[5]

For modern physics the importance of the point to which we have now come can hardly be overestimated. Part of the greatness of Galileo lies in the *way* in which he used mathematics, the *philosophical setting* in

3. A. C. Crombie, *Robert Grosseteste and the Origins of Experimental Science* (Oxford, Clarendon Press, 1953), "Mathematical Physics," chap. 5, pp. 143–45.

4. Galileo, "The Assayer," in Stillman Drake, *Discoveries and Opinions of Galileo* (New York, Doubleday Anchor Books, 1957), p. 263.

5. Ernest Cassirer, "Mathematical Mysticism and Mathematical Science," in McMullin, *Galileo*, p. 347; see E. W. Strong, *Procedures and Metaphysics* (1936).

which he placed this use in his own mind, and the connection he established between *mathematical representation and experiment.*

Perception and Representation in the Moment of Experience

Physics deals with *perceived* things or events. Great abstracter and physical theorist though he was, Galileo did not hold to a view that allows science to find its truth *only* in mathematical forms or relationships. The real world is there with all its complexity, even in small things:

> It always seems to me extreme rashness on the part of some when they want to make human abilities the measure of what nature can do. On the contrary, there is not a single effect in nature, even the least that exists, such that the most ingenious theorists can arrive at a complete understanding of it. This vain presumption of understanding everything can have no other basis than never understanding anything.[6]

Here in embryo is the now widely accepted view of physical truth as endlessly approximating to an external and rich reality by virtue of the method that physics comes to possess. One consequence is that, because of the richness of reality, physics is constantly prepared to have even its most comprehensive and integrated theories replaced in a short interval of time. If this were not true we could not even begin to pay proper homage to Galileo. From Galileo's work there came, among many other things, two great kinematic principles: the first is a concept of inertia, whereby a body continues at rest or uniform motion in the absence of any impressed force; the second is that the effects of forces in altering the motion of a body do not depend on the "amount of motion" that the body was already acquired. A relatively undeveloped notion of force, among other things, prevented Galileo from enunciating these principles in the exact form in which they are known to us today. Nevertheless his work made these great generalizations possible for Newton, and thus entered into the great Newtonian system. For all that, the best of Newtonian physics is now known to be a limiting case of a more developed mechanics expounded in Einstein's theory of special relativity and in quantum theory. The concept of force is no longer applicable in areas of physics such as quantum mechanics. Physicists are aware that this ongoing "revolutionizing" must be the case. In part, at least, this awareness stems from Galileo's maintaining that the richness of even the smallest natural effects constantly outstrips our theoretical comprehension of them.

---

6. Quoted by Bernardini, "Galileo's Influence," p. 30.

After perception of the thing, after initial observations, there comes the *representation* of it in a manner that leaves it susceptible to mathematical treatment. Isolated groups in Scholastic science had given examples of this in the 14th century. The Merton group at Oxford (Haytesbury, Swineshead, Dumbleton) had treated rectilinear motion in such a way as to extract the so-called Mertonian mean-speed law.[7] This law gave a way of computing the distance traveled by a body starting from rest and then receiving equal increments of velocity in equal intervals of time (i.e., undergoing uniform acceleration) (see Fig. 1). When this average velocity is multiplied by the time of transit, the total distance traversed is obtained. The Merton group used an arithmetical proof, but Orêsme and Giovanni di Casali adopted a more geometrical approach (see note 7).

In physics we not infrequently meet a physical magnitude that is extended in space or time, such as the temperature along a metal bar heated at one end, or the velocity of an accelerated body as time progresses. In 14th-century physics such cases were sometimes represented by a right triangle (see note 7). The base represented the space or time extension. The altitude above a given base point corresponded to the intensity of the physical magnitude at that point. The area of the triangle was regarded as representing the summation of the physical magnitude corresponding to the array of space points or time instants along the base. Such a device readily yields the Merton mean-speed law if the base represents time and the altitude the speed the body has acquired, and the triangle area represents the speed-time summation, or total distance traveled. This case serves as a very clear example of a way of applying mathematics to physics, which was to become systematic in the work of Galileo. The vital link is to conceive a representation of the physical phenomena — here speed and time — in such a way as to allow a mathematical treatment.[8]

The Merton mean-speed law was an important finding. We shall later see that from it one can directly obtain Galileo's famous law that bodies starting from rest and undergoing free fall or descent down inclined planes will traverse distances proportional to the square of the transit

---

7. E. A. Moody, "Galileo and his Precursors," in *Galileo Reappraised*, C. L. Golino ed. (University of California Press, 1960), p. 35; M. Clagett, *The Science of Mechanics in the Middle Ages* (University of Wisconsin Press, 1959). The important work by W. A. Wallace, "Galileo Galilei and the *Doctores Parisienses*," in *New Perspectives on Galileo* (Dordrecht and Hingham, Mass., D. Reidel Publ. Co., 1978), shows the great care that must be taken in researching the relationship between Galileo and the trends that preceded and surrounded him, a most valuable field for further research.

8. D. Dubarle, "Galileo's Methodology of Natural Science," in McMullin, *Galileo*, pp. 229–303.

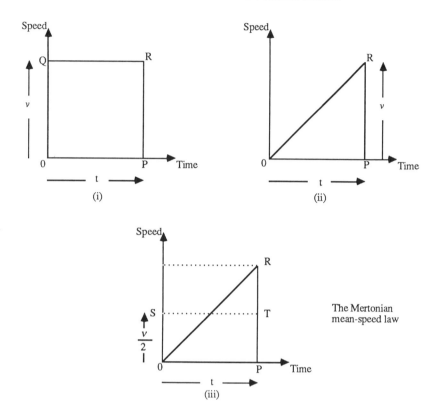

Fig. 1. A late Scholastic approach to the calculation of distances traversed by moving bodies. (i) A body traveling at constant speed "v" for a time "t" travels a distance vt, and this equals the area of the rectangle OPRQ. (ii) A body that starts from rest and increases its speed by equal amounts in successive equal lapses of time (uniform acceleration) has its speed-time graph rising linearly to its final speed v at R. (iii) The distance traversed by the uniformly accelerated body can be calculated by using the concept of its average speed $v/2$, represented by the horizontal dash line ST. The distance gone is then obtained by multiplying the average speed by the time, and this product is given by the area of the rectangle OPTS, which equals the area of the triangle OPR.

time. With Galileo this became part of a new unified kinematics armed with a new approach to physical reality. With the Merton group the mean-speed law remained bound within an erroneous Aristotelian concept of motion. Scattered groups of Scholastics had made considerable advances in mathematicizing physics. They even had a conscious aim of bringing the logical rigor of mathematics into reasoning about physical things. Roger Bacon wrote: "All categories depend on a knowledge of quantity, concerning which mathematics treats, and therefore the whole excellence of logic depends on mathematics."[9] Nevertheless such groups made only sporadic progress. It remained to Galileo to develop the perception-representation-mathematicization relationship into a general method with a fairly coherent philosophy, and this endures as one of his greatest gifts to modern science.

Galileo's work shows outstanding instances of the bold transition from perceived object to mathematicizable representation. Before him the Copernican heliocentric system had already provided an outstanding example. Immediate perception of the sun and the stars yields a naturally geocentric picture. The great transition is made when the reference system, conceived in some geometric way, is transferred as a *thought* representation to the sun, and then the mathematical consequences are fully worked out and *compared with observation*. A second example from Galileo's own work is his discovery of what is now called Galilean relativity. Answering the "Aristotelian" objection against earth-movement — that bodies dropped from a height would be left behind by the earth during their fall and would therefore have to follow a curved path of descent — Galileo affirmed, in an outstanding thought experiment, that a stone dropped from the masthead of a moving ship would hit the deck at a point vertically below the masthead. In this case the geometric representation that had to form itself in his mind, at least to some extent, was that of two frames of reference, one on the moving ship, the other on land. In the land frame of reference the stone and ship both had an equal forward velocity, and free fall at right angles to the stone's forward velocity had no effect on the latter. He was discovering the principle of composition of vectors (velocity being a directed physical quantity or vector), and also the general fact that the laws of physics remain invariant in a reference frame that is moving at constant velocity.[10] The advent of Cartesian reference axes and more sophisticated modern thought lets us develop our understanding of the nature of such frames, nowadays called inertial frames. Clear thinking about the relationships between such frames was a conceptual necessity for Einstein and others in the work leading to the theory of special relativity.

An instance of abstractive representation that proved very fertile for Galileo was his study of the pendulum. For Aristotelian science a heavy body tended to descend from an "unnatural" place (position of eleva-

---

9. *Opus Maius*, c.2 i, ed. Bridges, p. 103.
10. Galileo, *Dialogue Concerning the Two Chief World Systems*, Stillmen Drake, trans. (University of California Press, 1962), pp. 186ff.

tion) to a "more natural" place (lower position). A pendulum was constrained by its cord or chain so that it was forced to overshoot the natural place and made to reascend, until by a progressive damping of its motion it eventually reached its most natural position (of rest).

Galileo abstracted from all such considerations, and formed a representation of an "ideal pendulum" moving in a space free from naturality or unnaturality. This involves thinking about a bob attached to a "massless" string. The string is further ideal in that we neglect forces of friction, or "resistances," which would arise in it if different parts of the string had different times of oscillation (periods). In this representation the concepts of inertia and oscillating motion are involved.

Prior to Galileo considerable advances had been made in understanding these things. In the 14th century Buridan had developed a modification of the "impetus" theory, according to which a body receives from the agent launching it an impressed power.[11] In the case of a body thrown upward this power imparts an ability allowing it to ascend until progressive weakening of the power by gravity overcomes it and descent commences. In this form the impetus theory bespeaks an inertial principle, assigning to resistive tendencies (air resistance and gravity) the contrary factors that diminish the impressed virtue.

Buridan had also considered the oscillation of a plucked and taut string. Impetus or impressed virtue is supplied when the string is plucked, and is then weakened as the string is moved against the "resistance" of its tension; tension sends the string back, reimparting impetus, which builds up as the string returns to its midpoint, and so on. The bearing on the pendulum is obvious. Indeed Orêsme had sketched out the bearing of this theory on a stone swinging on a cord.

Galileo brought such partial findings into a more mature and integrated system of dynamics, in which the inertial principle is clearly related to free fall and to the horizontal motion of a body on a frictionless plane. From his work a systematic dynamics begins.

A last example of the outstanding intuitive representation, from the many that could be cited, was that of the relationship between the velocity of a body and the force or forces acting on it. Aristotelian physics rested on the immediate perception that if someone is pushing a cart at constant velocity on a level surface, for example, and then desists, the cart will sooner or later come to a stop. This was enough to allow the Aristotelians to affirm that the application of a constant force

11. An excellent discussion of this work with references to Galileo is to be found in E. M. Rodgers, *Physics for the Enquiring Mind: The Methods, Nature, and Philosophy of Physical Science* (Princeton Universtiy Press, 1960), chap. 19.

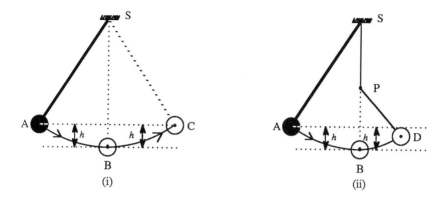

Fig. 2. The descent and ascent of a frictionless pendulum on an inextensible cord. (i) When the pendulum bob is released at A, it traverses the arc of a circle, passing through its lowest point B and then rising to the point C. The height "h," through which the pendulum bob descends from A to B, equals the height to which it ascends from B to C. (ii) A horizontal pin P is placed to intercept the cord as the pendulum swings through its lowest point B; the bob now travels along the arc of a smaller circle of radius PB. But once again the height of descent from A to B equals the height of ascent from B to D. This is true no matter how far pin P is placed below the support S. Galileo concluded that for bodies moving under frictionless conditions the height of ascent will always equal the height of descent.

to a body results in constant velocity. The difference between the Aristotelian "moment of experience" and the Galilean emerges very clearly in this instance. This difference lies in an inadequate induction on the part of the Aristotelians, a failure to think out the best representation of what is perceived. Galileo moved away from the bare fact of perception and recognized the role of the force of resistance from the surface of the earth and from the medium through which the body is being pushed. Some kind of picture of the interaction of oppositely directed forces is needed here. If the cart moves at constant velocity, then it is because the impelling force is being exactly balanced by the resistive forces so that no *net* force acts on it. By considering thought experiments on the rolling of a ball on an inclined plane with a variable angle of tilt, and combining these with the results of an actual experiment in which the string of a released pendulum encounters a pin in its path, Galileo was able to make his famous statement that in the absence of friction a body moving on an infinite horizontal plane would continue its state of rectilinear motion forever (see Fig. 2).[12]

12. "Dialogues Concerning Two New Sciences," beginning of the 4th day.

As Dominique Dubarle has written:

> The dynamics of Aristotle *is*, as has often been pointed out, quite close to the everyday experience we have, ever since our very first mechanical relationhips with reality. Nevertheless a whole multitude of facts cannot be brought under it. Throughout the three centuries that separate us from Galileo, scientists have reflected about this point more and more seriously. By now it has become quite clear that to transpose into abstract representations even the most obvious features of mechanical experience will not furnish us with a schema which is at the same time simple and general. It is necessary, therefore, to make an analysis of the fact of perception itself, before being able to grasp that in it which the representation will retain, not any more in a simple fashion, but by evoking different factors such as, on the one hand, the interplay of kinetic impulses, and on the other hand, that of dynamic forces and resistances of the environment. Abstract thought will therefore crystallize in intuition the true elements of science. It will no longer be sufficient to construct pure representations of movement. It will be necessary to know how to *think* in this way and to do that one will have to *learn* to think that which is to be represented.[13]

Some General Consequences of Galileo's Dynamics

Tracing the consequences of Galileo's mechanics for the science that followed him, we become aware of great intellectual stimuli. The pin-and-pendulum experiment mentioned above gave good support for another idea. A body released from a certain height, and able to follow a relatively frictionless descent path and then an ascent path, would ascend on the second path to a height equal to that from which it had been released. Galileo coupled this idea with the following "thought experiment" (see Fig. 3). Imagine a frictionless inclined plane A joined to a similar plane B, the angle of tilt of the latter being variable. If a ball is released on A, it should climb on B until it has reached a height equal to that from which it was released, and this should be true for any angle of tilt of B. Now imagine that in successive runs the tilt of B is progressively reduced. This will mean that in order to gain the same height the ball will have to travel greater and greater distances along the B slope. Ultimately, when B becomes horizontal, the ball should roll on forever.

Galileo wrote his famous passage:

> I conceive of a body launched on a horizontal plane, and by an effort of thought I assume all impediment to be removed. It is clear from what has been already said that its movement on the plane will be uniform and perpetual if the plane extends indefinitely.[14]

13. Dubarle, "Galileo's Methodology," pp. 302–3.
14. Galileo "On local motion," 3rd and 4th days of "Discourses Concerning the Two New Sciences."

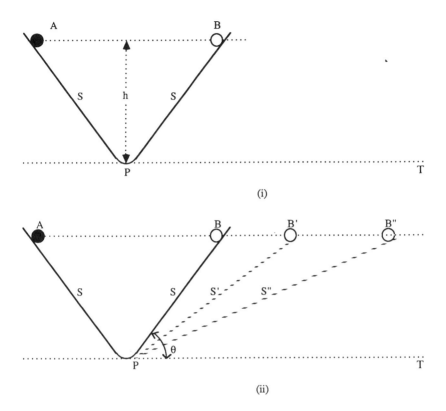

Fig. 3. A Galilean "thought experiment" on the rolling of bodies on frictionless surfaces. (i) the pin-and-pendulum experiment of Fig. 2. predicts that a ball released at A
on a frictionless surface S will climb to B, the height of ascent "h" above the base plane
PT being equal to the height of descent from A. (ii) If the angle of inclination θ of S
relative to the base plane is progressively reduced as in surfaces S' and S", then thc ball
will have to roll increasing distances PB, PB', PB", etc., to climb to the same height "h."
Galileo concluded that, ultimately, if θ were reduced to zero, the ball would continue
its rectilinear motion along an infinite horizontal plane forever.

This was later to be generalized by Newton as his first law of motion,
one of the cornerstones of the Newtonian system: "Every body continues in its state of rest or uniform motion in a right line unless it is
compelled to change that state by forces impressed upon it."[15]
In his general method Newton laid great stress on experimental
procedure as a foundation for a valid physical hypothesis.[16] This line of

15. Newton, *Principia*, book 1, "Axioms or Laws of Motion," Law 1.
16. Newton, letter to Oldenburg (July 1672), *Opera Omnia*, IV, pp. 320–21; see also

thought was subsequently developed into an "operationalist" approach to physical truth, a line of thought represented in the work of Mach, Poincaré, Duhem, and Einstein, until it became an articulate operationalism in the views of Bridgman, who wrote:

> If by convention we agree to use only those concepts in describing physical situations to which we can give a meaning in terms of physical operations, then we are sure there will never be need to retract anything.[17]

Hanson has discussed the consequences of trying to apply such an operationalist approach to Galileo's statement concerning the perpetual and constant rectilinear motion of a body moving on an infinite force-free plane.[18] To check rectilinearity of motion *operationally* we must have an *actual* (not imaginary), small but mass-possessing particle as the origin of our coordinate system, from which we lay out our coordinate line in order to check the nature of the motion. But as soon as our moving body appears, there must be a force of gravitational attraction between it and the coordinate zero-point anchor-particle. The "force-free" condition in Galileo's statement is thus vitiated at the outset. It would seem that either we must banish the law of universal gravitation or Galileo's formulation appears as an ideal but counterfactual statement. Then again if we wish to check the constancy of the motion, we must introduce a real measuring rod and a clock, which render the force-free situation even more impossible. "How can this ideal line be seen? How sad! There is nothing, absolutely nothing, that ever moves along this ideal line."[19]

Of course we are well aware that engineers successfully design structures using a geometry of circles and lines, though perfect circles and straight lines are never observed by us in nature. We take the mathematical concepts as limiting and ideal cases from which practical cases deviate. Indeed deviation from the limiting case yields valuable information about the practical case. This also operates in connection with Galileo's formulation. Although we have no operational procedure for directly checking the formulation itself, we can at least operationally study progressive deviations from it. If we observe two moving bodies,

continuation

Newton's letters to Cotes (London, 1713), in J. Edleston, *Correspondence of Sir Issac Newton and Prof. Cotes*, pp. 154–57.

17. P. W. Bridgman, *The Nature of Physical Theory* (Princeton University Press, 1936), p. 10.

18. N. R. Hanson, "Galileo's Real Discoveries in Dynamics," in Kaplon, *Homage* (note 1 above,) pp. 54–63.

19. E. F. Taylor and J. A. Wheeler, *Spacetime Physics* (San Francisco, W. H. Freeman and Co., 1963), p. 182.

one with greater impressed force beginning to act on it so as to oppose the motion, and the other with less, then Galileo's statement predicts that the body experiencing less force will approximate more closely that constant and perpetual motion in which it would have covered an infinite distance in an infinite time.

This last sentence brings us to the threshold of one of the great areas of debate that Galileo's work bequeaths to us in contemporary physics and its philosophy. We can approach the problem by asking how we can meaningfully assert of one body that it will travel "nearer to infinity" than another? Galileo's mechanics is full of processions to the *limit*, to frictionless surfaces, to infinite planes, to instants of time, to near-punctiform "mobiles," to rectilinearity, to constant acceleration. The relationship between such an approach and an operationalist physics has remained a profound puzzle to this day. Sometimes this puzzle bears on our most fundamental physical concepts. What is the bearing on our notion of space, for example? Returning to our operationalist method of verifying the "constancy of the motion," we would have to move our measuring rod to different regions of space to see if segments of the line traversed by the body in equal times are equal. But this presupposes that moving our rod from one region of space to another does not alter it.[20] Yet our rod experiences a force at least from the small anchor-particle that serves as the origin of our coordinate, and this force will be different from one space region to another.

In thinking about Galileo's formulation in modern terms, we are having to distinguish between an operationalist space, and a "more absolute" space. In the more absolute spaces which we need in order to understand Galileo's statement, we take it as an agreed property of rods (a convention) that they will not alter from one space region to another. Is the necessity for an absolute space implicit in Galilean-Newtonian mechanics, despite contemporary assertion to the contrary? The difference between absolute space and locally differing, matter-influenced space is one of the distinctions that has emerged between Newtonian and Einsteinian physics. Hindsight shows this distinction as perhaps already implicit in Galileo's work.

Mathematico-Physical Hypothesis and the Verification or Falsification Procedure in the Physics of Galileo

When we consider all this, something more of the greatness of Galileo becomes apparent. It is not that we are simply tracing out physical

20. Hanson, "Real Discoveries," p. 61.

discoveries whose ongoing threads have become woven into much subsequent physics. This achievement could be attributed to many physicists. Galileo managed to avoid the extremes of a purely abstract approach to physics and a strictly operational approach. He sought the rigor of mathematics, and an intuitive initial representation that could be mathematicized. Yet the abstract and ideal formulations that result should, wherever possible, be observationally or operationally verified or falsified. The abstract propositions are ordered to the reality of nature. The mathematicized representation is an initial feature; a deduced, correlated, and integrated hypothesis is an intermediary development; but neither of these is an ultimate.

Much has been written on Galileo as the great experimentalist, whose experimentalism was the "decisive step" in his break with Aristotelian science. Some writers have classified him as essentially an empiricist; other have seen him as rather reluctant in his appeal to experiment. It is not my purpose to enter into this complex debate, even if I had space to do so.[21] Galileo was conscious of the necessity and power of *authentic* abstraction in yielding the tractable representation and the testable, deduced hypothesis:

> The mathematical scientist, when he wants to recognize in the concrete the effects which he has proved in the abstract, must deduct the material hindrances. And if he is able to do so, I assure you that things are no less in agreement than are mathematical computations.[22]

> Of these accidents of weight, of velocity, of figure, infinite in number, it is not possible to give any exact description. Hence, in order to handle this matter in a scientific way, it is necessary to cut loose from these difficulties; having discovered and demonstrated the theorems in the case of no resistance, one must apply them with such limitations as experience will teach.[23]

The warning that application of hypothesis must stay within the "operational" limits of experience immediately raises the question of the necessity of "corrections" when parameters are altered, a fact of life so familiar in modern physics:

> These conclusions, proved in the abstract, will be different when applied to

21. The following works give summaries of the evidence for the various views of Galileo's status as an experimenter. Dubarle, "Galileo's Methodology"; Strong, "Metaphysics"; idem, "Galileo on Measurement," in Kaplon, *Homage*; Rodgers, *Physics*; T. B. Settle, "Galileo's Use of Experiment as Tool of Investigation," in McMullin, *Galileo*; W. L. Wilson, "Galileo's Scientific Method: A Reexamination," in *New Perspective on Galileo*, R. E. Butts and J. C. Pitt, eds. (Dordrecht and Hingham Mass., 1978); J. Losee, *A Historical Introduction to the Philosophy of Science* (Oxford University Press, 1972), pp. 55–58.

22. *Dialogo*, in the English translation by Stillman Drake, pp. 207–8 (= EN, VII, 234).

23. Ibid., pp. 252–53 (= EN, VIII, 276).

the concrete. . . . When we wish to apply our proven conclusions to distances which, though finite, are very large, we must find out, on the basis of demonstrated truth, what correction is to be made for the fact that our distance from the center of the earth is not really infinite, but merely very great by comparison with the small dimensions of the apparatus.[24]

Galileo's whole mathematical physics is essentially tied to physical reality: the physicist must "find a definition best fitting natural phenomena. . . . We have decided to consider the phenomena of bodies falling with an accelaration such as actually occurs in nature, and to make this definition of accelerated motion exhibit the essential features of observed accelerated motions."[25]

Although the physicist is thus ultimately tied to physical reality and to the empirical, the above passages are not operationalist. There is a power in the mathematicized representation and in mathematical reasoning that imparts an intellectual momentum and even a kind of necessity to the theoretical process, once it has begun: "The knowledge of a single fact through a discovery of its causes prepares the mind to understand and ascertain other facts without need of recourse to experiment."[26]

According to Galileo part of the power of mathematicized representation, feeding into mathematical deduction, lies in an inherent simplicity of law in nature:

> In all its works, nature makes use of the simplest and easiest means. When I notice that a stone falling from rest acquires successive increments of velocity, why should I not hold that these increments must occur according to the formula which is simplest and which suggests itself before all others?[27]

True empiricism is not subservience to common sense and a relatively crude "moment of experience," but is based on an element of simplicity in reality itself. The quest for unification and postulatory simplification lies at the heart of contemporary theoretical physics.

The preceding paragraphs of this section depict a balance between necessary chains of mathematical reasoning on the one hand and the need to terminate these in accord with experimental facts. But even in Galileo's mechanics this balance is by no means always clear. We are, after all, in one sense dealing with the influence upon modern science of a man forging methods, and not simply with a cut-and-dried methodological residue that he has bequeathed to us.

24. Ibid., pp. 251–53 (= EN, VIII, 270–71).
25. Ibid., p. 160 (= EN, VIII, 197).
26. *Discourses on Two New Sciences*, H. Crew and A. de Salvio, trans. (New York, Dover, 1914), p. 276.
27. See note 14, above.

Mechanics provided the best ground for Galileo's advancement of mathematical physics. It is when we pass on to his physical inquiries in nonkinematical domains and above all to his astronomy that we most clearly see limitations of the method described in the previous sections. There emerges a need to use a different method in these fields of scientific inquiry.

Empirical Methods and Logical Reasoning in Galileo's Astronomy and Physics

If we simply recount Galileo's discoveries in astronomy, we appreciate part of the enormous debt owed to him by modern science. Observation by astronomical telescope, appreciation of cosmic vastness, discovery of Jupiter's satellites (a kind of mini-planetary system), dynamic sunspots, the rugged moonscape — all these profoundly affected our subsequent scholarship.

In pre-Galilean astronomy a long controversy had unfolded as to whether astronomic hypotheses were simply convenient mathematical devices and nothing more, or whether they conformed to some physical reality.[28] All such hypotheses — Ptolemaic, Aristotelian, or Copernican — had to account for the actually observed motions of the sun, the planets, and the stars ("saving the appearances"). Copernicus had criticized the form of the Ptolemaic theory current in his day on the grounds that even though it saved the appearances to a large degree, *it contradicted fundamental physical principles*:

> Surely the ones who devise eccentricity, though to a large extent they may seem to have freed certain motions with consistent numbers by means of the eccentricity idea, still they permit other [things] which seem to disagree with the prime principles about the equality of motion.[29]

Such a statement makes it clear that Copernicus expected an astronomical theory to do more than simply save the appearances: *it must reflect a physical reality*. Kepler wrote in the same vein:

> [Astronomy] is a part of physics that inquires into the causes of things and occurrences, with the movements of celestial bodies being among its subjects, and which has as its one aim the tracing out of the conformation of the parts to the entire world structure.[30]

28. For an excellent summary of this debate, including the views of Galileo, see R. M. Blake, "Hypothesis among Renaissance Astronomers," in *Theories of Scientific Method*, E. H. Madden, ed. (Seattle, University of Washington Press, 1960).
29. *De revolutionibus orbium caelestium libri sex*, book 5.
30. *Opera Omnia*, VI, 119.

In turn Galileo adopted a clearly realistic approach to astronomical hypotheses:

> As to method the cosmographer is accustomed to proceed in his investigations by four means, the first of which comprises the appearances, otherwise termed phenomena, and these are nothing but the observations of sense. . . . In the second place come the hypotheses, and these are certain suppositions concerning the structure of the celestial spheres, and such as correspond to the appearances. . . . There follow, then, in the third place, geometrical demonstrations, in which, by means of the properties of circles and straight lines, are demonstrated the particular accidents that follow from the hypotheses. And, finally, what has been demonstrated by means of lines is then by arithmetical calculation reduced and distributed into tables, from which we can without difficulty and at our pleasure find again the disposition of the heavenly bodies at any moment of time.[31]

At first sight this seems to recall the sequence: perception-mathematicized representation-mathematical deduction-testing of predictions, discussed earlier in connection with Galileo's mechanics. But the only real instance of this sequence, in its pure form, encountered by Galileo in his astronomy was that already raised by the debate between the Copernican and Ptolemaic systems. It later fell to Newton to use such a sequence on a grand scale to *account* for the movements of the planets around the sun. Newton accomplished this after incorporating some of Galileo's kinematic findings into a comprehensive mechanics, and after postulating his own law of universal gravitation. But Galileo had to make use of a different method in his own astronomical studies. In the upshot this served to broaden his bequest to modern science. One should not make a fetish of the representations proper to mathematical physics.

Despite his methodological difficulties in astronomy, Galileo adhered firmly to his realist view of the subject and of the unity of cosmological and physical truth. In his opinion physical truth has such a priority in cosmology that one must even admit the possibility of purely mathematical devices that do save the appearances (Ptolemaic system) but which have no merit beyond a computational one. They do not accord with our understanding of physics and thus lack the vital element of realism, however limited that element of our knowledge may be at a given moment.

On the subject of Ptolemaic eccentrics, deferents, and such like, Galileo wrote:

> These, however, are merely assumed by mathematical astronomers in order to facilitate their calculations. They are not retained by philosophical

---

31. "Trattato della sfera ovvero cosmografia," in EN, II, 211–12.

astronomers who, going beyond the demand that they somehow save the appearances, seek to investigate the true constitution of the universe — the most important and most admirable problem that there is. For such a constitution exists; it is unique, true, real, and could not possibly be otherwise; and the greatness and nobility of this problem entitle it to be placed foremost among all questions capable of theoretical solution.[32]

The maintaining of this view, against all kinds of difficulties and oppositions, was indispensable for the birth of modern physical cosmology.

In his astronomy Galileo had to give first place to direct observational results, often gained by use of his telescopes. The "Letters on Sunspots," for example, contain reasonings that are, wherever possible, closely related to immediate observation. Consequently, in the astronomical writings of Galileo we may expect an affirmation of the great importance of the inductive moment of the inductive-deductive method advocated by Aristotle. The latter had stressed the primacy of observation and the moment of experience in the chain of scientific efforts, and we do indeed find Galileo taking this up:

> So when he [Aristotle] argued the immutability of the heavens from the fact that no alteration had been seen in them during all the ages, it may be believed that had his eyes shown him what is now evident to us, he would have adopted the very opinion to which we are led by these remarkable discoveries. . . . Hence they will philosophize better who give assent to propositions that depend upon manifest observations, than those who persist in opinions repugnant to the senses and supported only by probable reasons.[33]

The phrase "manifest observations" is interesting. In astronomy it was harder to get away from the brute or manifest fact to achieve a representation than it had been in mechanics. Yet Galileo had to do so, otherwise there remained a subservience to a piling of facts upon facts, accompanied by ad hoc theorizing. The alchemists accumulated masses of facts and manifest observations, but little remains of their science today. Galileo had to reason from the observed facts without the rigor of mathematical demonstrations. This was not only largely true in his astronomy but was sometimes the case in those parts of his physics in which he could not form the requisite mathematicizable representation. An example of such a situation was the problem of the relationship between liquid surfaces and bodies floating on them.[34]

In such circumstances Galileo fell back on his training in Aristotelian

32. "Letters on Sunspots," S. Drake, trans., in *Discoveries and Opinions*, p. 97.
33. Ibid., 118.
34. "Discourse on Bodies in Water," T. Salusbury, trans. (University of Illinois Press, 1960); EN, IV, 63–140.

and Scholastic logic, and on the principles of scientific reasoning developed in the later Scholastic period. Such principles included Duns Scotus's method of agreement,[35] Ockham's method of difference,[36] and Grosseteste's method of falsification.[37] In the 19th century Mill discussed these methods extensively and added his method of concomitant variations.[38] He endeavored to show that scientific discovery of causes was reducible to application of one or other of these methods. In particular he hoped that the method of difference eliminated doubt as to the validity of an assigned cause, a doubt stemming from the possibility that many causes can operate or cooperate to produce a given effect. Mill's conclusions are, however, nonrigorous. These methods do not allow us to argue from causes to effects with the rigor of mathematical demonstrations.

An elegant example of Galileo's use of the methods of agreement and difference occurs in his research on the the floating and sinking of bodies in liquids.[39] He had asserted that the densities of bodies governed their ascent or descent in liquid media. Opponents of his views cited experiments with ebony and water. Blocks of ebony sink in water, but a thin board of ebony can be floated on a water surface (a phenomenon now explained in terms of the surface tension of the liquid). From this experimental fact his opponents concluded that the shapes of bodies, not their densities, determined wheter they will float or sink. Galileo neatly refuted this argument by taking a ball of wax of a density lower than water. The wax floats, no matter what shape it is molded into, but if a piece of lead is added to the wax, the wax sinks, no matter what its shape (agreement and difference). Though he had refuted the general conclusion of his opponents, Galileo was not thereby able to explain the floating of the thin ebony sheet, although he did notice some of the pertinent details of this phenomenon.

It has been pointed out by Wisan that in his conscious employment of the resolutive method as a part of inductive-deductive procedure, Galileo is generally concerned with demonstration or proof rather than the discovery of new principles.[40] Resolution (or analysis) can be taken as examining the circumstances of an effect so as to discover an immediate cause, then trying to find a cause of the cause, and pursuing this

35. Duns Scotus, *Philosophical Writings*, Allan Wolter, trans. and ed., (Edinburgh, Thomas Nelson, 1962), p. 109.
36. See Losee, *Historical Introduction*, p. 34.
37. Crombie, *Robert Grosseteste*, the chap. on "Induction, and Verification and Falsification in Natural Science."
38. J. S. Mill, *System of Logic* (London: Longmans, Green, 1865).
39. Discussed by Wilson, "Galileo's Scientific," p. 17.
40. Ibid., p. 9.

regression until the true cause is found. Thus one hopes for a firm elucidation of the ultimate cause of the observed effect. But in Galileo's time there were two views as to the end of this process. In Scholastic natural philosophy the end of analysis was intended to be the *discovery* of the essential cause of an effect, or the discovery of more general principles entering into the makeup of a complex effect.[41] In mathematical analysis the aim is to derive a *proof* of the effect, by discovering, at the end of a regression, a formal principle already accepted as true. This latter method, stemming initially from the Greek geometers, seems to have been consciously intended by Galileo as the aim of his analyses. He comments that if from the senses, experiments, and observation a scientist has distilled a true conclusion, then "one may by making use of the resolutive method encounter some proposition which is already demonstrated, or arrive at some known principle."[42] If this is done, then the original conclusion induced from observation or experiment has been strengthened.

Even in astronomy Galileo greatly desires a certainty approaching that of the use of mathematical reasoning based on mathematicized representations. Perhaps for this reason he sometimes uses resolutive analysis more along the lines of the mathematicians than the natural philosophers of Scholasticism. In the end such a near-mathematical resolution can "with luck" arrive at a truth with strength and certainty:

> In investigating the unknown causes of our conclusions, one must be lucky enough right from the start to direct one's reasoning along the road to truth. When traveling along that road, it may easily happen that other propositions will be encountered which are recognized as true either through reason or experience. And from the certainty of these, the truth of our own will acquire strength and certainty.[43]

Eventually such truths can be "very little lower than mathematical proofs."[44]

Much more could be written, and has been written, about the use of empirical methods and logical reasoning in Galileo's science.[45] This is a particularly important topic for future research. The impression that it is intended to convey here is the overall one of scientists at the dawn of a comprehensive and articulate scientific method, struggling to use the best approaches to hand for their various purposes. Galileo's use of inductive and deductive procedures not infrequently yielded erroneous

41. Crombie, *Robert Grosseteste*, pp. 56–57, 64–65, 81–82.
42. EN, VII, 75.
43. Galileo, *Dialogue*, Drake trans., pp. 408–9.
44. Ibid., pp. 408, 410.
45. See Wallace, "Galileo Galilei."

conclusions. In astronomy it was much harder for him to intuit the authentic initial proposition than in a realm where he could mathematicize. But his persistence with these logical methods was of great value, helping to draw our attention to investigatory techniques possible for areas of nonphysical science in which mathematicizable representations are hard to come by.

Some Ongoing Implications of Galileo's Work in Physics.

It is possible to trace out a train of thought that leads straight to the heart of modern physics.

Let us go back to the Merton mean-speed law quoted earlier. It can be written:

$$\text{distance} = \frac{\text{final velocity} \times \text{time}}{2} \tag{1}$$

Acceleration is the increment of velocity per unit of time, and *if acceleration is uniform* (constant) and the body starts with zero velocity, then it follows that:

$$\text{final velocity} = \text{acceleration} \times \text{time} \tag{2}$$

Combining equations 1 and 2 we get:

$$\text{distance} = \frac{\text{acceleration} \times \text{time}^2}{2} \tag{3}$$

In his well-known studies of balls rolling on slopes, Galileo obtained the relationship that distance traversed is proportional to time squared. Consequently he had shown that on his slopes acceleration was constant, a point that he in fact derived by an ingenious geometric method. By considering slopes tilted more and more steeply, and by abstracting away from slope friction, Galileo eventually arrived at the proposition that *bodies falling freely experience constant acceleration*, and that the distances fallen from the point of release are proportional to the square of the time of fall. To this he added his famous investigation of the effects of the "massiveness" and shape of bodies on their acceleration of free fall, concluding that neither the size nor density of the bodies influenced their acceleration (although he knew that shape could sometimes do so on account of air resistance).[46]

Galileo lacked a concept of *mass*. Newton supplied this, partly as a result of considerations based on his first law, given above. Resonances

46. "Dialogues Concerning Two New Sciences."

of Aristotelian-Scholastic thought are often present in Newton's work. For him constant velocity and rest were more "natural" states than accelerated motion, consequently he introduced the notion of an impressed agent or *force* to account for the change of velocity that is acceleration. He considered that acceleration was proportional to applied force, and massiveness acted to oppose the accelerating action of a given force, and thus he arrived at the relationship:

$$\text{acceleration} = \frac{\text{force}}{\text{mass}} \qquad (4)11$$

From this it follows that in the case of free fall:

$$\text{gravitational acceleration} = \frac{\text{force of gravitational attraction by earth}}{\text{mass of falling body}} \qquad (5)$$

Newton advanced his law of gravitational attraction, from which it can be derived that for a body near the surface of the earth the force of attraction exercised by the earth on the body is given by:

$$\text{force of gravitational attraction} = \frac{\text{mass of body} \times \text{mass of earth}}{\text{earth radius}^2} \qquad (6)$$

For a body falling freely under the influence of the earth's attraction, we can thus combine 5 and 6:

$$\text{gravitational acceleration} = \frac{\cancel{\text{mass of body}} \times \text{mass of earth}}{\cancel{\text{mass of body}} \times \text{earth radius}^2} \qquad (7)11$$

The mass of the falling body, figuring in both the numerator and denominator of the formula, cancels out; Newton had returned via his reasoning process to Galileo's demonstration that *the mass of a body is without effect on its gravitational acceleration*, a demonstration that Newton himself experimentally confirmed. Galileo's work had entered into the heart of the great Newtonian system, which was to give a beautiful and direct explanation of Kepler's famous laws of planetary motion. The explanation of Galileo's finding was a signal success underpinning Newtonian mechanics.

As we saw earlier, Galileo was deeply convinced of the unity of physical and cosmological truth. Nowadays we see the search for the unification and simplification of physical theories as one of the most fundamental features of contemporary physics, a great intellectual pattern already spanning four centuries. At the dawn of this great process there stands Galileo Galilei. We currently know of five fundamental kinds of interactions in nature between physical entities: gravitational, electrical, magnetic, the weak interactions (responsible for the emission of fast-moving electrons from atomic nuclei), and strong interaction (responsible for "glueing" nuclei together). Figure 4 represents the progress made and being made toward their unification. In this scheme celestial and terrestrial gravity are shown as initially separate domains of understanding.

The first effective unification of celestial and terrestrial gravity stemmed from Newton's law, already quoted, that gravitational attractive force acts universally between all pairs of particles with a strength proportional to the product of their masses and inversely proportional to the distance between them. In celestial phenomena we have seen that this allowed him to calculate the orbits of the planets in agreement with Kepler's empirical laws of planetary motion. In terrestrial phenomena it not only allowed him to obtain the mass-independent gravitational acceleration observed by Galileo; it also permitted him to calculate the trajectories of projectiles, in accord with observations. Celestial and terrestrial movements were thus comprehended by a single theory.

In the 19th century James Clerk Maxwell obtained a set of differential equations describing the properties of the electomagnetic field, and this unified electrical and magnetic phenomena. In the present century electromagnetic phenomena have unified with the weak interactions by the work of Salam and Weinberg. The dash lines in Figure 4 show the areas in which an intense theoretical effort is being made in contemporary physics to achieve a comprehensive unification via the grand unification theory and studies in the field of superunification (e.g., through supergravity).

The penetration of Galileo's work into the process of unification is even deeper than Figure 4 depicts. Returning to equation 7, we see that the constancy of gravitational acceleration for all masses falling in a vacuum appears as a cancelation of mass between the numerator and denominator. But the numerator mass is mass active in gravitational attraction (*gravitational mass*, equation 6), whereas the denominator mass is mass active in its inertial role of resisting the accelerative tendency of force (*intertial mass*, equation 4). Their cancelation to yield equation 7 suggests a numerical equivalence between inertial and gravitational mass in nature. Using very sensitive techniques, the identity of the gravitational acceleration of pieces of aluminum and gold has been verified with an accuracy of three parts in one hundred thousand million, so that Galileo's original finding has become very firmly supported.[47]

47. P. G. Roll, R. Krotkov, and R. H. Dicke, *Annals of Physics* (1964) 442.

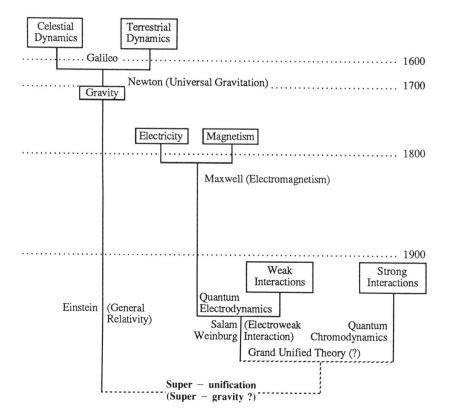

Fig. 4. Schema of Major Unifications of Physics.

Einstein found the equivalence of inertial and gravitational mass to be a particularly striking fact, and suspected that it rested on a great physical truth. He formulated his principle of equivalence, in which it is considered that acceleration of a frame of reference remote from any source of gravitational attraction can produce effects in it identical with those that would result, according to Newtonian dynamics, if the same reference system were placed in the gravitational field of a planet. *In a small laboratory in free fall in a homogeneous gravitational field, the laws of mechanics are the same as those observed in an inertial frame in the absence of a gravitational field.* Such a principle accounts for the identity of inertial and gravitational mass. The conservation of the laws of mechanics in a ship moving with uniform velocity (inertial frame), as noted by Galileo and described above, is here united with free fall in a way that became one of the sources of general relativity.

Another essential element in Einstein's formulation of general relativity is the concept of a curved space-time manifold, with matter concentrates able to influence the local curvature. Although mathematicians (Lobachevsky, Bolyai, Riemann) were able to develop the geometry of curved spaces independently of any needs of physics, it proved to be the case that at a certain stage of its development physics, from its own side, required such geometries. As Reichenbach has written:

> If several kinds of geometries were regarded as mathematically equivalent, the question arose, which of these geometries was applicable to physical reality; there is no necessity to single out Euclidean geometry for this purpose. Mathematics shows a variety of possible forms of relations, among which physics selects the real ones by means of observations and experiments. . . . After the discoveries of non-Euclidean geometries the duality of *physical* and *possible* space were recognized. Mathematics reveals the possible spaces; physics decides which among them corresponds to physical space.[48]

The situation depicted at the outset of this paper has returned upon itself, greatly enriched. Now, on the basis of its highly elaborated content, mathematical physics chooses for itself geometries according to its needs. It could not do so without the valiant struggles of the man who at the outset grasped that a conceptualization of space without finalistic domains, space considered essentially as extension, could yield generalizations framing our great picture of the cosmos. We can see even further. In the physics of our present century the idea of space is being enriched beyond the simplicity of extension that Galileo isolated for his purposes. Relativity unites space with time in a manifold of four dimensions. The absolute nature of the velocity of light yields the texture of Minkowskian space-time. Quantum field theory regards space as everywhere premeated by physical fields, excitations of the fields denoting localized particles. Even in particle-free domains, where there are no excitations, the fields are concomitants of space. In theories that lie at the forefront of contemporary research, dimensions other than those of space and time may possibly extend the dimensionality of our universe beyond the number four.

Already we can see a great justification of Galileo's method of abstraction in general and of his kinematic space in particular. Initial concentration upon a pure extension of space, and the subsequent development of a kinematic system in such a conceived space, has not forever limited the space of physics to a paucity of properties, nor does

48. H. Reichenbach, *The Philosophy of Space and Time*, M. Reichenbach and J. Freund, eds. (New York, Dover, 1957), p. 6.

it necessitate a permanent *philosophy* of a space devoid of other attributes. Galileo was right. He was not afraid to prescind away from the relatively rich space of Aristotelian thought, or from a division into celestial and terrestrial domains. In a conceptually simple space, suitable for a science of kinematic "accidents," there lay the real key to advance toward an ever-richer physics, a physics developed with the deepest rigor of logic so far known to the human mind.

8

Galileo and Contemporary Scientists

Georges J. Béné

Over the last twenty years or so, numerous personal or collective appeals have been addressed to various organs of the Catholic Church to institute a "review" of the case of Galileo, with the aim of improving relationships between the church and science. It is important to take account of the deep significance of these appeals. What motivated them? Are they representative of the opinion of the whole scientific community?

Reply to these two questions rests on a precondition: that of knowing what scientific circles think about Galileo and the Galileo affair today. Certain appeals would lead one to think that scientists have a common opinion on the question. Is this true? It seems to me important to try to nuance a reply in relation to the type of scientific activity, the philosophical conceptions, and the feelings and intellectual traditions of those concerned. Such an analysis should lead to a better judgment of the opportuneness of this or that initiative.

The task so defined would be a considerable one and certainly beyond my reach. It would call for a painstaking investigation over a fairly short time, involving a large number of truly representative scientists.

Because I lack the means of carrying out such an examination, it seems to me useful to describe briefly the conditions in which the material here presented has been assembled. At the outset it should be made clear that it was in the summer of 1964 that I began to be actively interested in the Galileo problem. The celebration of the fourth centenary of his birth occasioned many contacts with others; which were followed up with a view to assessing the opportuneness and the conditions for an eventual review of the question by the authorities of the church following a suggestion made at the Second Vatican Council.[1]

In the course of the last two decades I have been in touch with scientists, above all physicists — either by direct discussions with them, or by reading their writings — from many countries with diverse orientations and spheres of competence. From the above it should be clear that it has not been a purely informative inquiry, but one aimed at taking action.

As a result, what follows is of the nature of a personal witness with gaps and limitations. I have listened to my colleagues rather than interrogated them.

The period covered by the present work, 1964–1982, might seem long. As will become apparent, the evolution of opinion during this period was minimal, and took place in an atmosphere of "de-dramatization" of church-science relationships, particularly discernible in more recent years, coupled with interest in the scientific work of Galileo, which has been on the increase over the whole period.

Current Interest in Galileo in Scientific Circles

These preliminary remarks will allow me to get to the heart of the matter by replying to certain questions. What are the scientific circles? There is a tendency to apply the word "science" in all directions, but I will hold to its strict sense: scientific circles comprise those who advance the natural sciences by observation, by experimentation, and by the application of mathematics, not excluding those who teach these branches of knowledge or who scrutinize them rather more at large (historians and philosphers of science). The border between these groups is in any case not clear-cut: eminent physicists are often teachers, and secondarily may be, or have become, historians or philosophers of science. In the totality of these groups one can also include the somewhat heterogeneous category of scientific journalists.

It should be noted that it is often the case that when scientists express themselves in the name of the "scientific community," it is rarely true that such opinions are really representative of that community: rather it is a matter of the national and philosophically homogeneous groups to which they belong. Accordingly the greatest prudence should be observed in considering such opinions.

Another point appears essential when one gathers together the opinions of scientists on Galileo: his personality was so rich, he was active in

---

1. There is in the text on religious freedom presented by Bishop de Smedt a passage to the effect that "in 1964 a reparative homage could be paid to the memory of Galileo, who was born in 1564."

so many fields, that it is rare for anyone to be aware of the "wholeness" of his personality.

The aspect best known to scientists is certainly Galileo as a man of science: constructor of an astronomical telescope of exceptional characteristics, discoverer of many important celestial phenomena, initiator of fundamental laws of mechanics. This aspect will be touched on only briefly, because it does not raise any serious problems.

But this man of science was also the pioneer of a new way of grappling with the science of nature, and his contributions to the methodology of science have always been the subject of impassioned studies.

In a quite different sector, Galileo proposed a new interpretation of sacred texts — rejected by the authorities of his time, but the rule now for more than a century.

He was also someone who led a tormented life, a troubled yet outstandingly brilliant thinker, and above all the "man on trial."

Finally it is interesting to ascertain the circumstances of those who speak about Galileo. Works on the science of Galileo, as well as serious historical works on his life or his trial, seldom reveal a motivation stemming from a particular historical context: it is often the discovery of new documents or a deeper study of as yet unexplored material that motivates new writings. Even if they often constitute the most important contribution to a better knowledge of Galileo as a scientist or as a person, such works only concern a very limited number of specialists.

Around the various aspects of this many-sided person, particularly the last mentioned, there is added the weight of a legend, with inexact data, maintained or periodically revived for nearly four centuries. At first it is generally not easy to identify to which side of Galileo's personality and to which tradition scientists are referring when they write or speak about him, but the source reference, once discovered is always essential. It appears clearly enough when something stirs up a church-science conflict. Galilean anniversaries (centenary celebrations of his birth or death) up to the end of the 19th century focused on the person of Galileo and his conflict with the church; those of the 20th century bear more on Galileo as scientist. But public opinion (even that of the scientific community as a whole) has not followed suit. Attention has remained focused on Galileo taken as a whole, symbol of scientific freedom, and of the struggle of science against the church.

Many occasions in the course of the last two decades have provided such opinions an opportunity for expression:

- the celebrations of the fourth centenary of his birth: congresses, notably in Italy and the United States, and more limited meetings

in many important research centers and universities;
- interventions at the Second Vatican Council, involving requests from Catholic scientific circles or declarations by conciliar fathers;
- the publication of the work of Fr. Paschini on the life and work of Galileo (1964), completed in 1942 (third centenary of the death of Galileo), though its publication was deferred;
- the address by Cardinal König, then president of the Vatican Secretariat for Non-Believers, on the occasion of the Nobel committee meeting in Lindau (1968);
- and finally the interventions of Pope John Paul II, notably his address at the Pontifical Academy of Sciences, November 10, 1979.

These events, and others less well known, have given scientists occasion to comment, by personal interventions or through the journals of scientific societies, on the current reality of the Galileo question, and its repercussions on the relations between science and society, but above all the relations between science and religion.

Commentators accentuate the aspect of Galileo or his legend that best accords with their own particular view or with the problems that preoccupy them. The observed reactions clearly bear the mark of the conflicts at the end of the 19th century and of their emotional content.

The Attitudes of Scientists to Galileo

The attitudes of scientists can be reduced to four groupings, though with some oversimplification:

1. An important group is comprised of those who are completely disinterested in Galileo as a person: for them he is a name or a qualification (as when one speaks of a "Galilean frame of reference," for example); or, outside the purely scientific domain, he is a cliché from the past to be ranked with the Inquisition, the Crusades, the Renaissance popes. He concerns an utterly played-out past that should be forgotten in order to get on with that which is important today; this group is particularly important outside Europe.

2. Then there are those who react in the media and who, unfortunately, often have very meager information or merely legends. According to their religious or philosophical persuasions, they are more concerned with parallels that can be drawn between the Galileo case and current situations that they consider analogous. It is these commentators who feed an ever lively polemic

based on information that is not always exact. Among atheists, Galileo is lauded as a champion of free thought or a martyr of the Inquisition, an argument for attacking the church. Among Christians, there is felt either the need to justify at all costs the decisions taken against Galileo, or to show that these decisions, considered unfortunate, do not lessen the authority of the Roman magisterium. In most instances, the fact that the church has quietly, but clearly, retracted earlier decisions has created a feeling of guilt that remains very much alive.

3. Then there are the historians and philosophers of science whose regular and relatively frequent contributions keep a certain public interested and help to inform it correctly. It is scientists, in a broad sense, who make up the bulk of this public. Such a contribution is often of great value and the works of recent decades have largely helped in "de-dramatizing" the question and in pursuing the work currently being done under the aegis of the Holy See.

4. Finally there is the most numerous group, consisting of those who are interested in Galileo as a scholar, as a scientist. Basically it includes university graduates in the exact sciences who have come to know there the works of this scholar. It also comprises researchers who ponder the works of Galileo in order to locate them in the history of science or to judge them in the light of current knowledge.

Accordingly, it is in the light of this "classification" that I shall attempt to situate reactions on the subject of Galileo encountered in scientific circles.

CONTEMPORARY SCIENTISTS AND THE PERSON OF GALILEO

The Man of Science

I will not press this point, even though certain aspects of Galileo's scientific activity are directly related to the difficulties that he encountered. Let us note that the general interest of scientists in the *science* of Galileo was already present in outline in the celebrations on the occasion of the third centenary of his death, but had become almost exclusive during those of 1964 — the fourth centenary of his birth. All the congresses, notably the six in Italy and those in the United States, almost without exception dealt with current scientific problems in relation to the scientific work of Galileo.

It must be stated that for some considerable time the discoveries or hypotheses of Galileo have been the object of deepened criticisms. He was wrong in his explanation of the cause of the tides (due to lunar attraction, not to the movement of the earth), a point on which his contemporaries and notably Pope Urban VIII saw matters correctly. There was also his confusion between relative and absolute motion. Moreover he did not take into account that if the phases of Venus and the satellites of Jupiter prove the falseness of the Ptolemaic representation, they favor, but are not proofs of, the Copernican representation (notably the immobility of the sun). In his controversy with Bellarmine on relative movement, it was Bellarmine who was right, not Galileo.

These few examples demonstrate the contemporary interest in Galileo on the scientific plane, which is shown not only by publications or congresses of circumstances, but by an integration of the thought and the scientific work of Galileo in the science of today. These works aid in placing "the Galileo problem" in a more correct perspective.

The Philosopher of Science

Contemporary interest in Galileo goes far beyond the milieu of scientific specialists or informed persons in astronomy; the new concepts that he has developed in scientific methodology are still present and vital. After his astronomical discoveries, some of his adversaries claimed that the objects seen in the telescope did not exist or were of minimal importance, or they purely and simply denied the existence of things unknown to competent authorities (letter of Sassetti to Dini, 1622).[2] Here is Galileo's reply:

> If the existence of objects depends on the knowledge of whether they are known or not, it follows that they have not existed before they were known. Now that is absurd.

The objectivity of the real world, defended notably by St. Thomas Aquinas, has here found a particularly persuasive advocate!

The controversy concerning the mountains of the moon, which he had discovered, and their height, which he had estimated from the length of their shadows and the angle of the sun's rays, already clarifies for us his conceptions of "scientific truth," conceptions that are retained today. He rejected, for example, with a cutting distrust, the first theories of "hidden variables," especially Clavius's hypothesis (to the effect that the valleys and mountains of the moon are covered with an absolutely transparent substance that permits the heavenly body to be spherical

2. EN, XI, 103.

despite its appearance). Galileo's reaction? It is a beautiful invention . . . it only needs to be proven.

His conceptions of truth were contrary not only to the traditional doctrine of the church, but they also ran contrary to the logic of the epoch. Galileo had broken the scientific rules then in vogue, and in doing this had created from them new ones now universally accepted.[3]

This new concept of truth implies the necessity of taking into account that which one sees, and truth is thus reduced to a model that allows prediction (and consequently inclusion) of new facts (as was, for example, the case with the system of Kepler in comparison with those of Copernicus or Ptolemy). The criterion of simplicity (of "logical beauty") is equally essential. It decides in favor of Copernicus and Kepler, but does not affirm the reality of an absolute model, but rather one capable of further perfection.

Galileo and Biblical Exegesis

Other planes on which Galileo's conceptions were expressed have always been the object of passionate studies and discussions. The famous letter to the grand duchess Christine, in which Galileo set forth his views on exegesis and the interpretation of the scriptures, has recently been translated into several languages and discussed.[4] By common accord it has been recognized that scripture often speaks in a language comprehensible to the ordinary people to whom it was first addressed:

> The truth of the Bible, for those who wish to affirm it, without as a result rejecting the discoveries of science, should not be sought for in a literal interpretation of such episodes as the six days of creation, the miraculous halting of the sun during the battle of Joshua, or the star of Bethlehem. Such a judgment confirms what Catholic[5] and Protestant theologians have long accepted. It equally clarifies the current controversy between Darwinian evolutionism and so-called creationism (O. Gingerich; see note 3, below).

On this point Galileo's arguments have contributed to his current notoriety. His behavior vis-à-vis the authorities of the Catholic Church is admired by eminent Catholic scientists. Thus the Italian physicist A. Zichichi notes in an interview:

3. This is well shown in Gingerich, *Pour la science*, Oct. 1982, pp. 68-79.
4. Notably, in English, Prof. Stillman Drake, *Discoveries and Opinions of Galileo* (New York: Doubleday Anchor Books, 1957) and in French, *Galilée, aspects de sa vie et de son oeuvre* (PUF, 1968).
5. See the encyclical *Providentissimus Deus* of Leo XIII (1893) and more recent documents.

Galileo, man of faith, went down on his knees before the church — the church that condemned Joan of Arc to the stake and has subsequently canonized her.[6]

He proposes nothing less than that Galileo also be canonized. Why?

Galileo invented science. His sanctity consists in the fact that he, as a man of faith, bowed before the church: a great act of humility, which could, even today, be demanded of Catholic scientists. He was too far ahead of his time in his scientific discoveries.

Historical Works

Galileo's person, the details of his life and his struggles, have been scrutinized in detail and largely contribute to the image formed of him by scientists of today. But once again in this matter the great majority of scientists have no sources of information other than those available to the public, and legends can circulate just as well among scientists as elsewhere.

A certain number of eminent scientists are known as specialists in the history of Galileo. There are Gerlach and Heisenberg, to mention only the most illustrious. But many scientists of distinction, after a life devoted to science, show an interest in the history of the sciences, and Galileo is one of the subjects that most often comes up in this new orientation. In this way, by original historical discoveries, they have contributed to a better understanding of the man, his work, and the intellectual environment in which he lived. Whether or not these discoveries have been made by scientists, their impact on the world of science is often considerable.

The discovery, announced in the U.S.A.,[7] of the texts of courses taught at the Jesuit Roman College in the 16th century, in which there was an underlining of the role that experimentation and application of mathematics could play — fundamental ideas for Galileo — shows that his ideas were in the air and that the scientific revolution progressively emerged from the Middle Ages.

Other authors — scientists — express themselves in the same fashion in letters to the editor of the American review *Science*: "The popes of the end of the Middle Ages were not persecutors but protectors of science" (Holt, 1964). "One should not attach too much blame to the judges of Galileo in 1633" (Stephanon, 1965).

---

6. *Gente*, December 16, 1978, interview by G. Grieco.
7. See the contribution by Fr. William Wallace, chap. 2, above.

During the period 1615–1623 the following was taught in Savoy, at Annecy:

What is found affirmed in Holy Scripture by ignorant men, profane or natural philosophers, has no other authority than that of its writers. . . . Thus when Joshua, ignorant of astronomy, commanded the sun to stand still, he spoke according to his opinion. . . . Scripture speaks of the things of nature according to human feelings, and because humans commonly hold that the sun moves and that the earth is motionless, it keeps to the same language.

Reference has also been made to the choice of a scientific career by Galileo:

The precarious financial conditions of his family led his father to direct him toward medical studies, which were agreeably remunerated; happily university life gave him the occasion to initiate himself in applied mathematics and to realize his real vocation as a physicist. Though he knew that this new orientation would make him a pauper, he did not hesitate to interrupt his medical studies, without passing the final examinations, and to work at the physical and mathematical sciences at home (Heidelberg, 1976).

The discoveries of J. M. Jauch in connection with the secret injunction, of which mention is made during Galileo's "trial," have stirred up fresh interest in the question. Let me quote an extract from a letter of G. B. Venturi, a Galileo historian, to M. Delambre of the Academy of Sciences of Paris (1820), published by Jauch in 1973:

In fact the judges had little reason to condemn him [Galileo]. But the persecution did not in fact come directly from them, but from Urban VIII, who until then had treated Galileo with much friendliness, but who was then piqued by what Galileo in the dialogues put in the mouth of Simplicius in mockery, arguments that the pope had earlier advanced against the Copernican system. Here is the real cause of Galileo's misfortunes. I have authentic proofs in my hands, and I will have them printed with all the rest.

Truth and Legends

Despite all this, legends and inaccuracies live a long life. It is not uncommon to find a university lecturer beginning a course that involves heliocentrism and geocentrism with the famous *Eppur si muove*, "But it does move!" — words that everyone should know were never uttered by Galileo. For many scientists it is a "historic phrase." The opinions of scientists who have not pondered the problem have inherited, willy-nilly, all the legends that have come into being around Galileo. For example, an opinion, which is quite current, is that, "thanks to the telescope with diverging eye-lens, which he invented in Venice, he was able to confirm the theses of Copernicus and eliminate those of Ptolemy, teaching us that the earth rotated" (France, 1980).

In general, everyone has grasped more or less correctly the relationship between Galileo and Copernicus (the decisions of 1616 against Copernicus form the counterpart of the condemnation of Galileo in 1633). This becomes a twofold stroke against the church of the time, "enemy of science." The true role of Giordano Bruno in this context is less well known.

Bruno, a philosopher, condemned by the church a short time before Galileo, played an important part, precisely because of his philosophy, in the positions taken up by the church in 1616 and 1633. By an extrapolation (one could say a distortion) of the ideas of Copernicus, as E. Namer has shown, Bruno constructed a metaphysics that involved the entirety of Christian dogma.[8] Inasmuch as, according to Copernicus, the earth had lost its position as the center of the universe, there was no reason to retain outside the planetary system the sphere of "fixed stars," a step that allowed the limits of the universe to be pushed back to infinity. The earth and the solar system lost their unique character. Bruno spoke of countless planetary systems, and matters were heading for a kind of pantheism:

> Many philosophers and letters of that epoch teach that the sun was the center of the universe and the earth a simple planet, deducing immediately that the history of terrestrial humanity was not in any way special, each planet also having its own history, with its own fall and its own redemption, and that for all these reasons the scriptures were pure inventions (C. Piron, Geneva, 1980).

It therefore seemed to the Catholic authorities of the time that the unproven theory of heliocentrism led to the metaphysics of Bruno. Bellarmine, who had taken part in the trial of Bruno, was thus aware of the inauspicious consequences of the Copernican system for the Christian faith.

Another point on which serious confusion is apparent in scientific circles is the role of the "index" in the 16th and 17th centuries. The trial has been essentially made into a conflict between "free secular research and the authority of the church." It is clear that at that time the nondistinction between scientific truth and religious truth could have allowed such a confusion.

But let us look a little more closely. The "Dialogue on the Two Principal Systems of the World" claims to prove the movement of the earth by the phenomenon of the tides. The proscription of the book —

---

8. E. Namer, *Giordano Bruno* (Paris, Seghers, 1966).

emanating from an authority responsible for profane science as well as Catholic doctrine — is comparable to the rejection of a work considered inaccurate by the editorial committee of a serious scientific journal today. A problem of faith is mixed into this matter, but the two propositions were declared philosophically false, and further, *only in the case of one of them*, contrary to scripture.

The famous phrase, erroneously attributed to Galileo, *Eppur si muove*, has conferred long life on a serious inexactitude: the proposition contrary to scripture (and for this reason declared heretical by Galileo's judges, who on this point exceeded their competence) *is not the movement of the earth* (a proposition declared scientifically false by his judges, and only "dangerous" as far as the faith was concerned) but the immobility of the sun (which contradicts the biblical text taken literally):

> Finally, the church did not condemn the theory of the relative motion of the planets, the sun, and the earth, in terms of a supposedly immobile sun, but upheld that, in the absence of manifest proof, an immobile sun should be considered as a depiction allowing for a simpler accounting of the facts, vis-à-vis certain difficulties with the scriptures and not as being reality (C. Piron).

I have touched on certain lacunae, but how many more need to be touched on! Fortunately, healthy reactions come to light, and the concern of scientists for truth — even if it is sometimes limited to hunting down the false — shows itself in a relentless fight against the legends and inaccuracies that encumber the Galilean tradition. Such reactions, from authors of very diverse or even opposed philosophical and religious convictions, help to cleanse the historical bases of popular opinions on Galileo.

Reference sometimes has been made to "obstinate theologians," whereas it was a matter of experts in astronomy who were not prepared to reject the Ptolemaic system and replace it by that of Copernicus, for reasons that were at that time valid:

- the demonstration given by Galileo was recognized as false;
- the elementary "experiential" feeling that the earth is at rest had been established;
- as long as one held to circular movements, the simplification was not great: the 80 circles of Ptolemy were reduced to 34, and their center was not coincidental with the center of the sun.

A present-day theologian, specialist in the philosophy of science, has expressed regret that those who opposed Galileo were so expert in astronomy and at the same time such sorry theologians. A rather more serious study of St. Thomas, in particular, would have permitted them to avoide the snare of confusion as to the aim of scripture when it refers to observable phenomena (Kaelin, 1964).

GALILEO IN CURRENT CONFLICTS OF IDEAS

Antireligious Polemics

The interest of present-day scientists in the scholar and polemicist Galileo is undeniable, but it is clear that interest is even greater in Galileo considered not as an "end" but as a "means." Many reflections, occasional writings, and even studies in depth, use facts concerning Galileo to defend a viewpoint that does not directly concern him. It must be remembered that at the end of the last century, the decision of the judges of 1633 and the stance of the Holy Office in 1616 were made the object of a bitter debate on the dogma of papal infallibility, which had just been proclaimed. But nowadays the dispute has changed its objectives.

This was particularly evident when Cardinal König, speaking before the Nobel committee meeting in July 1968, proposed a reconciliation between science and religion by various steps, notably by a reinstatement of Galileo. By presenting the point of view either of their editorial boards or of individual scientists, many scientific journals addressed these two points in extenso.

As far as throwing light on the trial of Galileo is concerned, reactions were almost unanimous:

> If the Church were to openly admit it had been deceived, and that it recognizes the fault committed by preceding officialdom, how would this in any way change the actual situation?[9]

For physicists the initiation of a new investigation of Galileo would be without great significance, and they would look upon it as one more spectacle staged by the Catholic Church.

For A. Mussard (Geneva, 1980) "the urgency of such a review . . . seems somewhat doubtful."

Christians as well as non-Christians think that today there are more important problems. "The Church can reinstate Galileo, but does not do as much for the living, which would be really important" (*Science*, 1968).

Physics Today posed a facetious question: "and what if Galileo is

9. E. Brücke, *Phys. Blätter*, 1968 (RFA).

again condemned?" (1968). In France some think that a "review would be ridiculous." For McMullin (U.S.A.), it is more important to engage in the ethical problems raised by biology at the present time. In sum, there is no interest in going back to the trial, and if one wished to do something for Galileo, it would be better to pay homage to him for his suggestions concerning the problem of interpretation of the scriptures (I have heard this point made in the U.S.A., Spain, and France).

According to Brücke such a review will not solve the problem of the relations of scientists with the Catholic faith, because there remain "dogmas unacceptable to them, which are in part of a fairly recent date, but which chill scientists as being rather medieval errors." Quoting scientist and theist Max Planck, Brücke adds:

> Step by step, belief in miracles should retreat before science, which advances surely and incessantly, and we should not doubt that sooner or later there will be an end to miracles.

He recommends a pure and simple setting aside of dogmas (above all, the last to be proclaimed, the assumption of the Blessed Virgin). For him, the encyclical *Humanae Vitae* does not take into account the reality of overpopulation and the threat of famine. "These realities show that the successor of St. Peter is still endowed with the same spirit that condemned Galileo in his day."

One does not find only negative reactions, even among nonbelievers. For R. Féynman (Paris, 1979), for example, "the science-faith conflict belongs to a past that has ended."

It should be remarked that among many Catholics the point of view is clearly different, but leads to similar conclusions. The battles of the 19th century, coming after the advent of an awareness in the church as to the bad decisions of 1616 and their upshot (the condemnation of Galileo), have led the majority of believing scientists to a guilt complex, which is not absent from the form and content of their appeals to church bodies (the Second Vatican Council, for example). The majority of these scientists seem to be unaware of the reactions of the Holy See in this matter since the 18th century.

This guilt feeling is particularly clear in an extract from a collective letter (Paris, 1963) of Catholic scientists to the bishops of the Second Vatican Council:

> The condemnation of Galileo, one of the principal and greatest founders of modern science, declared guilty of having upheld in the matter of astronomy propositions that in fact were scientifically founded, has always been deeply resented by the whole of the scientific world as one of the most evident proofs of the suspicion with which the church has regarded and still regards the intellectual undertakings of science. No subsequent indication

of esteem or of benevolence with regard to science has effaced, in the spirits of many scientists, the impression that the Catholic Church and its faith are, at their very roots, adversaries of science. The solemn condemnation of Galileo seems to them to demonstrate this proposition irreversibly.

One cannot reasonably say that the theory of the tides — which Galileo proposed and which is at the basis of his condemnation — was "scientifically founded!"

R. Lavocat is also categorical:

> The scientific crisis, felt by the church since the dawn of modern times, with the condemnation of Galileo as its starting point, has marked the breaking off of a dialogue. . . . A gulf has begun to open, which only grows larger, between the church and the international community of scientists.[10]

According to a commentator on a meeting of an ecumenical council of churches in Boston, 1979, which, among other things, dealt with problems of science and faith, "the time is past when theology, which had become an instrument of power, could claim to dictate to scientists (Copernicus or Galileo) the correct use of their method" (E. Fuchs, Switzerland).

Even Catholic authors refer to the condemnation of Galileo as "the expression of a conflict between scientific and religious conceptions, between the freedom of secular research and the authority of the church."

Some judgments of physicists are so abrupt as to strain credibility. For example:

> For a long time the Church, Catholics, have been impervious to science (L. Michel, 1982).

> Over the centuries, attached to the beliefs that it made into dogmas, the church has profoundly mistrusted and has persecuted those who serve it. (J. Lamotte, 1982).

> South of a line that divides the European countries of the Reformation from the integral bastion of Catholicism, the universities were sterilized by the Holy Office and the condemnation of Galileo in 1633 (P. Caro, 1981).

That the church urged prudence on scientists who dealt with heliocentrism — incidentally, in a nonmonolithic fashion — is certain; but in all other domains, scientific development has in fact experienced no hindrance.

Even in the field of astronomy, it was not long before criticism stirred in France. The decision of Galileo's judges was criticized as early as

10. R. Lavocat, *L'Eglise et la communauté scientifique.*

1642 (Gassendi). Pascal's pamphlet against Galileo's judges is well known (1657). In Italy, in the very year of the death of Urban VIII (1644), Argoli published his *Pandosium sphaericum*, in which he dared to argue in favor of the rotation of the earth.

It is clear that science developed outside the Catholic Church after the Reformation; half of Europe was no longer under its jurisdiction and the church only very rarely intervened (very passively after the 17th century). It is probably this silence that is interpreted as disinterest or systematic opposition![11]

Marxist and Anti-Marxist Propaganda

Exploitation of the thought of Galileo, to defend or attack currently fashionable ideas in philosophy, is clear in Marxist circles, where Galileo enjoys a particularly favorable press.[12] In the first place he serves as a justifying argument in the anti-religion, and particularly anti-Christian struggle, a fact particularly noticed after the proposal of Cardinal König mentioned above (1968).

According to Mtchedlov, it is a matter of a new strategy of the church:

> Aware of the decline of its influence, the Catholic Church is of late mobilizing all its possibilities in order to insert itself into modern civilization or, at least, in order not to appear as a patently foreign organism. Ideologists of Catholicism launch efforts to demonstrate that a collaboration between the church and scientists is possible, desirable, and even indispensable in the interests of humanity, its welfare and its progress. In this respect, the theses presented by the archbishop of Vienna [Cardinal König] are very indicative of the new climate that prevails in the Vatican, and of its desire to widen its contacts with the world of today in order to find partners and allies.

> It is the 20th century that obliges Catholic ideologists to work out a new attitude with respect to science and scientists, and to envisage in a new way the place and role of science in social life . . . Scientists have no need at all of theologians! (*Litt. Gaz.*, April 16, 1969).

The *Encyclopédie Philosophique* (Moscow, 1960) maintains that "Galileo had a profound influence on the development of the purely materialist representation of the world." Galileo demonstrated the infinity of the universe and interpreted natural phenomena as a "mechanistic materialist." In addition, Galileo "would never have accepted the

---

11. *Science sans conscience* (Geneva, Labor et Fides, 1980).

12. This question of the confrontation between Marxist philosophy and Christian thought in connection with science-faith questions has been developed in G. J. Béné and C. Piron, *Rev. Quest. Scient.*, 151 (1980) 391–407. See also René Coste, *Marxist Analysis and Christian Faith* (Maryknoll, N.Y., Orbis Books, 1985).

idea of the creation of the sun and planets by God, except as "an initial mechanical state."

"It is pointless to insist on the tendentious, or at least inaccurate nature of such assertions!" (*Athéisme et Dialogue*, Rome, June 1980, pp. 80-81).

In his *Galilée* (French trans., 1973), Kuznetsov turns Galileo into a forerunner of Marxist philosophy. In his preface he writes:

> In his conception of the world and his style, every great thinker reflects his epoch and his environment. But he also reflects the past and the future, as well as other social or national settings, in which his ideas have formed, resounded, or evolved. The history of nature proves . . . the indissoluble bond between ideas and modes of thought peculiar to various nations, united in scientific progress and cultural community.

Throughout the work these arguments are applied to Galileo wherever possible. But, for Kuznetsov, who knows his sources well, "One . . . characteristic that ties Galileo to the past is his imprecise attitude vis-à-vis the problem of the infinite universe" (p. 16); "infinite empty space is not featured on the Galilean coat of arms." Kuznetsov contradicts, therefore, the *Encyclopédie Philosophique!*

Exceptional scientists "seem to me to be only those who have known how to express the objective historical logic of the unidirectional evolution of science" (Kuznetsov).

It must be remarked that if Galileo has been "recruited" by Soviet Marxists, he has equally supplied arms to their adversaries. The trial of Galileo is compared with all the Soviet trials of scientists who have not respected the criteria of Marxism. Whether as to biology (Lysenko) or cosmogony (big-bang reckoning), the list would be too long to print here.

Brecht's "Galileo," which has had the honor of being presented in the People's Republic of China, being written in the period of Nazi Germany and then in a new version after the great Moscow trials, is still of current interest (if one thinks of events in Poland, for example). "Woe to a country that needs hero-intellectuals," because no honest researcher can promise not to be dissident.

Such manipulation of the Galileo affair has given many scientists occasion to examine their conscience.

The Scientist and Society

Those who think that science has a social role to play find in Galileo a convinced partisan. In fact he chose to express himself in Italian, because the public understood that language. The choice of Italian for the *Dialogo* is certainly at the root of his difficulties. He himself explains why he chose Italian:

> I write in the vernacular, because it must be the case that everyone can read me; that is why my last treatise has been published in that language. I have been led to this by observing that many set to work though remaining indifferent to the profession they have chosen — medicine, philosophy, etc., . . . and without having any aptitude for it. At the same time, others, who are talented, are absorbed in family concerns or other occupations far from the profession of writing because, as Ruzzante says, although talented, they remain all their lives unable to understand the contents of Latin works, being persuaded that these books contain very important things on logic and metaphysics inaccessible to their understanding. For all this, nature has given them, just as it has given philosophers, eyes with which to see her works, and she has also given them intelligence so as to be able to understand them and assimilate them (Letter to Fr. Gualdo of Padua).[13]

Einstein, on the contrary, is of the opinion that Galileo was much too worn out to convince his public:

> As far as Galileo is concerned, I picture things quite differently. Without doubt, he sought for truth, more passionately than many others. But it is hard to understand that a mature man would work unremittingly to impart this truth to a public that was superficial and corrupted by paltry interests. Did he, then, attach such importance to this task that he consecrated the rest of his life to it? . . . It is without real necessity that he went to Rome to fight the popes and the other politicizers. This whole picture does not agree with the idea I have formed for myself of the independence of spirit of the ageing Galileo. I cannot, for example, visualize myself doing as much to defend the theory of relativity. In Galileo's place I would have said: truth is stronger than I am. Defending it by bestriding Rosinante, sword in hand, would have seemed to me ridiculously Quixotic.[14]

These points are the subject of a permanent debate in the journals of scientific societies.

Many other aspects of the current interest in Galileo deserve emphasis. Those that have been mentioned show the variety of questions for which a reference to Galileo naturally comes to mind.

It is certainly regrettable that this current interest, this radiation of an exceptional personality, should be often — unfortunately, much too often — based on inaccurate or distorted information, on legends that each century sees reborn, transformed, or enriched.

The best service we can render to our contemporaries — scientists, philosophers, teachers, and all those for whom the history of human thought is a source of reflection — is to offer a more exact, more precise

---

13. EN, XI, 327.
14. Cited in B. Kuznetsov, *Galilée*, p. 92.

knowledge of who Galileo truly was, of the real message that he brought to the world. This message, like the fishing net of the Gospel, contains strengths and weaknesses, includes discoveries and errors; as a whole, however, it transmits a Lesson that is still valuable today..

Epilogue

"The Greatness of Galileo is Known to All"

Pope John Paul II

During the centenary commemoration of the birth of Albert Einstein,[1] celebrated by the Pontifical Academy of the Sciences on November 10, 1979, Pope John Paul II spoke on the profound harmony between the truth of faith and the truth of science in the following terms.

I feel myself to be fully one with my predecessor Pius XI, and with the two who followed him in the Chair of Peter, in inviting the members of the Academy of the Sciences and all scientists with them, to bring about "the ever more noble and intense progress of the sciences, without asking any more from them; and this is because in this excellent proposal and this noble work there consists that mission of serving truth with which we charge them."[2]

The search for truth is the fundamental task of science. The researcher who moves on this plane of science feels all the fascination

---

1. Albert Einstein, illustrious scientist of our time (1879–1955), was the discoverer of the theories of special and general relativity. According to special relativity, measurements of space and time depend on the speed of light which transmits signals. One of the most remarkable consequences of special relativity is the equivalence of mass and energy ($e = mc^2$, c being the velocity of light). Whereas special relativity introduces time as a coordinate of all measurements (four-dimensional space-time), general relativity geometrizes the distribution of material masses, by assigning to each point of space-time a curvature determined by the mass located there. In addition, general relativity predicts that a moving mass will emit gravitational waves, a prediction that seems to have been recently confirmed in radio astronomy by experimental means. The hypothesis of universal gravitation, proposed by Newton, must thus be revised, and the conceptual difference between inertial and gravitational mass disappears. Traditional concepts of mathematics and physics are thus radically transformed.

2. Motu Proprio *In Multis Solaciis* of October 28, 1936, concerning the Pontifical Academy of Sciences: A.A.S., 28 (1936) 424.

of St. Augustine's words, *Intellectum valde ama*,[3] "love intelligence greatly," and its proper function, which is to know the truth. Pure science is a good in itself which deserves to be greatly loved, for it is knowledge, the perfection of human beings in their intelligence. Even before its technical applications, it should be loved for itself, as an integral part of human culture. Fundamental science is a universal boon, which every nation should cultivate in full freedom from all forms of international servitude or intellectual colonialism.

The Freedom of Fundamental Research

Fundamental research should be free vis-à-vis political and economic powers, which should cooperate in its development, without fettering its creativity or enslaving it to their own ends. As with all other truth, scientific truth has, in fact, to render an account only to itself and to the supreme truth that is God, the creator of humankind and of all that is.

On its second plane, science turns toward practical applications, which find their full development in various technologies. In the phase of its concrete applications, science is necessary for humanity in order to satisfy the just requirements of life, and to conquer the various evils that threaten it. There is no doubt that applied science has rendered and will render humankind immense services, especially if it is inspired by love, regulated by wisdom, and accompanied by the courage that defends it against the undue interference of all tyrannical powers. Applied science should be allied with conscience, so that, in the triad, science–technology–conscience, it may be the cause of the true good of humankind, whom it should serve.

Unhappily, as I have had occasion to say in my encyclical *Redemptor hominis*, "Humankind today seems constantly to be menaced by what it constructs. . . . In this there seems to consist the principal chapter of the drama of human existence today" (§ 15). Humankind should emerge victorious from this drama, which threatens to degenerate into tragedy, and should once more find its authentic sovereignty over the world and its full mastery of the things it has made. At this present hour, as I wrote in the same encyclical, "the fundamental significance of this "sovereignity" and this 'mastery' of humankind over the visible world, assigned to it as a task by the Creator, consists in the priority of ethics over technology, in the primacy of person over things, and in the superiority of spirit over matter" (§ 16).

This threefold superiority is maintained to the extent that there is

---

3. St. Augustine, *Epist.* 120, 3, 13; P.L. 33, 49.

conserved the sense of human transcendence over the world and God's transcendence over humankind. Exercising its mission as guardian and defender of both these transcendences, the church desires to assist science to conserve its ideal purity on the plane of fundamental research, and to help it fulfill its service to humankind on the plane of practical applications.

The church freely recognizes, on the other hand, that it has benefited from science. It is to science, among other things, that there must be attributed that which Vatican II has said with regard to certain aspects of modern culture:

> New conditions in the end affect the religious life itself. . . . The soaring of the critical spirit purifies that life from a magical conception of the world and from superstitious survivals, and demands a more and more personal and active adhesion to faith; many are the souls who in this way have come to a more living sense of God.[4]

The Advantage of Collaboration

Collaboration between religion and modern science is to the advantage of both, and in no way violates the autonomy of either. Just as religion requires religious freedom, so science legitimately requires freedom of research. The Second Vatican Council, after having affirmed, together with Vatican I, the just freedom of the arts and human disciplines in the domain of their proper principles and method, solemnly recognized "the legitimate autonomy of culture and particularly that of the sciences."[5]

On this occasion of the solemn commemoration of Einstein, I wish to confirm anew the declarations of Vatican II on the autonomy of science in its function of research into the truth inscribed in nature by the hand of God. Filled with admiration for the genius of the great scientist, a genius in which there is revealed the imprint of the Creator Spirit, the Church, without in any way passing a judgment on the doctrine concerning the great systems of the universe, since that is not its area of competence, nevertheless proposes this doctrine to the reflection of theologians in order to discover the harmony existing between scientific and revealed truth.

Mr. President, in your address you have rightly said that Galileo and Einstein have characterized an epoch. *The greatness of Galileo is known to all*, as is that of Einstein; but with this difference, that by comparison with the one whom we are today honoring before the College of

4. *Gaudium et Spes*, § 7.
5. Ibid., § 59.

Cardinals in the Apostolic Palace, the first had much to suffer — we cannot conceal it — at the hands of men and departments within the church. The Second Vatican Council has recognized and deplored certain undue interventions: "May we be permitted to deplore" — it is written in § 36 of the Conciliar Constitution *Gaudium et Spes* — "certain attitudes that have existed among Christians themselves, insufficiently informed as to the legitimate autonomy of science. Sources of tension and conflict, they have led many to consider that science and faith are opposed." The reference to Galileo is clearly expressed in the note appended to this text, which cites the volume *Vita e opere di Galileo Galilei* by Pio Paschini, published by the Pontifical Academy of Sciences.

In order to go beyond this position adopted by the Council, I desire that theologians, scientists, and historians, animated by a spirit of sincere collaboration, deepen their examination of the Galileo case, and, in a loyal recognition of errors, from whatever side they come. I also desire that they bring about the disappearance of the mistrust that, in many souls, this affair still arouses in opposition to a fruitful concord between science and faith, between the church and the world. I give my full support to this task, which can honor the truth of faith and of science, and open the door to future collaboration.

The Case of the Scientist Galileo Galilei

May I be permitted, gentlemen, to submit to your attention and your reflection, some points that seem to me important for placing the Galileo affair in its true light, in which agreements between religion and science are more important than those misunderstandings from which there has arisen the bitter and grievous conflict that has dragged itself out in the course of the following centuries.

He who is justly entitled the founder of modern physics, has explicitly declared that the truths of faith and of science can never contradict each other: "Holy Scripture and nature equally proceed from the divine Word, the first as dictated by the Holy Spirit, the second as the very faithful executor of God's commands," as he wrote in his letter to Fr. Benedetto Castelli on December 21, 1613.[6] The Second Vatican Council does not differ in its mode of expression; it even adopts similar expressions when it teaches: "Methodical research, in all domains of knowledge, if it follows moral norms, will never really be opposed to

6. Galileo Galilei, "Letter to Father Benedetto Castelli," December 21, 1613; EN, V, 282–85.

faith; both the realities of this world and of the faith find their origin in the same God."[7]

In scientific research Galileo perceived the presence of the Creator who stimulates it, anticipates and assists its intuitions, by acting in the very depths of its spirit. In connection with the telescope, he wrote at the commencement of the *Sidereus Nuntius*, ("the starry messenger"), recalling some of his astronomical discoveries: *Quae omnia ope perspicilli a me excogitavi divina prius illuminante gratia, paucis abhinc diebus reperta, atque observata fuerunt,*[8] "I worked all these things out with the help of the telescope and under the prior illumination of divine grace they were discovered and observed by me a few days ago."

The Galilean recognition of divine illumination in the spirit of the scientist finds an echo in the already quoted text of the Conciliar Constitution on the church in the modern world: "One who strives, with perseverance and humility, to penetrate the secret of things, is as if led by the hand of God, even if not aware of it."[9] The humility insisted on by the conciliar text is a spiritual virtue equally necessary for scientific research as for adhesion to the faith. Humility creates a climate favorable to dialogue between the believer and the scientist, it is a call for illumination by God, already known or still unknown but loved, in one case as in the other, on the part of the one who is searching for truth.

Galileo has formulated important norms of an epistemological character, which are confirmed as indispensable for placing Holy Scripture and science in agreement. In his letter to the grand duchess of Tuscany, Christine of Lorraine, he reaffirms the truth of Scripture:

> Holy Scripture can never propose an untruth, always on condition that one penetrates to its true meaning, which — I think nobody can deny — is often hidden and very different from that which the simple signification of the words seems to indicate.[10]

Galileo introduced the principle of an interpretation of the sacred books that goes beyond the literal meaning but is in conformity with the intention and type of exposition proper to each one of them. As he affirms, it is necessary that "the wise who expound it show its true meaning."

The ecclesiastical magisterium admits the plurality of rules of interpretation of Holy Scripture. It expressly teaches, in fact, with the

---

7. *Gaudium et Spes*, § 36.
8. Galileo Galilei, *Sidereus Nuntius, Venetiis, apud Thomam Baglionum*, MDCX, fol. 4.
9. Ibid.
10. Galileo Galilei, "Letter to Christine of Lorraine"; EN, V, 315.

encyclical *Divino Afflante Spiritu* of Pius XII, the presence of different
genres in the sacred books and hence the necessity of interpretations
conforming to the character of each of them.

An Honest and Loyal Solution of Long-standing Oppositions

The various agreements that I have recalled do not by themselves
solve all the problems of the Galileo affair, but they help to create a
point of departure favorable to their honorable solution, a frame of
mind propitious for an honest and loyal resolving of long-standing
oppositions.

The existence of this Pontifical Academy of Science, with which
Galileo was to some extent associated through the venerable institution
that preceded the academy of today, in which eminent scientists
participate, is a visible sign that demonstrates to all, with no racial or
religious discrimination, the profound harmony that can exist between
the truths of science and the truths of faith.

About the Authors

GEORGE J. BÉNÉ, born in 1919 in France, is professor of experimental physics at the University of Geneva, Switzerland. A specialist in scientific research on the application of nuclear magnetic resonance in medical diagnosis, and in the relations between science and faith, he has published many papers on these subjects, and is a consultant to the Roman Secretariat for Non-Believers.

IAN CAMPBELL, born in 1921, obtained his doctoral degree at the University of London. His research has included studies of the reactions of atoms consequent upon their nuclear activation, of the effects of radiation on solid lattices, and in radiometry. He was formerly senior lecturer at the University of Manchester, and was elected a professor of the Polish Academy of Sciences. While at the University of Manchester, he was ordained to the Anglican ministry, serving as curate in a parish of the Chester diocese and then as a chaplain in Hong Kong, being later received into the Catholic Church. He has written a number of articles in the science-faith area.

PIERRE COSTABEL, born in 1912, attended the École Normale Supérieure. He has held a fellowship in mathematics, and has the licentiate degree in theology. He is a priest of the Oratory of France. He has taught at the Catholic Institute, Paris, and was research director at the École Pratique des Hautes Études. He has been permanent secretary of the International Academy of the History of Science since 1965. He is the author of many works, including *Leibnitz et la dynamique en 1962* (1960; 2nd ed., 1981); *Malebranche et la Réforme mathématique en France de 1689 á 1706* (1968; 2nd. ed., 1979); *Les Nouvelles Pensées de Galilée par le P. Marin Mersenne*, 2 vols. (1973); *Démarches originales de Descartes savant* (1982); *Correspondence Varignon-Jean Bernoulli* (1983); *Le "De Solidorum Elementis" de Descartes* (1983).

BERNARD JACQUELINE was born in 1928 in Saint-Lo, France. Ordained a priest in 1944 and a bishop in 1982, he is at present the apostolic pro-nuncio in Burundi, after having been under secretary of the Roman Secretariat for Non-Believers. A doctor in canon law and in letters, he has been professor of philosophy at Cherbourg and director of research in juridical sciences. He has published many works, notably *Le droit pontifical selon saint Bernard*, and numerous papers on history. He is in charge of the publication of the collected writings of Charles de Foucauld.

PAUL CARDINAL POUPARD, born in 1930 in Anjou, France, has a doctorate in history and theology, a diploma from the École Pratique des Hautes Études and is a laureate of Academie Francaise. He was ordained arch-Bishop in 1979 and raised to the cardinalate in 1985. Pope John Paul II appointed him President of the Vatican Secretariat for non-Believers in 1982 and of the newly created Pontifical Council for Culture. He is the author of the *Dictionnaire des Religions*, and 12 other books, including, *Eglise et Culture*; he is editor of two quarterlies *Atheisme et Dialogue* and *Cultures et Dialogue*. Many of his works have been translated into German, English, Korean, Spanish, Hungarian, Italian, Japanese, Polish and Portuguese.

FRANÇOIS RUSSO, S. J., was born in France in 1909. A student at the Ecole Polytechnique, he is a specialist in the history and philosophy of science. He has been editor of the review *Etudes*. At present he is affiliated with the International Catholic Center for UNESCO, and a consulter of the Roman Secretariat for Non-Believers. Author of numerous articles and works, he has published *Nature et méthode de l'historire des sciences* (Paris, 1983).

MARIO VIGANÓ, S. J., was born in Seregno, Italy, in 1905. He was ordained a priest in 1937. He has a licentiate degree in philosophy and theology, and a doctrate in physical sciences (University of Padua). He has been professor of cosmology in the Faculty of Philosophy of Garete, Varese, and at the Pontifical Gregorian University, Rome. He has published a number of articles on philosophy and science, and a book, *Il manacato dialogo tra Galileo e i teologi* (Rome, 1969).

BERNARD VINATY, O. P., was born in 1933 in Verdun, France. He was ordained a priest in 1963. He has a licentiate degree in theology from Le Saulchoir, and in philosophy from the Angelicum, Rome. He is professor of epistemology and a specialist in the philosophy of science. He was in charge of a special edition of the review *Angelicum* devoted to Galileo (vol. 60, no. 3, 1983). At present, he is working on the text of and a commentary on Galileo's "Discourse on the Ebb and Flow of the Sea," to be published by the Pontifical Academy of the Sciences.

WILLIAM A. WALLACE, O. P., born in 1918 in Washington, D.C., entered the Dominican Order in 1947, and was ordained a priest in 1953. He has a doctorate in philosophy and theology, and is professor of philosophy at the Catholic University of America, Washington, D.C. He is president of the Leonine Edition of the works of St. Thomas Aquinas, and associate editor of *The Thomist*. He has published many scientific works on the philosophy and history of science.

Index